Chosen FROM AMONG THE WORST

Pablo Yoder

CHRISTIAN LIGHT
PUBLICATIONS

CHOSEN FROM AMONG THE WORST

Christian Light Publications

Harrisonburg, Virginia 22802

©2021 Christian Light Publications, Inc.

Printed in the United States of America

ISBN: 978-0-87813-342-0

Second Printing, 2022

Cover & Interior Design: Elizabeth McMurray

Cover & Interior Graphics: Jacinto Yoder, Getty Images

DEDICATED

TO JONATHAN MILLER, who was my son-in-law and Omar Montenegro's best friend. God chose to take Jonathan home to Heaven on June 9, 2012.

TO JESSICA, my dear daughter, who as a widow kept up her close friendship with Omar and Yuri's family.

AND TO ABNER, the godly man who tenderly took Jessica's grief-battered family into his heart. I thank you for also becoming one of Omar's best friends.

I LOVE YOU, DAUGHTER AND SON!

CONTENTS

1

POOR MAMA!

JANUARY 14, 1975

The windowless bedroom was gloomy, with bare, thick adobe walls and a dirt floor. Sunlight streaming through the open door fell upon a hard wooden bed covered with a threadbare blanket.

Miriam Obregón lay on the bed, pale and panting. The midwife and the short stocky neighbor lady hovered nearby, concern written on their sweaty faces. They worried for the young mother as the hours ticked by.

"This can't go on much longer," the midwife clucked, "or the baby will die. Oh, what can we do?"

Miriam moaned from the bed and then croaked, "I'm going to die!"

"Don't worry, I will help you," the neighbor lady purred, scrambling onto the bed. "As long as there are women here to help, you won't die. Everything will be all right. Can you sit up?" Embracing Miriam from behind, the woman squeezed as hard as she could—and the baby was born.

"It's a boy!" the midwife cheered.

But the tiny infant did not cry. He lay still on the bed, his face purple from lack of oxygen. "He's dead!" wailed the neighbor, burying her face in her hands.

The midwife rushed into action. "Bring some water!" she gasped. As she picked up the tiny boy by his feet, the neighbor shoved a bowl of water onto the bed. With her free hand, the midwife splashed water onto the baby's back and began smacking him gently. The neighbor joined in, splashing water and pounding on the little body.

Suddenly the baby gasped. His thin feeble cry echoed through the house. Miriam smiled through her stupor. Little Omarcito Montenegro was going to live!

Later that day, the baby was breathing normally at Doña Miriam's breast when Grandma Ester came back from town with little Jáqueling, Miriam's first child. Jáqueling was a petite, lovable three-year-old. Not only was she as cute as a button, but she was also highly intelligent and perceptive.

Grandma Ester led the little girl to the bedroom. "Jáqueling, guess what!" she whispered. "Your mother had a baby. Now you have a little brother."

Jáqueling stalled just inside the doorway. She shook her head, staring at her mother and the little bundle at her side.

"Let's go see him," Grandma coaxed.

But Jáqueling refused to move. Giving her head a little jiggle, she said quietly but clearly, "My poor mama!"

Three months later little Jáqueling contracted measles and died.

The Montenegro family never forgot the little drop of borrowed sunshine they had called Jáqueling. Nor did they forget what she had said when she first met her baby brother. When Omar Montenegro grew up to be a wild, rebellious youth, his mother Miriam suffered.

Years later, in Los Angeles, California, Omar's life spiraled deep into sin and crime. He was wanted by the authorities and hated by all. Even his mother was afraid of him.

Was Omar destined to always be an arrogant, violent man? Was Doña Miriam destined to suffer so intensely all her life? Would the Montenegro family forever shake their heads and whisper little Jáqueling's sad words, "Poor Mama"?

2

GUARDIAN ANGEL

GRANDMA ESTER WAS never really a grandmother, nor even a mother, for she and her husband Don Cruz were not able to have children. But if anybody in the Regadío Valley of northern Nicaragua had the heart of a mother or a grandmother, it was Grandma Ester.

The Cruz home was always open for anyone, especially the needy. When Doña Ester cooked a meal, hungry people soon found their way to her house. Though quiet old Cruz never said much, his grin indicated that he was in agreement with his wife's generosity.

Grandma Ester could afford to be generous. Don Cruz was a hard worker, and the couple owned land. In the Cruz house, there were always beans, corn for tortillas, salty homemade cheese, and even some money now and then for extras.

Years before Omarcito was born, Don Cruz's sister Chepa had quarreled with her husband. Destitute and homeless, she and her four children had moved in with her brother and his generous wife. Doña Ester promptly tucked the family into her heart and loved the children as her own grandchildren.

But Doña Chepa was still young and pretty. A neighbor man started courting her, and soon she went to live with him in his parents' house down the street. Chepa's children didn't want to leave Grandma Ester. The oldest, nine-year-old Miriam, stood her ground. "I am not leaving with Mama!" she declared to her younger sister Gladys. "Not if she leaves with that horrible man!"

"If you stay, I want to stay too," Gladys echoed. And that's how Grandma Ester acquired her first two foster daughters.

Doña Chepa took the two little boys with her. But since they lived close by, the boys spent more time with their sisters at Grandma Ester's place than with their mother and stepfather. So one day Grandma Ester asked Chepa if she could keep the two little tykes as well. Since Doña Chepa cared more about her new man than about her children, she readily agreed.

Even though Don Cruz and his wife Ester never legally adopted Chepa's children, they fed and dressed them, put them through school, and raised them to adulthood. All their lives the children called Ester their Mimita.[1]

With extra mouths to feed, Grandma Ester started a small store to bring in a bit of income. Neighbors came for a kilo of beans or a liter of oil and a friendly chat. But after Miriam grew up to be a beautiful young lady, Ester was disturbed when a dashing young man, Fermín Montenegro, came often to hang out at the store. He dressed like a man from the city and handled himself like a king. He often brought them meat and stayed to eat the food that Miriam and Grandma Ester prepared.

Many times Grandma Ester reminded Miriam that Fermín was a married man who had abandoned his first wife only months after he had married her. "Sure, he owns a butcher shop, but he never gets ahead financially, and he doesn't own an inch of land, not even a house," she warned.

Miriam did not heed the warning. She married Fermín after he divorced his first wife. Fermín promptly moved into Don Cruz's already full house and became part of Grandma Ester's tribe.

Fermín and Miriam's first child, Jáqueling, was born in 1972. Little Omarcito arrived in 1975, just before Jáqueling's death. In 1976 another little girl was born and also named Jáqueling. A year later a second girl, Cándida, joined the family. Fermín and Miriam and their three children lived with Grandma Ester in the big house on Regadío's main street.

---

1   Mimita: endearing term for *mother*.

In the 1970s, Nicaragua was ruled by Anastacio Somoza, who was not very concerned about education or the betterment of the poor working class. He ruled the country with an iron hand, ruthlessly ridding it of opposition. By the time Omarcito was three years old, the country tired of the Somoza dictatorship, and a guerrilla force called the Sandinistas began to oppose the government. The Somoza government tried to squash the opposition, but the more guerrillas they killed, the more the Sandinista movement grew. All of Nicaragua, including the village of Regadío, groaned under the political unrest.

A stiff November wind shuttled puffy white clouds across the turquoise sky arching over Regadío. The tall eucalyptus trees scattered throughout the village bowed as the wind swooshed through their long straggly leaves. Dust devils swirled on Regadío's rocky main street.

Grandma Ester, her straight black hair coiled into a bun and tied with a scarf, muttered as she swept the leaves that had fallen in front of her house. The wind snatched the leaves and spun them down the road.

When the little woman looked down the street, what she saw made her heart lurch. In the distance, a long row of armed men in green camouflage came marching toward her. "The EEBI!"[2] she exclaimed under her breath as she ran for her house.

When the EEBI knocked on her door, Grandma Ester faced the soldiers bravely.

"Where's your husband, Don Cruz?" the commander barked, his black eyes glistening.

"He's out harvesting corn," Ester answered, calming her thundering heart.

"Hand over your husband's pistol!" the commander demanded, stepping into the living room.

Because the pistol was registered, they had no right to demand it, but Grandma Ester was so flustered that she handed over the gun without protest. The EEBI left, marching up a side street.

---

2   EEBI: Somoza's soldiers, the *Escuelas de Entrenamiento Básico de Infantería* (School of Basic Infantry Training).

Although Grandma Ester was used to trouble, this raid had taken her by surprise. Desperately she looked around, wondering what she could do. Then she remembered that her husband's pistol had legal papers. She rummaged through his belongings until she found them.

Little Omar stood watching her, his wide innocent eyes showing the uncertainty of a three-year-old. Little Omar Montenegro couldn't understand what was going on, but he knew something was very wrong. The events of that day would forever be seared in his brain.

Clutching the papers, Grandma Ester hoisted the little tyke up onto her waist and ran out the door. Maybe the soldiers would respect a toddler.

In a few moments, she heard anguished cries. As people fled the village, the news ran like fire: "They took Felipe!"

Who was behind this? The EEBI was trained to slip into villages and round up enemies of the government. When the EEBI struck, people were often killed. Two of Felipe Flores' grown children had joined the guerrilla forces, and Felipe himself was cooperating with the guerrillas. *But no one must know that*, Ester decided. The EEBI couldn't prove that Felipe was a traitor. A good man like Felipe Flores must not die!

Grandma Ester hurried up one of Regadío's steep side streets leading toward La Presa. The rocky street was flanked by unkempt barbed wire fences and bushy hedges. As she marched, she whispered into the little boy's ear, "Today you will be my guardian angel!"

Grandma Ester's mind raced even faster than her feet. *Surely they intend to kill Felipe Flores. But I can't allow that to happen because he is a good man!*

The usually active village of Regadío seemed like a ghost town. The only people Ester saw along the way were EEBI members standing guard at strategic places. The residents had either holed up in their houses behind locked doors or escaped into the hills. Everyone was terrified of Somoza's soldiers.

She topped the ridge and followed the street on down into La Presa Valley. Even before she got to the first house, she saw the movement of armed men under the trees. Fearlessly she charged onto the scene.

Little Omarcito's sharp eyes saw what was happening even before his grandmother did. The soldiers had Felipe tied to a tree, with his hands behind the trunk. His head lurched as a burly soldier slapped him in the face. "Traitor!" the soldier screamed. "Stupid guerrilla, talk!"

Another soldier raised his gun, ready to slam its butt onto Felipe's head when the feisty little woman burst into the circle, panting, her eyes on fire. "What are you doing to this poor man?" she cried. "Stop! I am here to tell you that Felipe Flores is innocent. He's not a guerrilla!"

The soldiers stared at Doña Ester, whose unkempt hair was straggling out from under her scarf. They weren't used to being interrupted. What nerve this woman had to approach them, especially carrying a little boy!

"Did you know that Felipe's son and daughter have joined the guerrillas?" the commander demanded angrily.

"Of course I do!" Doña Ester snapped. "Everybody knows that. But that doesn't mean their father is involved. I guarantee that he has nothing to do with the guerrillas."

"What can you tell me about the other neighbors?" the commander asked.

"I am not here to intercede for anybody else," Ester rejoined. "I am here to defend Felipe Flores whom you are beating shamelessly without a cause."

"Really, it's none of your business!" one of the soldiers snarled. "Now back off and let us finish our job."

"Another thing," Doña Ester said, handing the commander the papers in her fist. "Give me back my husband's pistol. It has legal papers."

Then she retreated and stood under a gnarled tree, Omarcita's little body trembling in her sturdy arms. The soldiers huddled together, keeping a vigilant eye on Felipe and several other men also tied to trees.

Suddenly one of the soldiers marched over to Doña Ester. She recognized him as a fellow from a neighboring town. When she saw he was smiling, her heartbeat slowed to normal. "Look," he whispered, glancing back at the commander and handing her the pistol. "We had orders to kill Felipe Flores. We received an accusation that he was a guerrilla supporter. But, like you explained, he apparently is innocent."

Grandma Ester nodded in relief.

Patting the little woman on the back, the soldier whispered, "Rest assured, Felipe Flores won't die today."

Regadío was subdued as evening crept into the valley and Felipe Flores came limping home. The wind had died down and the eucalyptus trees drooped, their long fronds hanging down like matted braids. The villagers who had hidden earlier sneaked back home. The EEBI had beaten Felipe with the butts of their guns and tortured him emotionally. But when they found no proof of his involvement with the guerrillas, they had turned him loose.

At the time of Omarcito's birth, most of the men in the Regadío Valley worked for the rich Briones family. But not Fermín Montenegro. He was proud of his own little business of buying cattle, butchering them, and selling meat to the community.

Don Chema Briones was a rich landowner with over 1,600 acres in Regadío. His hacienda occupied most of the valley with its fertile black soil, and no other ranches in the area were as large and prosperous as his. The Briones' sprawling ranch buildings, perched along the main road and flanked by a large rock corral and a sugar factory, served as the center of industry in the valley.

Before Omarcito was born, old Don Chema died and his sons took over the Briones' haciendas. Just as Nicaragua was ruled by the Somoza dynasty, the economy of Regadío Valley was controlled by the Briones dynasty.

In many ways the Briones were good to their workers. Though they paid meager wages, they allowed the workers to build their own houses on the Briones' land. The workers cut down lumber for these houses from the ranch and used the Briones' oxen to haul it. Though the workers could never own the land, they could live in the simple homes they had built as long as they worked for the Briones.

The Briones ran hundreds of head of cattle in the hill country surrounding the valley, and they milked up to a hundred cows in the big rock-walled corral behind the house. They allowed each worker with little children to choose a cow from the dairy. They would graze the cows on the Briones' land, but they could milk them at their own houses and use the milk for themselves. The calves belonged to the Briones, of course.

But what really prospered the Briones' hacienda was their sugarcane setup. The Briones paid the workers to plant dozens of acres of sugarcane, corn, and beans for the ranch. In addition, they also gave the workers land that they could till for themselves. Every worker could have up to two or three acres to plow with the Briones' oxen and plant their own sugarcane. At harvesttime, eighteen months later, the workers used the Briones' oxen to haul the cane to the Briones' sugar plant. There the workers processed it, going fifty-fifty on the dulce,[3] the finished product. Dulce was one of the best cash crops in the area at that time besides cattle, so this setup ensured cash for both the ranch owners and their workers.

The Briones weren't as ruthless as the Somozas; however, they did reign supreme in the Regadío Valley. It was difficult for the workers to ever own land, which limited their opportunities. But if they were willing to work, they always had plenty to eat.

This was little Omarcito's world—a world of inequality. Even though his father didn't work for the Briones, their lives still revolved around the rich man's world. When the Sandinista guerrillas started showing up, the Briones became nervous, and life in the Regadío Valley grew unsettled.

Who could have known, when Omarcito protected Doña Ester from the soldiers, that another guardian angel would have a full-time job watching over this rambunctious little boy who seemed destined to folly?

---

3   Dulce: brown sugar cakes that were sold as a cash crop.

3

TERROR ON ANGOSTURA

THE MAGNIFICENT OLD pine tree on the top of the cliff held out its green arms, inviting the cool wind to rustle its glistening needles. The sun had been up for several hours and was trying its best to warm the land. Several hundred feet below the sheer cliff, a bellbird bounced from branch to branch at the tip of a bare ceiba tree, emitting bell-like bonks and flutelike whistles.

The peace of this wild and beautiful scene was broken by the ring of hoofbeats coming down the rocky trail skirting the mountaintop and the edge of the cliff. The buckskin mare's hide glowed, revealing good care and excellent health.

The rider was well-dressed in a checkered shirt, blue jeans, and cowboy boots. He wore a .22 pistol in his belt, and a black felt cowboy hat adorned his neatly slicked hair.

But the man was disgustingly drunk.

Behind the saddle, five-year-old Omar clung like a monkey to his father's waist. This narrow pass at Angostura[4] always frightened the little boy. Every time he dared to peep over the edge of the cliff, the depth below made his heart stop.

---

4   Angostura: "the narrow place."

Not only was he drunk, but Fermín Montenegro was also angry and sick of his empty life. His own vanity was a burden almost too heavy to carry. It seemed that every one of Fermín's financial endeavors failed. A cattle deal had fallen through, and the money he hoped to make had gone swishing down the drain. At this rate, he would never be able to pay his debts.

Living in with old Cruz and Doña Ester had its drawbacks. Since Omarcito's birth, three girls had been added to the family: Jáqueling, Cándida, and the newest baby, Ninozca. Just girls! And so many mouths to feed! Fermín sighed bitterly.

The evening before, Fermín had taken little Omar with him and ridden to San Luis to talk with an uncle. Of course, after telling his uncle all about his failed plans, they started drinking. Fermín drank into the night, trying to forget his woes. His inability to stop drinking only made Fermín more angry and bitter. More and more, Miriam fussed at him for his irresponsible ways.

This morning, riding along the trail and sweating out an awful hangover, all of Fermín's woes hung heavily on his shoulders. He never had enough money to buy groceries, much less build a house for his family. Why couldn't he find work or at least discover a good way to make money?

As Fermín rode across the crest of Angostura, the morning seemed to hold its breath. The wind died down and the old pine tree held still for once. The bellbird fell silent.

Crazed by drink, Fermín suddenly spurred his horse toward the wide rock slab that hung out over the abyss. Omarcito clutched his father's shirt in shocked terror. Surely his dad wouldn't make the horse jump out over the cliff! Peeping around Fermín's back, Omarcito saw that the mare had pranced out onto the rock and was nearing the edge.

But the mare was even more frightened than Omarcito. As soon as she saw the abyss open up in front of her, she disobeyed her rider's instructions and pawed to a stop, her shod hooves scraping loudly on the rock. She took the bit, spun around, and headed back onto the trail.

Sawing at the bit and cursing, Fermín brought the mare around again. Once more he spurred the mare, forcing her to gallop toward the cliff. He swore, giving the mare's ribs a terrible raking.

Omarcito pinched his eyes shut as they closed in the second time. Terror clutched at his throat. Was his father going crazy?

But the mare couldn't make herself do it. Again she pawed to a stop at the cliff's edge. Just as she fought the bit, a shout rang out.

"Don Fermín!" A rider was coming along the trail from the opposite direction. "What's wrong with you, old man? Are you planning to kill yourself along with that boy?"

Ashamed, Fermín reined in his mare and went up the trail to meet his friend Luis, also from Regadío.

"What was that all about?" Luis asked, looking Fermín over closely.

"I wanted to die," Fermín answered sheepishly. "Had too much drink…"

As they traveled home, Fermín was quiet, still in his drunken stupor. Not once did he acknowledge his little son trembling behind him. Fermín didn't seem to realize, or even care, that Omarcito had just had the worst scare of his life. The little fellow would carry its scar all his life.

The dark rocks of the old stone corral on the Briones' deserted hacienda were dressed in frilly patches of light gray lichens. At one end of the corral, an immense tangle of cactus vines waved spiny green arms into the sky. Just beyond the wall, a gnarled old acacia tree spread its thorny branches, creating an immense green umbrella that provided shade from the sun. A pair of wrens chattered to each other, hopping from limb to limb in the tree's topmost branches.

Tucked in under the edge of the shady umbrella sat skinny seven-year-old Omar, troubled thoughts wandering through his head. Young as he was, he understood that times were hard.

Things had changed drastically in the past two years for Regadío and its inhabitants. After several attempts, the guerrillas had finally taken control of the city of Estelí[5] in 1979, and several days later they seized Managua. When the Somoza dynasty of Nicaragua saw they were beaten, they fled the country. Some of the family went to the United States. The last dictator,

---

5   Estelí: a big city, the seat of the department, that lies fifteen miles east of Regadío.

Anastacio Somoza, ended up in South America. Daniel Ortega, one of the guerrilla leaders, took Nicaragua's reins into his hands.

Suddenly there wasn't room in Nicaragua for the rich lords anymore. The Briones family, lords of Regadío, also fled the country. Some of the Briones ended up in Miami, others in Honduras and Costa Rica.

The Briones' sixteen-hundred-acre hacienda was confiscated and divided out among the poor. Many of the Regadío poor working class suddenly became landowners. They formed several cooperatives, but unfortunately, these working class people had no business experience, nor did they have money to develop the land. Two years after the revolution, the Briones homestead had been abandoned.

Omarcito hunched over on the stone wall, gazing at the sugar mill. The long beam that stuck out from the center gearbox, like an old man's bony index finger, pointed due north as if complaining, *That's the direction our masters fled.*

Seldom was a pair of oxen harnessed to the beam anymore. The circular ditch the oxen's hooves had carved out, going around and around as they squeezed out the cane juice, was now an abandoned trench the Regadío boys played in when they had nothing else to do. The cane press, made of three squat iron rollers that used to revolve into each other as they ate up the cane were still, as if they had lost their appetite forever.

The sugar mill had once been the busiest place on the hacienda. Omar could remember the hustle and bustle of the mill during better times. But he would never have the privilege of working on one of the sugar mill's shifts. Times had changed. Now the people bought dulce when they had money, which wasn't often. Or they consumed plain white sugar that was rationed at the stores.

Things were worse now than when Nicaragua had been under the Somoza dictatorship. Not all Nicaraguans were pleased with their new president, Daniel Ortega. They had expected the new government to be a true democracy. So when Ortega chose to take the country in a communistic direction, they rebelled. Many Nicaraguan men and boys took up arms and fought in the civil war against the Sandinista regime.

As Omarcito whiled away the time high up on the old stone wall, he only dimly comprehended the political troubles of his country. What bothered him more were the problems at home. Everybody at home was angry all the time, it seemed to Omarcito. His dad Fermín took his anger out on the children.

More and more often, his dad drank on weekends. Even worse, his mother fussed day and night because her husband wasted their hard-earned money on drink. And now rumors were flying that Fermín was seeing other women, which only escalated his mother's complaints.

Why did Daddy have to drink? Why did Mama have to complain all the time?

One cheerful ray of light in Omarcito's darkening world was the baby Emilio, nicknamed Milo, who had been born while Omarcito was in first grade. Finally he had a little brother! Milo wasn't old enough to sit with him on the stone wall, but he was big enough to coo when Omarcito played with him. *Someday Milo will grow up and we will be playmates.* The thought made Omarcito smile.

But then his thoughts darkened again when he remembered last evening. Daddy always drank Saturday evenings. That was nothing new. But before last night, he had always come home, albeit late and disgustingly drunk. Mama would be patient with him when he returned, saving her scolding until the next morning when he was miserable from a hangover. But last night Daddy hadn't come home, and Omarcito was worried. When he overheard Mama say she wondered if he hadn't run off with another woman, his heart had gone cold.

Bitterness crept into the heart of the pensive little boy. He yearned for a home where he could feel love. Someday, he wanted a home of his own where there was peace, not fighting.

"Omar!" The call startled him from his reverie. Three Regadío boys his age, slingshots in hand, had stumbled upon Omarcito's hiding spot as they meandered past the corral.

"Come rabbit hunting with us!" Fabricio shouted. "We couldn't figure out where you were. Maybe we can catch a rabbit or at least shoot a bobwhite."

Forgetting his troubles, Omarcito jumped nimbly off the stone wall and raced toward his buddies, clutching his own slingshot. He quickly assumed his usual role as the aggressive leader of this inseparable pack of boys. Now eight bare feet padded along the dusty trail leading to the lagoon.

Although it was already dry in December, nobody in Regadío expected rain till May. But one wet treasure that the whole town cherished was the lagoon, fed by an opulent natural spring at the lower end of the town. A jungle of plants and grasses, it was a young boy's paradise for birds and animals. Omarcito and his friends knew it like the palms of their hands.

As the boys approached the jungle growing lush and green in the otherwise dry landscape, they slowed their steps and loaded their slingshots.

Omarcito led the way, taking a trail through the brush to an open field beyond. This was where the bobwhites roamed, and among the grasses that surrounded the town the rabbits hid until eager boys flushed them out.

As they crept noiselessly along the trail, Omarcito whispered, "Maybe we'll at least see a roadrunner. I've seen them around here before. Wouldn't it be great if we could shoot one?"

The boys skirted town, hunting along the creek, but found nothing on which to use their pockets full of stones. As the afternoon ticked by, they tired of their sport. "Pshaw!" Omarcito complained. "We should go to La Presa. There's a rabbit hole up there that might bring us some luck."

"La Presa is far away," René ventured. "But if there are rabbits there, why not? We sure aren't having any luck over here!"

A half hour later the four lads were sneaking through a rocky field, the tall weedy grasses as high as their heads. "Look," Omarcito whispered. "Last week I chased a rabbit into a den that's just around this cluster of trees. Maybe if we sneak up quietly, we can catch him."

"How would we do that?" Fabricio asked, sounding doubtful.

"I don't know, but if I see him," Omarcito bragged, patting his slingshot, "I will shoot him dead with this gun."

Suddenly Omarcito froze. Sure enough. Peeping through the high grass, he could see the little rabbit fast asleep at the doorway of his den. Instinctively, he pounced.

But all the wild pounce did was separate the rabbit from his den and set his feet on fire. He was gone in a split second, zigzagging across the pasture, four youngsters hot on his heels.

The next half hour was one wild tracking experience. The rabbit hid; the boys flushed him out; the rabbit ran for his life. Again and again the scene was repeated as the four boys and the rabbit worked their way over a hillside, closer and closer to the town of Regadío.

As they stumbled over the rocks that lay right above the road to La Presa, Omarcito hissed, "I saw him run into the weeds over here! That rabbit is tired."

"And I'm tired too!" Anibal fussed. "Let's give up. We'll never catch him."

But Omarcito was determined. *He's got to be around here somewhere,* he thought as he climbed over yet another boulder, his buddies scrambling along behind. Something moved in the weeds ahead of him. Pushing his way through the last stand of tall grass, Omarcito crouched, ready to grab the rabbit. He was sure his time had come.

But as his eyes finally landed on the rabbit, Omar froze. The rabbit was there, all right, but something else was there as well, the rabbit securely fixed in its jaws. It was the biggest rattlesnake Omarcito had ever seen.

Falling backward in his haste to get out of there, Omarcito croaked, "A rattler! A huge rattler!"

The four boys fled the field faster than they had come barging in. Pale as sheets, they regrouped down on the street that ran over the hill from La Presa. "That was the biggest rattlesnake I've ever seen!" Omarcito gasped. "He had the rabbit in his jaws, and so near I reached down to grab the poor rabbit."

Hunting was over for the day. As the bloodred sun dropped to rest on the western horizon, each of the boys headed home. Though dazed, Omar had one clear thought: *So nearly that rattler bit me!*

4

THE LITTLE RED HEN

OMARCITO DREAMED OF being a cowboy. Coming back from school one afternoon when he was eight years old, he was dreaming again. Passing a neighboring store, he saw a flimsy rope lying in the yard near the store's front door. Omarcito nonchalantly picked it up and headed on home. *Nobody needs it anyway,* he decided.

Omarcito's dad had taught him how to make several lassoing knots. In a minute, Omarcito had formed a noose. Swinging his newly acquired lariat around his head, he imagined himself to be an expert cowboy in a rodeo. In his daydream, he was hurtling across the Regadío plains on a spanking stallion, racing after a steer that needed to be branded. He threw the noose at a post beside the road, but it flew on past, missing the post. He needed more practice, but someday he would learn to rope as well as his daddy.

Omarcito gathered up his fancy lariat and deftly rewound it. By the time he reached his house, it was ready again. Galloping into the front yard, he flung the rope at his mama's favorite rosebush and lassoed it grandly.

"Omar, where did you get that rope?"

Omarcito stopped abruptly at the sound of the gruff voice. He hadn't seen his father leaning in the doorway. Expecting to be scolded for ruining Mama's rosebush, he quickly unwound the rope from the bush.

CHAPTER 4

"I asked you where you got that rope!" Fermín barked, his voice rising in anger.

"I picked it up on my way home," Omarcito answered lamely.

"I asked you *where* you got it!" Fermín was shouting now.

Omarcito started to shake. He knew too well where his dad's anger was headed. With trembling lips, he confessed he had picked it up in front of Bayardo Sanchez's store.

Before Omarcito was done explaining, his dad had jerked a set of horse reins from a nail on the wall. Omarcito didn't dare run. That would only make matters worse—much worse. He stood still until the rein bit into his back and legs. Then he danced in pain, taking the lashing bravely, till his dad was satisfied.

"Now take that rope and put it back exactly where you found it!" Fermín commanded, panting from exertion. "I don't want any of my boys turning out to be low-down robber skunks, do you hear?"

Blubbering and still in pain, Omarcito ran for the store. He hid behind some bushes and waited till the coast was clear. Then he ran into the yard and dropped the rope exactly where he had found it.

Though Omar remembered the pain of that lashing, he eventually understood that a lot more than pain was involved in the rope incident. Even though his dad was often cruel and unreasonable, on that day an important lesson was settled in Omar's heart: *Thou shalt not steal!*

A mile or two west of the Regadío Valley, a steep, rocky road opened into another valley, called Paradise Valley, that lay between the same two mountain ranges as Regadío. After topping the hill, the road meandered through a wide expanse, flanked on one side by an old stone wall and on the other by open green fields. Beyond the stone wall, the land was rolling, covered by tall grass that had acquired a golden hue as it leaned in the wind during the beginning of dry season.

To the left of the little country road lay vast fields, dressed in green grass, shorn short by cattle. Beyond the fields, green hills reached for the skies, interspersed with clusters of blue-green pines. No wonder the valley was called Paradise Valley. It resembled a calendar picture of an alpine valley in Switzerland.

At the entrance of the valley, right beside the rocky road, a rickety wooden house perched on stilts among some *carbón* trees, subject to the wild winds that whipped through the valley most of the year. That is where Omarcito's grandparents lived.

Fermín's parents, Paulino Montenegro and his wife Cándida, were very poor. But Paulino's rich cousin, Leonardo Montenegro, had allowed them to build their two-story wooden house on his ranch.

Paulino and his son Fermín had several things in common—drinking, working hard, and starting projects. But it seemed as though nothing they tried ever got off the ground. When the neighbors shook their heads and whispered, "It's bad management," the Montenegros blamed it on bad luck.

Paulino and Fermín often borrowed money they couldn't repay. Relatives took pity on them and bailed them out of debt time and again. Leonardo tried to help Paulino get ahead. He gave Paulino work when he was sober, and he lent him land for planting. But whatever money Leonardo lent him, Paulino spent for drink.

Fermín's brother Gilberto, whom everybody called Bato, was the one who helped Fermín. Bato worked in the States and made good money. Every time he came back to visit his family in Nicaragua, Bato tried to help his brother financially. But, like their dad, everything Fermín tried turned out to be a flop.

When Bato was in the States and not available to help his brother, Paulino allowed Fermín to plant vegetables on Leonardo's land. Some time after the rope incident, Fermín was cultivating a tomato patch on Leonardo's land, and he had brought Omarcito with him. Rather than walking back to Regadío every evening, he and Omarcito were staying nights with his parents.

Omarcito enjoyed staying in Paradise Valley with Grandpa and Grandma Montenegro, and he loved when his dad considered him man enough to work shoulder to shoulder with him. But one thing scared him—Paradise Valley was known for its coyotes, and Omarcito was deathly afraid of coyotes.

One evening, Omarcito sat on a board that ran along the side of his grandpa's living room, listening as Paulino told a thrilling story. The flickering light from the kerosene lamp made red-gold colors swirl on Grandpa's face, creating a spooky atmosphere. The coyotes were howling in the distance. The sound was wild and sad, making Omarcito's hair stand straight up. His eyes grew bigger and bigger as Paulino's story developed.

"Several months ago the coyotes got bolder and bolder," Paulino said. "They started coming into the downstairs area and stealing the missus' chickens. I finally decided it was enough. I stayed up one night, machete in one hand and flashlight in the other.

"As soon as I heard the chickens squawk, right at midnight, I rushed down those steps." Paulino laughed.

"What were you planning to do to the coyote?" Fermín interrupted. "Did you think you could catch him?"

"I didn't know what I was going to do." Grandpa shifted in his hammock. "I didn't have a plan—I just wanted to scare that old beast away."

Grandpa paused, prolonging the suspense. Omarcito's mouth was so dry he couldn't open it to urge his grandpa to hurry with the story.

"As I came down those steps, shining ahead with my flashlight, I saw the biggest hairiest coyote you could imagine, staring at me, his eyes shining red in the light. He had a chicken in his mouth, but he didn't run. His glare seemed to say, 'Leave me alone! I'll take as many chickens as I want.' "

"What did you do?" Fermín asked, shaking his head and laughing.

Paulino chuckled. "I tried to yell, but it felt as if I had something stuck in my throat. All that came out was a croak."

"Then what?" Omarcito managed to gasp.

"I came back up those steps a lot faster than I went down!" Paulino roared with laughter. "Right then and there I decided that it was okay if the coyotes stole my wife's chickens."

But Omarcito was not laughing. His enormous eyes and pale face betrayed the terrible fear in his heart.

The next afternoon, a neighbor boy rode up to Paulino's house. "Don Fermín," he said, "one of Pedro Moncada's cows fell and broke its leg. He wonders if you would buy the animal and sell the meat in your butcher shop in Regadío."

Pedro Moncada's ranch was adjacent to Leonardo's, but both homesteads were built back a ways off the road. Very soon Fermín, Omarcito, and the neighbor boy were on their way up into the foothills, Fermín leading a packhorse, with Omarcito riding high on its wooden packsaddle containing a selection of Fermín's butcher knives and several sacks.

By the time Fermín and the neighbor boy had killed the cow, carved the bulk of the meat off the bones, packed it into sacks, and tied it on the packhorse, it was getting dark.

"Omarcito, take the packhorse down to Moncada's ranch house," Fermín said sharply. "Get somebody to help you unload. Then come back for the rest of the meat. Be quick about it."

Omarcito's heart froze. "But, Dad, it's getting dark!" he wailed. "I'm scared of the coyotes!"

"Yes, it's late," Fermín acknowledged, frustration written all over his face. "That's exactly why you need to hurry. It's still early enough to get back to the ranch house before it's pitch dark. I've told you a thousand times that coyotes won't attack a human. So get going!"

As the sunset faded from red to purple to black, Omarcito padded along, leading the packhorse down the lonely path. Eventually even the stars were blacked out by shadowy clouds driven by a stiff wind. Suddenly the quiet of the night was shattered by the *yip-howl* of a pack of coyotes. Omarcito's blood ran cold as he jerked on the sluggish horse's reins.

He almost screamed. How many coyotes were in the pack? Twenty? He was too scared to cry out—he could only moan. What a yapping, howling throng! Were they after the meat on the horse, or were they after *him*?

Once again the coyotes yowled their deepest feelings into the dark night. Long eerie howls rose and fell, punctuated by staccato yips, yaps, and barks. They sounded closer than before! Omar hurried even more, but his responsibility for the packhorse kept him from making a wild dash for safety.

It was pitch dark now, and Omarcito stumbled as he tried to follow the unseen trail. He jerked at the horse's reins, running aside into the grasses and banging his bare toes on the rocks beside the trail.

Finally in desperation, he bent over and found the trail with his hands. Crouched like an ape, he kept feeling the ground for the fine dust of the path that ran between the grasses and the stones, tripping along the best he could. Then the coyotes howled again, and Omarcito started to cry.

Groping along the dark trail, with coyotes howling in the background, Grandpa's tall tale from the evening before didn't help Omarcito's nerves at all. It seemed that the darker the night grew, the louder the coyotes howled, and the harder Omarcito cried.

At last the young boy topped a hill and saw the lights of Pedro Moncada's homestead. Crying tears of relief, he hurried down the hill as fast as the old nag would let him. The coyotes hadn't eaten him after all. But he had to go back!

When Pedro Moncada's mother saw Omarcito running into the house as pale as a sheet, she realized what had happened. She was furious. "What in the world?" she fussed, drying Omarcito's tears. "I can't believe Fermín would be so mean. Omarcito is still a child, and he makes him do a man's job on such a dark night. Anybody can see he's scared to death."

Summoning the hired man, the grandmother commanded, "Take this flashlight and go with this little boy back up the mountain to bring in the rest of the meat. He must not go back up there alone."

Don Cruz had a brother called Tomás. Unfortunately, Tomás had not turned out to be a hard worker like Don Cruz. He drank too much and moved his growing family from place to place. He had three children with his first woman, and after she left, he shacked up with a woman named María. Eventually, Tomás had taken his family to the Yalí area, three hours by bus from Regadío plus an hour's walk back in toward the mountain.

Tomás acquired a small piece of land and built a small house. There he lived with the three older children plus the children he had with María. Soon after her sixth child was born, María died.

About a year later, Doña Ester took the bus to Yalí to assess the situation. She was saddened by the living conditions and the dire lack of food. Tomás's oldest daughter pulled Ester aside and whispered, "Please take these children, Auntie. I can hardly stand it anymore. My dad never provides enough food. You know how he drinks. Lately he has been offering to give these children away to anybody. Please take them, Auntie, and give them a real home."

"I don't know . . ." Ester hesitated. "I need to talk to Don Cruz first."

"But they are his nieces," the girl pled. "He'll be okay with it."

The next morning, Doña Ester made up her mind. She would adopt Tomás's poor children and give them a real home.

Doña Ester looked like the Little Red Hen followed by a string of chicks. But the little woman with the ever-generous heart wasn't leading chicks. She was leading children—five of them, to be exact. She was carrying the sixth and littlest one, who was just over a year old.

When they crawled off the bus at the stop closest to Regadío, Ester's brother Guillermo happened to be there. He shook his head and moaned, "Sister, what have you done? Don't tell me you're bringing these youngsters home for keeps! You must be off your head!"

"Do I come to *your* house to beg when the corn and the beans are all gone?" Doña Ester snapped. "Do you bother to help keep food on our table? Just mind your own business. I know what I'm doing!"

The bus stop was two miles from Regadío, and the road was hot and dusty. So when a big, battered, flatbed truck stopped, Doña Ester was glad for the ride. After loading the children and their bags, Doña Ester crawled up and sat on top of the high load among the children. The children were hot and sweaty and dressed in tattered clothes, but Doña Ester sat with her head lifted high, as if she were a queen surrounded by princes and princesses. Her tired smile was a sight to see.

Everybody at home was expecting her back that day. Omar had been whiling away the afternoon on the porch, hoping to be the first to see his dear Mimita again. He *was* the first to see her, perched high on the back of the flatbed. But who were all the children surrounding her?

As Grandma Ester helped unload the brood of children, a hush fell over the whole street. Neighbors came to the doors of their houses. Don Cruz had just come back from his farm, and the rest of the children gathered around. Everybody stopped and stared.

"What's going on?" Don Cruz asked, as Doña Ester herded the children toward him on the porch.

"Well, these are your nephews and nieces." Doña Ester smiled bravely. "As you well know, their mother died. Their older sister begged me to take them because their dad is threatening to give them away, one by one, to anybody who comes by. And as you see, these poor children are half-starved. I knew that you wouldn't want them given away like candy or dying from starvation, right?"

"I guess not." Don Cruz sighed, looking the poor skinny children over. "Yes, I guess you had no other options. Anyway, here we have plenty to eat. Come on in out of the hot sun."

"And we will get decent clothes for them," Grandma Ester added as she ushered the children into the cool living room. "And we'll put them through school. And above all, we'll give them love, just like we did your sister Chepa's children, won't we?"

Don Cruz nodded.

Omar's mother Miriam sat in the corner, nursing her own month-old addition to the family—a little boy named Melvin. Fermín would have fits when he found out what Mimita had done. But what a big heart Mimita had! These children surely needed help—just like Miriam and her siblings had needed help years before. Miriam would help all she could to make them all one big family.

Since Melvin's birth, Omar had five siblings of his own. Now Grandma had brought home yet another brother and five more sisters. That would make a dozen children in this house, Omar figured.

Doña Ester started the introductions. "This is baby Fátima," she said tenderly, bending over so little Milo could see her. "See how skinny she is? If we wouldn't have adopted her, she might have died. And next is little Chepita; she's three. Cristina is five, Juanita is seven, and Tomasa is nine. And this big boy is Cristóbal, and he is eleven."

Then Grandma Ester, who could not have children of her own, hurried to the kitchen where she helped finish one of the biggest meals she had ever served. That night a dozen children were tucked into their makeshift beds, their tummies tight with rice, beans, and tortillas.

5

SOMEDAY I WILL BE BIG

MOST OF GRANDMA Ester's household accepted her decision to take in a new batch of orphans. Even the town of Regadío, often brutal in their gossip, eventually lifted their hats to the brave Little Red Hen. But one person was not happy with the situation. Every time the proud rooster Fermín came home and saw the six new chicks playing with his, it ruffled his feathers.

Fermín couldn't complain about misbehavior in Doña Ester's family. The orphans appreciated their new home, and Miriam's children accepted their new siblings. Doña Ester continued to rule the house with a firm hand. Old Grandpa Cruz loved to take Omar and Cristóbal out on the farm with him to help whenever they could. The first year with the house full of a dozen children was a good year for them all—except Fermín, whose pride suffered.

When Fermín's younger brother Bato came back from the United States for a visit, he bought a section of land on the outskirts of Estelí and divided it into lots for each of his brothers and sisters. Fermín grabbed for the chance to move his family away from the charity of the Little Red Hen.

Fermín's older sister Irma was married to Toño Sanchez, a guerrilla. Because Toño was usually away from home, Irma's teenaged son Andrés had taken on the responsibility of building a house on Irma's lot. Their house was finished by the time Fermín started building his house next to Irma's. As soon as Fermín's house was half-built, he moved his family to Estelí.

The house was simple, with a tin roof, cement walls, and a dirt floor. During their four-year stay in Estelí, Fermín and Miriam had two more children, Selene and Alvaro, bringing the total to eight.

Problems developed between the two families living so close together. The five Sanchez cousins were older than Fermín and Miriam's children, and it was hard for them to put up with the children's antics in the house next door. They found Omar's pranks especially annoying.

Fermín built a little meat stand on Main Street and started butchering steers and selling meat, a trade that he knew well. Omar, now ten years old, became Fermín's right-hand man. Life became very busy for the boy, yet he still found opportunities for mischief.

The evening sky was a pale peach toward the west. The sun had just set, and the air had cooled off fast. The Estelí evening was gorgeous and still. A pygmy owl offered his evening toots for anybody to hear. But Omar, sneaking around the outside of Auntie Irma's kitchen, wasn't paying any attention to the owl's song.

Right above Doña Irma's open-fire cookstove was an opening to the outside, partially covered with a wooden lattice. A small treasure clutched in his hand, Omar snuck closer. Standing on a rock under the opening, he peeped into the kitchen. As usual, Auntie Irma's fire burned hot, and Omar could see the cook herself, stirring up the evening meal. Omar bided his time.

Just as he expected, Doña Irma eventually meandered off to the main part of the house to set the table. Still Omar waited. He had to pop his surprise just when she was returning. *Here she comes!* he cheered inwardly. Then he dropped his treasure into the fire.

Innocently, Doña Irma approached the stove where the beans were boiling and the tortillas curling on the hot grill. Just as she reached her hot stove, the evening was shattered. *Boom!*

Doña Irma jumped back, clutching her throat. "That almost killed me!" she gasped, leaning against the wall. And then, realizing that she was unscathed and understanding perfectly well what had happened, she yelled, "You ornery troublemaker!"

Omar just giggled and ran off. What fun it had been to drop a bullet into the hot coals of Doña Irma's cookstove!

Aside from such pranks, life was tough for Omar in Estelí. Despite Fermín's drinking problem and his inability to prosper financially, he taught his boys to work hard. Anybody working under Fermín, young or old, had to be diligent and prompt. Fermín gave orders like an army sergeant, and Omar learned early to jump to his tune.

While they lived in Estelí, Omar was expected to get up with his dad at three o'clock in the morning to butcher the animal of the day: a steer, a cow, a bull, or a hog. By the time the sun was peeping over the horizon, Omar was usually pushing his little wooden cart, delivering choice meats to the restaurants. That was his job till 11 a.m.

Then he had to rush home to shower and get ready for school. Omar's school period was from 12:30 till 5 p.m. After school, it was his job to go from restaurant to restaurant to collect the money from the morning's deliveries. Then he needed to clean and wash down the little wooden butcher shop. Life was far too busy for a ten-year-old. Often as not, he would crash into bed an hour or two after sundown, too tired to even think.

Sometimes on weekends or school holidays, Omar went with Fermín to buy a cow or hog and help chase it home. One Saturday they left early in the morning for Regadío. By midmorning, Fermín had bought two Brahman cows to butcher. Instead of lassoing them, Fermín decided they would chase them along the road. Neither Fermín nor Omar realized how ornery those two cows were.

It took a lot of maneuvering and hollering just to get the cows out of their field and onto the road. Fermín, who rode his horse, had cut himself a long pole. Omar was walking, carrying a lariat. Of course, he wouldn't dare try to lasso such big angry cows, but he swung the rope to help chase them. With Fermín brandishing his pole and Omar swinging his lariat, they both yelled till they were hoarse. Finally the cows were on the road, heading toward Estelí. By then Fermín was angry.

Fermín knew of a shortcut before they reached La Comarca, where they could take the road south toward Estelí. It was little more than a trail, easy to miss among the tall roadside weeds. But Fermín chased the cows up the incline, hollering at them as they crashed through the brush. "Omar!" he yelled. "Run up ahead and cut those cows off so they don't try to head back home. Don't you dare let them get through!"

Omar ran ahead like a deer. Sweating and tired, he stood in the bright sun right in the middle of the road twirling his rope. Fermín, his face as red as a beet in spite of his wide-brimmed hat, chased the cows along, brandishing his stick and hollering, "Ja! Ja! Ja!"

As the two cows approached the road, they suddenly swung around and charged back the brushy trail toward home, dodging Fermín on his big horse.

Omar saw what was going to happen, clenched his teeth, and prepared to stop them. Both cows were running straight toward him. Knowing how mad his dad would be if he failed this test, Omar stood his ground. Nobody expected what happened next. The lead cow lowered her head, pointed her long horns straight at Omar, and charged.

Anybody else in his right mind would have leaped out of the way. But Omar stood still, yelling as loud as he could. As the cow closed in, he smashed his rolled-up lariat against her head. Then he lost control, and the cow jumped right over him, knocking him flat.

The cows ran past, crashing through the weeds, and Fermín's curses sliced the air as he galloped toward Omar. "I told you to stop those cows!"

Omar cringed as he got up off the ground, so far unhurt. He knew what was coming. Before he could run or hide, it happened. "You good-for-nothing!" his dad screamed as the pole zipped through the air. All Omar could do was whip up his hand to take the blow instead of letting it land on his back. The pain was excruciating. Fermín plunged into the weed patch to start the rodeo all over again.

That's the way life was for Omar, working with his dad. He never knew what to expect. Even so, Omar respected his dad and tried to please him.

But he never felt good enough for Fermín, who demanded perfection from everyone but himself.

As Omar neared his twelfth birthday, his mother convinced him to start catechism in the big Catholic church that stood proudly at the head of the children's park in the center of Estelí. So every Sunday morning, an hour before Mass, Omar joined a large group of youth his age for catechism.

One Sunday, the young lady who taught the catechism spoke to the youth about the importance of asking for forgiveness when guilty and of forgiving when wronged. It left an impression on Omar's young heart, and very soon he had an opportunity to put it to practice.

Playing in the park just two blocks from the Catholic church was a lot more fun for Omar than studying religion. Among the playground's delights, the favorite for Omar and his cronies was the swing set. It had a big metal frame and three swings with little metal seats.

As soon as catechism was over, Omar and half a dozen of his buddies sped for the park, racing to get the first chance to swing. As usual, Omar got there first, and by the time the others panted onto the scene, he was already in the air.

Two other boys plunged for the swing right next to Omar's. As they fought for the seat, Betito was not watching Omar's airlifts. The next thing Omar knew, his metal seat had kissed Betito smack on the forehead. The next thing Betito did *not* know was that he was flat out, blood streaming from his eyebrow.

Fear struck Omar's heart as he saw his buddy lying hurt and motionless. In one wild leap, he abandoned the swing, the park, and his buddies. He didn't stop running till he was several blocks away. Then he sneaked into his house quietly, not telling a soul about what had happened. But he was nervous all day, expecting the police to come pick him up at any time.

The next Sunday came too quickly. Though Omar was terrified about discovering Betito's fate, he had to go if he wanted to take his first Communion the following Sunday. The first thing Omar noticed when he arrived at church was Betito with his head wrapped in gauze, a red stain visible above the left eyebrow.

At least I didn't kill Betito. Omar sighed with relief, eyeing his buddy all through the class. *Plus, I didn't do it on purpose.*

After catechism, the boys did not race to the park as usual. They met outside on the street. Feeling guilty, remembering the catechism class the Sunday before, Omar sidled up to Betito and whispered, "I'm sorry I knocked you over last Sunday."

"What?" Betito cried, stepping back as if afraid of him. "So *you're* the one who just about killed me? I should have known!"

Not only Omar, but all of his buddies, had abandoned Betito the day of the accident. Omar never found out who called the ambulance to pick up the unconscious boy, but somebody, probably the park guard, had helped him. Since Omar's buddies hadn't tattled, the only way Betito found out who had hit him was through Omar's voluntary confession.

Betito remained Omar's enemy for the rest of their stay in Estelí. Unlike Omar, he apparently hadn't learned a bit from the teaching they had received on forgiveness.

The next Sunday was the big day—the first Communion for the catechism class. Omar dressed in his best school clothes and headed expectantly for the Catholic church.

Omar was filled with awe as he tiptoed into the big church and took his seat among the several dozen youth about to take their first Communion. He felt strange when it was his turn to confess his sins to the priest. Edging up to the cubicle that hid the priest from view, Omar waited nervously.

"What are your sins?" a deep voice intoned from within the confessional.

"I-I sometimes lie," Omar stuttered, wondering why he had to tell a total stranger, whom he couldn't even see, what his sins were.

"What else?"

"I sometimes steal money from my dad."

"What else?"

"I get mad sometimes."

"What else?"

"That's all I can remember," Omar faltered, wishing the ordeal were over.

The priest then explained to Omar how many times he should say the Lord's Prayer and recite Hail Marys. He concluded, "If you do this, your sins will be forgiven."

When the confessions were finished, the youth stood in line to receive the host for the first time. When it was his turn, Omar allowed the priest to place the thin wafer on his tongue. It tasted like a soda cracker and melted before he was able to chew it.

Omar left the Catholic church that day, feeling confused. None of the rituals really made sense to him, nor would they have any lasting effect on his life. Though in his heart he harbored a strong longing to be good, he wasn't convinced that what he had experienced that day was really going to help him achieve what his soul desired.

Omar sat on a little stool at the meat stand, surrounded by hanging pieces of beef. He would finish sixth grade that day, and he was looking forward to not having to go to school anymore. But right now he was disgusted. The usual hustle and bustle of market day had passed, but the cow's head, eyes bulging, still hung in the open-air window. At least the stomach was gone—that thing stank!

More and more, the load of being the man of the house was falling on Omar's frail shoulders. Omar had delivered the best cuts of meat early that morning while his dad sold at the stand. As soon as Omar got back, his dad had turned the selling over to him, took the money, and disappeared. Omar knew where.

Only two blocks away was a bar that Fermín visited more and more often. Midmorning, Fermín had come back to the stand. "Give me the cash," he had coaxed. "I need it."

This irritated Omar. His dad's habits were familiar to him; Fermín had always kept himself well supplied with alcohol. But Omar was old enough to realize that it really wasn't fair for his dad to spend money at the bar when there was never enough for necessities at home.

Omar also understood why his mom complained. The needs of the family, a load that Miriam mostly carried, were slowly being shared with the older children. It made Omar feel good that his mother depended on him. Still, he resented the constant nagging. More and more, Omar sensed the lack in his home life. He longed for security and closeness, but instead he faced constant bickering.

Sitting at the meat market, Omar had time to brood. Not only was home becoming less and less inviting, but his country's government was in shambles too. The Sandinista guerrillas, who had caused so much trouble when he had been a toddler, were now the ruling power. The Contras, a new guerrilla group sponsored by the United States, were the topic of the day, and the whole country was involved in a vicious civil war.

Just the week before, there had been serious combat two miles north of Estelí. As the *boom! boom! boom!* echoed in the distance, Omar felt oddly exhilarated, watching the flocks of people running toward the center of town. *Maybe someday I will be a Contra,* he dreamed.

As he whiled away the afternoon, Omar thought of happier times in Regadío with Grandma Ester and Don Cruz. How he longed to be back in the country where he could ride horse to his heart's content and roam the dry hills with his friends. In Estelí, it seemed he never had time to play.

Omar was too young to realize he was being prematurely pushed into an adult's world. Though his circumstances were making a man of him, he was being deprived of many of the joys of youth, and bitterness was slowly overpowering him.

Later that afternoon Omar sauntered into the kitchen to find Jáqueling and Cándida crying, and the rest of the children standing around in shock. His mama had her back turned, so Omar couldn't read her feelings. "What's going on?" he demanded, eyeing his mother.

Doña Miriam didn't answer. She seemed too troubled to speak.

"Andrés beat Daddy!" little Cándida sniffled.

"Andrés did *what?*" Omar demanded, facing his mother squarely. "Tell me the truth, Mama!"

Doña Miriam turned slowly. "It's true. Your cousin Andrés beat up your daddy."

"Why did he do that?" Omar's anger smoldered.

"Your daddy was drunk again," Miriam admitted sadly. "When he came back from the bar, he started hollering at the whole Sanchez household, and I guess Andrés just couldn't stand it anymore. First he knocked him over, then he dragged him around, beating him all the while."

"Why didn't somebody stop him?" Omar shook his head in disbelief.

"No one else was around over there—just Irma," Miriam answered. "And Andrés thinks he's too big to obey her anymore."

"Where is Daddy now?" Omar asked anxiously.

"He's back at the bar," Miriam answered nervously. "But just let it go, Omar. It was as much Fermín's fault as Andrés'. Since he was drunk . . ."

"But who ever heard of a man beating up a drunk?" Omar complained. "Of course, Daddy was at fault, but Andrés is stupid to beat up a drunk. He's going to pay."

Omar slipped out of the house to see if he could find Andrés, but his older cousin had left for an errand in town. *I'll get him later!* Omar vowed.

The very next day he had his chance. Coming back from butchering, Omar spotted Andrés digging a hole for a new latrine behind their house. The hole was chest deep, and Andrés was down in it, digging hard. Omar sidled up to the hole and challenged, "Why did you beat my dad?"

"None of your business, kid." Andrés laughed. "I beat up your dad because I wanted to. Plus, he deserved it. He was cursing our family up and down."

"But he was drunk," Omar snarled, picking up two rocks that were handy. "You're a coward to beat up a man when he's drunk."

"Look, kid, lay off if you know what's good for you!" Andrés commanded. "If you insist on bugging me, I'll beat you up too."

Two things happened simultaneously. Andrés popped up out of the hole, and Omar threw his first rock as hard as he could.

Andrés dodged the rock, and in an instant he was after Omar like a cheetah after a rabbit. Omar could have easily outrun Andrés if he hadn't been busy throwing rocks as he ran. In his anger, he snatched up and threw rock after rock. But Andrés was too fast, and Omar was too angry to hit Andrés even once with his vicious throws. Omar antagonized Andrés even further by hollering at the top of his voice, "Cursed Contra! Cursed Contra!"

True enough, Andrés had joined the Contras for a short time, but then he had turned himself and his arms in, and the Sandinistas had forgiven him. But it was not to Andrés' best interests to have somebody announce to the public that he had been sympathetic to the Contra cause. Omar was really asking for trouble!

On the street in front of the two houses, Andrés caught the angry young boy by his arm. Ripping off his belt with his free hand, he gave Omar a lashing he would never forget. Though twelve-year-old Omar was full of hate and anger, he didn't stand a chance against Andrés, a seventeen-year-old ex-guerrilla.

After the lashing, Andrés shoved Omar away and hurried back to his digging. Omar stood his ground, tears of rage streaming down his cheeks. As Andrés crossed over the fence, Omar yelled, "Andrés, someday I will be big. Then I am going to kill you!"

6

BATO'S PREDICTION

ONCE MORE, OMAR'S life took a big turn. From being a city boy helping in the butcher shop and going to school, he became a farm boy, living on what might someday become a grand ranch.

Fermín's brother Bato had come from the United States again. This time he bought a hundred-acre farm near the village of Naranjita, about six miles south of Regadío. He offered to trade the little house Fermín had built in Estelí for the farm in Naranjita. Tired of city life, and still struggling to make a living, Fermín accepted the trade with alacrity.

Omar loved the change and took to the farm like a coot to a marshy lagoon. The years in Estelí were fast becoming only a bad memory of endless work and heartbreaking troubles.

On the farm, Fermín built a small house. Then he moved Miriam and their children to Naranjita. Fermín had brought his horses along to the farm and bought a few cows, and now they were deep into farming. Or at least Omar was.

Miriam was bothered by how much time Fermín was spending in Regadío, leaving the work to the rest of the family. But it didn't bother Omar. He enjoyed the farmwork and relished his role as the man of the house. His pay was a lot of time to do the things he loved. Since his dad wasn't home much, Omar ran his own schedule and did what he wanted.

They hadn't lived in Naranjita long until the Montenegro family started hearing rumors from Regadío about Fermín and a young woman called Eva.

Eva was a pretty, spoiled, unmarried young woman with a little girl of her own. She lived with her parents and a string of siblings. Just as Miriam had done years before, Eva was falling for Fermín's fine clothes and high-falutin manners. She didn't seem to care what she was doing to Fermín's family in Naranjita.

But Fermín was still Omar's hero. At thirteen, Omar blindly believed his dad was in the right and that his mother was wrong to complain. Resenting Miriam and her quick tongue, Fermín turned Omar against her and the rest of the family. He also convinced Omar that he had to find other women because Miriam and her tribe were so terrible. Omar, quick at catching his dad's hints, wouldn't even allow some of Miriam's family to come visit them. Slowly but surely, Omar's heart turned bitter toward his mom and his sisters, who took Miriam's side.

In spite of the family troubles, several things about Naranjita brought Omar great satisfaction. Eventually, he would call the three years in Naranjita the best years of his youth.

One special thing about Naranjita was Onel. Miriam's Uncle Gustavo owned the farm adjacent to theirs, and his house was nestled just across a gully among the trees. Onel was Uncle Gustavo's son.

Omar turned fourteen soon after the move to Naranjita, and Onel had just turned twelve. Like Omar, Onel was outgoing and afraid of almost nothing. Being the oldest of the two, Omar became the natural leader in their inseparable friendship.

Another good thing about Naranjita was that Omar's little brother Milo, now eight years old, was starting to do things with him. Just as Fermín had been Omar's hero for so many years, Omar was fast becoming Milo's hero. If Omar wanted wild, adventurous companionship, he chose Onel and made Milo stay at home. But when Omar wanted to go some-where close or take care of the duties around the farm, he was happy to have Milo tag along. Little Melvin, now seven, often followed too.

But the best thing about Naranjita was that his dad gave Omar a colt. Omar had always loved horses. Back in Regadío, Omar had excelled at riding. Even in Estelí, Fermín had kept several horses on the outskirts of town. Omar took interest in them, and riding was his joy.

Now Omar had a horse of his own, even though it was still a baby. The colt's mother was just an ordinary nag, but Fermín had bred her to Bato's fancy black stallion. The little brown colt, born soon after they moved to Naranjita, showed signs of becoming a great horse.

Omar's lonely heart attached fiercely to his colt. He called him Golondrino after the swift-flying bird by that name. Even while the colt was still nursing, Omar tamed him by handling him almost daily. Soon the colt followed Omar around about as much as he did his mother. Omar dreamed of the day he could train Golondrino and ride him like the wind.

Tall mountains loomed around the Montenegro homestead in Naranjita like immense, friendly beasts protecting the inhabitants of the narrow little valley. The names of the two tallest mountains were Los Terreros, "earthly one," and El Volcán, "the volcano." One May afternoon at the end of a very dry season, huge black clouds billowed up over the two Naranjita mountains. The land was thirsty, and so were its people.

As the first raindrops fell, Omar and his siblings ran out onto the dusty road by their house. Like little Golondrino when his tummy was full of milk and the cool morning air made him frisky, the children kicked up their heels and played tag as the storm pounced. Even Omar's sisters, Jáqueling, Cándida, Ninozca, and little Selene, joined the boys in their play. A streak of lightning dropped behind El Volcán, the cone-shaped mountain right behind the house. A clap of thunder followed, and then the rain fell copiously.

The children, the yard, the mountain, and the whole Estelí region drank the water thirstily that afternoon. The children didn't stop playing in the rain until they were sopping and tired. Bursting into the house, they found their rooms to change their clothes. It didn't matter that they were soaking the dirt floor—it was as dry and thirsty as the yard had been.

Two hours later the rain stopped, leaving the land drenched and refreshed. Miriam fixed some delicious beans and served them with tortillas and salty cheese. It didn't take the children long to soak up the food just like the land had soaked up the rain. The tiny cracks left in their tummies were filled with piping hot black coffee, saturated with sugar. The family was content that night, appreciating the house that protected them from the elements.

Just one thing was lacking. As it got later, they all knew that Fermín would not be coming home for the night.

"I wonder where Dad is," Jáqueling said, frowning deeply. "Why isn't he coming home for the night?"

"I'm sure he's with Eva again," Miriam complained.

Angrily, Omar jumped up from his chair, spilling his coffee onto the dirt floor. Startled, the yellow cat sailed out the door. Omar shouted, "Don't you dare judge, Mama! You don't know what Daddy's doing."

Miriam shut her mouth. Omar was becoming an angry young man who was hard to get along with. She knew better than to try to explain the situation to the fuming boy glaring at her. She fled to the kitchen. Still upset, Omar slipped into his room and went to bed.

Several days after the hard rain, Omar walked out behind the house after the morning milking and yodeled across the gully, "*Oi*, Onel, let's go hunt iguanas." Minutes later Onel appeared.

Recently Fermín had brought home a borrowed assault rifle. "Man, since we're at war, I can find all kinds of goodies!" he had said with a chuckle. "They also gave me a quarter gunnysack full of bullets."

Now Onel and Omar had the choice of three guns—the old .22 that Fermín had owned for years, the .30-30 he had acquired when they moved to Naranjita, or the assult rifle that Omar hadn't tried yet. Picking up the AK-47, Omar bragged, "I can shoot this baby, because I watched Dad use it."

Onel shrugged. Who was he to tell his overly confident cousin what to do?

Picking up a machete and their fishing lines, the two boys called their mutts and headed out across the gully and into the hills. Between El Volcán and El Terrero lay a deep canyon with a rocky bed. Carrizal Creek chortled its merry way through the walls of stone and jungle. "I'm sure we can scare up some iguanas along these banks," Omar announced as his cousin followed him down the trail.

The land that had been powder dry, showing only browns and grays just days before, was flaunting fresh new colors. A sheen of light green was swallowing up the drab colors. After the seemingly endless dry season, Naranjita Valley was reawakening to life.

Omar and Onel dropped down into the creek bed flanked by trees of all shapes and sizes. The thick stand of brush embraced the creek like a cool green tunnel, blocking out the bright sky.

As Omar and Onel stepped into this unique passageway, a colorful tropical bird flung itself deeper into the woods, its long tail streaming behind it like a tail after a kite. The last cicadas of the season rasped their dying shrieks. The dogs ran ahead, sniffing the banks for iguanas. This was the wild world Omar loved.

Shifting the heavy assault rifle, Omar announced, "Let's hunt iguanas on the way downstream, and then we'll fish our way back. If we don't get any iguanas, we can at least take a mess of minnows home so Mama can make us fish soup."

The creek bed was mostly solid rock, and the clear water gurgled from pool to pool. Some of the pools were small and shallow and some were large and deep. Omar and Onel had tried them all on previous jaunts.

As the boys tiptoed along the waterway, they scanned the rocky banks and overhanging trees for iguanas. "Mama will be so happy if we bring several iguanas for lunch," Omar whispered. "I'm getting hungry already!"

"We've gotta find 'em first," Onel answered. "And then we have to shoot 'em, and you've never shot that gun yet, have you? If you do blast an iguana with that big gun, there probably won't be much meat left."

Just as they approached the deepest widest pool, Omar and Onel heard a rasping roar followed by the unmistakable *puk-a, puk-a, puk-a, puk-a* of a helicopter. "It's the army!" Omar exclaimed as the roar got louder. "I bet they're out looking for Contras."

"I wonder if they can see us." Onel gazed expectantly up into the trees.

Just as the green camouflaged chopper popped into sight, a crazy idea popped into Omar's head. "I'm going to shoot at that machine!" he yelled over the din, hoisting the gun to his shoulder.

"You're crazy!" Onel rasped, bending over and covering his face.

It didn't take long for Omar to pull a bead on the big chopper looming above them as it scouted the length of the canyon. But neither did it take him long to see something else that made him change his mind fast. Standing in the open doorway of the helicopter was a soldier scanning the bottom of the canyon like a hawk—and holding a bigger and deadlier machine than Omar's.

"Let's get out of here," Omar yelled over the drill of the helicopter's beating rotors. "They're gonna shoot us!"

The noise drowned out Omar's next sentence—"They might see us and think we're Contras!"

The two boys ran back upstream like a pair of spooked coyotes. All of Omar's desire to be part of the army and all of his ideas of shooting down helicopters gushed down the drain about as fast as the water gushed down each waterfall in the creek bed. All he could think was, *What if that man in the helicopter starts shooting down like I thought of shooting up?*

As Omar and Onel ran, the deafening noise slowly diminished. Satisfied that there were no Contras in the area, the chopper swerved and headed back the way it had come. Soon the boys' hearts, that had seemed to be competing with the *puk-a, puk-a, puk-a* of the helicopter's blades, were beating normally. As they walked along, panting and laughing, they forgot all about the iguanas and fish they had planned to catch.

The civil war didn't rage as severely in the Regadío Valley as it did in other parts of Nicaragua. The powerful city of Estelí kept its department under control. Very few Contras were ever able to approach the city, and that made life easier for the Naranjita folks. It also allowed Omar and Onel to enjoy the daily adventures that Naranjita offered them.

Music throbbed from the Montenegro farmhouse into the dark Nicaraguan night. Fermín's home was crammed with people. His boom box almost bounced on the table, and several kerosene lamps and a dozen candles lighted the scene.

Omar's uncle Bato sat in a chair in the middle of the little living room. He wore a gold neck chain and an expensive wristwatch, and a diamond ring flashed on his finger. His white teeth shone as he kept the crowd laughing with his jokes. Omar couldn't stop staring at him.

Bato had arrived earlier that evening and given out expensive gifts for everybody in the family—clothes, shoes, and trinkets. Omar received a rust-red leather vest with fringes and a pair of snazzy cowboy boots.

The family was prepared for Bato's visit, and Miriam had served a delicious meal of chicken soup with plenty of tortillas. It was avocado season, and Bato split the fruits one after another and downed the flesh with a sprinkle of salt. At the end Miriam served pumpkin cooked in dulce. Immense amounts of the rich, sweet stuff found their way into Bato's mouth, swished down with cup after cup of black coffee. It was astounding how much the big man could eat. Bato was tall, showing signs of obesity, but he was still an elegant man.

After the meal, Bato brought out several bottles of expensive whiskey. To Miriam's horror and Fermín and Omar's delight, Bato wanted everybody to drink. But what Omar liked even better than the whiskey were the stories about life in Los Angeles.

Every time Bato came to visit, often twice a year, he showed off wads of cash, carelessly carried around in his pockets and spent generously for everybody. Omar wondered where his uncle got all his money.

According to Bato's stories, his life in Los Angeles was full of fancy cars, luxurious restaurants, beautiful girls, sparkling casinos, and exciting bars. Bato made it all sound so glamorous. Apparently acquiring money was no problem at all.

Bato had gotten his green card and could work legally in the United States. He had a work contract that included providing watchmen for fancy businesses. What Omar didn't realize was that no one could possibly make as much money as Bato hauled around by being just a night watchman.

Later that evening, as the liquor was making everybody tipsy, Bato singled out Omar. "Come here, Omar. I'm proud of you. I can see that you're making a man out of yourself," Bato bragged. "You're the bright, tough kind. You're the kind of man that knows no fear. Your future isn't here in Regadío. Your future is in the great United States of America."

Omar smiled broadly, basking in the attention, but not saying a word. In his heart, Omar was willing that every word Bato was saying would come true. *Someday I will go to the great United States of America,* he dreamed. *I'll have money and I'll become famous.*

"Why would you want to spend the rest of your life in this sleepy place where there's no future?" Bato continued, draining a glass. "There's no excitement here—no fun. And worst of all, no money. You're too young yet, Omar, but get ready. You're not the kind to stay here. Within several years I'll come and take you to the States myself. You just be ready. Meanwhile, be a man. Have another drink, my boy!"

Milo and Melvin stood in awe. Knowing Omar's strong will, they surmised that what Bato was saying was going to come true. Omar's sisters stared at their legendary uncle. They, too, knowing Omar's fierce determination and his big dreams, had no doubt that someday Omar would travel to the States and become a great man.

Fermín sat back in his chair with a gleam in his eyes, grinning. Of all the people in the room, he was the happiest to see how Bato picked Omar out and lifted him to the skies. Hadn't he, Fermín, raised and trained his son to become as tough as nails and a daredevil through and through? Yes, he was sure Omar would do all those big things he had never been able to do himself.

Bato clinched his speech by picking up a glass of spirits and offering it to Omar. "Let's toast, Omar! You're the nephew that's most like his uncle Bato. Here's to our future together in that fancy city called Los Angeles!"

Omar and Bato laughed heartily as their glasses clinked together.

Only one person in the room did not like Bato's speech. Miriam's heart fluttered in fear and dread as she remembered her late daughter's words, "Poor Mama!"

Miriam didn't like Bato's lifestyle. She didn't like Bato at all, nor the things he represented. He was too much like Fermín, too proud. Together, Omar's father and uncle were poisoning her son's mind. She feared they would only lead him into trouble and much sorrow. Miriam sighed, feeling as if she could cry for a week. She breathed a little prayer. *Oh, Lord, don't let all this happen to my firstborn son!*

7

GOLONDRINO

THE NOONDAY SUN blazed down on the lush green knoll. Sprinkled all across the hillside, dozens of worshipers dressed in their colorful Sunday best knelt among the rocks. Near the top of the knoll stood a concrete shrine with an eighteen-inch white stone virgin standing inside. The little replica of Santa Ana, Regadío's patron saint, wore a golden crown and a purple silk dress.

Standing before Santa Ana, a priest in a somber black robe intoned words out of a little book. The worshipers repeated each phrase reverently.

A stiff wind whipped up the hillside, ruffling Santa Ana's dress. It also whipped the words out of the priest's mouth, making it hard for the worshipers to hear.

The wide flat area below the hillside ritual was bustling with activity, as noisy as the hillside was reverent. Perched in the center of the expanse of trimmed grass and a sprinkling of trees, a crude wooden house teemed with ladies cooking food for the celebration of Santa Ana Day.

There were more folks in the valley preparing for the party than there were worshipers on the hillside. Men stood around the house, smoking cigars and talking about the weather. Wild youth laughed and joked, bragging about their horses or their sinful pursuits. None of this made any difference to Santa Ana, because she was just a white limestone carving who knew nothing.

Fermín, having no respect for the stone statue, was not up on the hillside. He was hanging out with the men in the valley, and his mistress Eva was helping with the cooking. Doña Miriam and the younger children were at home in Naranjita. They would never go to such a place, mainly because they knew Eva would be there.

Omar and Onel were also in the valley, talking with their friends about the fun they were about to have. Fifteen-year-old Omar felt grown-up in his brand-new blue jeans, a red checkered shirt, and his rust-red leather vest. His dad had recently bought him a cream-colored cowboy hat, and his black cowboy boots glistened from a recent polishing.

Golondrino was still too young to ride, so on this Santa Ana's Day, Omar was riding Califa—his dad's best horse—a fancy paint with four white stockings. Tied under one of the shade trees, Califa was waiting for his part in the festivities.

That morning, the procession from Regadío to Las Nubes had been a sight to see. A dozen men walked ahead with the priest, taking turns carrying the shrine containing the little virgin. Close to a hundred people slowly tagged along, chanting Hail Marys as they left Regadío and trailed up the mountain toward Las Nubes.

After the worship ceremony, the real party began. In the valley, food and drink vendors sold meat tamales steamed in banana leaves, different breads made from corn, fried meat with tortillas, and of course, lots of liquor. Even the religious worshipers abandoned their ritual and started eating and drinking.

Sometime after the feast, Omar was holding Califa in at the edge of the crowd. Califa was prancing around, his muscles rippling under his shining red coat, mingling with the rest of the excited horses. It was then that Omar's cousin Sandra approached him shyly. "Omar, remember you promised to give me a ride on Califa someday? Would you give me that ride now?"

"Sure!" Omar answered proudly. He trotted the steed over to a rock and reined him in. Sandra scrambled onto the rock and bounded up into the saddle in front of Omar.

Sandra held Califa in as they trotted to the end of the valley. Then, swinging the mount around, she gave Califa full rein. This would be the fastest ride Sandra would ever get, Omar realized as he hung on for dear life. Califa seemed to have sprouted wings!

The horse flattened out and streaked across the valley. Sandra leaned forward, screaming and laughing, her long hair whipping in the wind.

They ate up the ground terribly fast, and suddenly a stand of trees appeared just ahead. Sandra hauled on the reins, but Califa had lost his head. Too excited to heed his rider, he took the bit in his teeth and plunged into the cluster of trees. The crowd watching from a distance gasped. "They're going to kill themselves!"

Sandra took the brunt of the blow as the two riders crashed into the branches of two trees and were ripped from the saddle. Califa sailed on, slipping between the two trunks, free of his riders.

Omar and Sandra got to their feet slowly. "Are you hurt?" Omar asked anxiously.

"No, I don't think so. Are you?"

"Naw, I'm all right," Omar drawled. "I don't know why Califa went crazy . . . sorry."

"All's well that ends well." Sandra laughed, brushing off her clothes. Other than several rips in their clothes and a bump here and there, the two were unhurt. But it was hard on Omar's pride, walking out across the valley to catch his horse.

After the racing, the musicians in the crowd pulled out their instruments—guitars, mandolins, violins, accordions, and trumpets. As the sun set, the music rose, and the people started to dance, drink, and carouse. The fiesta lasted all night long.

As the first streaks of daylight peeped over the Las Nubes Mountain, Omar was ready to head home. He had no idea where his dad was, and he was so drunk that he didn't really care. Omar paid no attention to the glorious sunrise. All he remembered later was the awful headache from the hangover and the drunks strewn along the trail from the top of the mountain down to the town of Regadío.

"Golondrino!" Omar yelled, stepping out of the yard one afternoon. On the hillside across the road, the handsome colt raised his head. The silhouette of the dark brown colt against the white clouds on the horizon etched a lovely scene, making Omar catch his breath.

Golondrino abandoned the lush grass he was cropping and cantered down the hill. *What a fortunate young man I am!* Omar gloated, as he opened the gate and let Golondrino slip through. *Soon I'm going to ride my own horse.*

Golondrino followed Omar to the wooden box on the porch where corn was kept. While Golondrino nibbled the corn, Omar brushed him, talking to him all the while.

"Golondrino, someday you'll be a grand horse. You and I are going to be the best of friends. We'll go many places together."

Omar slipped his right hand down Golondrino's front leg, caressing all the while. Then Omar lifted the colt's front hoof. Tapping on the hoof with his index finger and grinning, he whispered, "And this is the way I will shoe you any day now."

Omar went through the same procedure with all four legs, and the horse took it in stride. He was perfectly used to such handling. "Soon you will be the grandest horse in Estelí," Omar promised, hugging his horse's neck. "And I will be the grandest rider!"

Omar brushed and handled Golondrino almost every afternoon. Almost a two-year-old, Golondrino followed him around like a puppy. Omar could call him from anywhere, even from inside the house, and the horse would come immediately. Golondrino would walk right in through the front door and into the living room if Omar was there.

Golondrino wasn't the only thing that brought excitement and enjoyment into Omar's life in Naranjita. Almost always Onel was part of the plans. The two cousins often went hunting all through the hills of Naranjita. They spent hours fishing along the creek.

Several evenings a week, Onel and Omar would ride into Regadío where a communal building was set up for folks to watch movies. Regadío had no electricity yet, but a generator provided power to run old-time films.

Omar especially enjoyed watching the rodeos. Bullfighting and bull riding were among his favorites.

Inspired by the movies, Omar and Onel were soon deep into riding calves down on the Naranjita farm. Omar would pick out the feistiest calf, and Onel would help him snub it to a tree out in the field. Next, they would tie a rope tightly around the calf's chest, just behind its front legs. Then, taking turns, they would crawl onto the calf's back. Once they were ready, left hand wrapped well into the flank-strap, they would yell, "Let him loose!"

The next several seconds were exhilarating for Omar. He loved the challenge of letting his body whip around with the calf's movements while keeping his balance. He soon learned that the secret was to keep his spurred feet clamped tightly around the calf's belly. "Someday I'll become a professional bull rider!" Omar would brag to Onel.

Fermín had moved Miriam and the younger children back to Estelí. He claimed this was so the girls could have better schooling, but the rumors were that he wanted to bring Eva to the farm. Because Omar took Fermín's side, and since, at age fifteen, he was already general manager of the farm, Fermín was happy to let Omar run the setup.

Whether the rumor about Eva moving to the farm was true or not, Miriam was determined not to let it happen. Every weekend she and a couple of the girls came home, ostensibly to cook for Omar and make sure things were okay. As long as Miriam was coming back regularly, she was sure Eva would be too proud to move to the farm.

So now Omar was on his own from Monday through Friday. Not only did he do most of the farmwork, but he also had to cook for himself. He didn't really mind cooking, but he felt like a slave, having to work the farm and cook for himself too.

One afternoon when Omar was alone and bored, he yodeled over the gully. Onel immediately popped up.

"Did your dad give you permission this quick?" Omar wondered.

Onel winked at Omar. "No, I sneaked away."

"Do me a favor," Omar coaxed. "I need bread. I'm tired of being the housewife, and I'm totally out of cooked food. I don't want to cook this evening. If you'd run to Regadío and buy me some bread, we could just eat bread with coffee."

Onel hesitated. "Can I use one of your horses?"

"Sure! Go saddle up Dad's black mare."

Minutes later, Omar handed Onel a fifty-córdoba bill. "Bring me a bag of bread, and we'll throw a party when you come back."

After Onel left, Omar finished doing the evening chores, his thoughts seething. He was sick and tired of living alone. His dad was gone half the time, and he could hardly wait till school was out so Miriam and the girls could be home again.

Oh, well, at least this evening I won't have to cook, Omar told himself. *I'm going to make a big batch of coffee, and Onel and I are going to have a bread and coffee party.*

Dusk was sneaking over the mountains by the time Onel rode in. The coffee was hot, and Omar's mouth watered because he hadn't had anything but rice and beans and salty cheese for a week. He was hungry for that bread!

Onel stopped the horse in front of the house. "And the bread?" Omar growled, his eyes looking over Onel and the big white sack on the saddle in front of him. It looked as if he had bought enough groceries for two weeks. "Where's the bread?"

Onel stared back at him, looking puzzled.

"Where's the bread?" Omar barked, his anger beginning to rise.

Onel cringed, knowing that trouble was brewing like a storm in May. Omar's capacity for patience was very small. By the look in Omar's eyes, there had to be some big misunderstanding. Onel pointed at the bulging sack in front of him and answered weakly, "Here's the bread."

"What?" Omar yelled, reaching up and jerking the sack off the horse. "How much bread did you buy?"

"You told me to get a sack of bread."

By now Omar had opened the sack and was staring into it, his eyes almost as wide as the sack's mouth. "What on earth!" he scolded. "You bought enough bread for several months!"

Onel jumped off the horse, confused. Should he get out of here? Was Omar going to hit him?

Suddenly Omar threw back his head and burst out laughing. "How much bread did you buy, anyway?"

"Fifty córdobas worth . . ." Onel stuttered. "That's what you gave me. I knew you were hungry for bread, so I figured you wanted a lot."

"I only wanted a small bag of bread!" Omar roared. "Maybe five córdobas worth. I expected you to bring me a whole pile of change. Instead of that, you brought me enough bread for the whole neighborhood!"

Suddenly Onel knew that the danger of getting hit by his buddy was over, and he, too, saw the humor in the situation. "I'll come over every day, and we'll eat bread for breakfast, lunch, and supper!" Onel cackled.

"We'll eat bread until we get sick of it!" Omar threw in. "We'll give some to the neighbors, feed some to the dogs, and live it up! But what will Dad say when he realizes I spent all of the money so fast?"

Onel only laughed harder.

"Well," Omar snapped. "Come on in. The coffee's ready. Let's start eating that bread. That's what you brought it for, right?"

8

HIGHWAYMEN

AFTER THE SCHOOL year was up, Miriam abandoned Estelí against Fermín's wishes and brought all of the children back to the farm in Naranjita, determined not to lose it to a woman who hadn't worked for it. Even though Omar was mean to the family, Miriam pitied him, realizing he carried a heavy load.

Fermín denied all the rumors Miriam repeated to him. But one afternoon Miriam, goaded by a friend, followed her husband into Regadío and caught him walking boldly to a birthday party with Eva by his side.

As Miriam returned to Naranjita, the stiff wind whipped fiercely at her tear-stained face. By the time she got home, it was dark. The girls had made a simple meal of beans, tortillas, and cheese. As the family gathered in the kitchen to eat, Miriam told them about her encounter with Fermín and Eva. Miriam's hair was unkempt, her eyes distressed, and her face sad. For once, Omar found a bit of pity in his heart for his mother. So he held his tongue.

But Omar still admired his father. Something good had happened since they had moved to Naranjita. Fermín had stopped drinking. Was it because Eva was religious and warned him that she wouldn't pay him any attention if he drank? Did he finally see that alcohol was killing him and ruining his family? The whole family, even Omar, was relieved that Fermín had been able to stop drinking.

But about the time Fermín stopped drinking, Omar began to acquire the habit. Whenever Omar heard about a party in Naranjita or Regadío, he showed up. Onel's dad never let him go with Omar to these events, and Milo and Melvin were too small to accompany him, so often Omar went alone. He began associating with a rowdy crowd of youth who were making a bad reputation for themselves in Naranjita.

Though Fermín had stopped drinking, that didn't stop him from attending wild parties—in fact, he usually helped plan them. On every special holiday, Fermín was on the planning committee, and when the party was held in Regadío, he took Eva with him.

Out on the stretch of road between La Comarca and the Pan-American Highway, remnants of the civil war were still causing trouble. Bands of well-armed highwaymen sometimes stopped vehicles and pedestrians alike and stripped them of their belongings, sometimes even taking their shoes. These outlaws were well-armed with assault rifles, and people avoided traveling at night for fear of being detained.

One night, when Fermín was at home for several days, the family had gone to bed at 7:30 as usual. Like they often did, they were talking back and forth in the dark. Suddenly the dogs started barking behind the house. The barking was nothing new. People often came past on the road after dark.

But why were the dogs barking behind the house? Then the family heard feet shuffling outside the back door. "Somebody's out there!" Fermín hissed, jumping out of bed. Omar's feet also hit the floor.

The sound of metal rasping against metal made their blood run cold—they recognized it as the cocking of a gun. Barely had the terrifying sound sunk in when the dreaded command came. "Open up!"

Omar peeped through the cracks, just like his dad was doing. What they saw was a gang of well-armed men standing right outside the doorway.

Fermín, Omar, and a cousin named Rogelio, who was staying overnight, gathered inside the back door, nerves tense. Fermín looked at his son and whispered, "Well, we have no other options." Then he threw the door open.

A man dressed in camouflage and cradling a loaded assault rifle ordered the three men into the backyard. "Get facedown!" he ordered, as soon as Fermín had handed over the bit of cash from his pocket.

Omar understood what was happening. Fermín had just recently taken out a loan from the bank in Estelí to buy cattle. Fortunately, he had already paid for the cattle. Somehow these men had found out about the loan, but they were one day too late!

Though Omar felt little fear, and even though he wanted to stand up to the highwaymen, he followed his father's example. Once the three men were flat on the ground, the robbers milled around while the boss talked to Fermín.

"Where's your pistol?" he snarled, pointing his AK-47 at Fermín.

"I don't have one," Fermín lied, his face in the dust.

"Yes, you do!" The robber spat the words out between his teeth. "We know you do."

"If you don't believe me, search the house," Fermín answered. "I don't have a gun."

While the leader questioned Fermín, a few robbers went into the house and took everybody's watches and the big recorder. One of the robbers ordered the ladies to prepare food. So the women slipped out to the kitchen and stirred up the fire.

When there was a lull, Fermín whispered to Omar, "Look, if something happens to me, you know what your job is. I stuck the pistol under the bean barrel before I opened the door."

Omar nodded eagerly in the dark, and his heart burned. *Yes, if Dad dies tonight, I will take revenge!*

The commander ordered Fermín to get up, and several robbers took him farther out into the darkness while another robber guarded the two boys. Omar expected to hear gunfire any minute. *They're going to kill my dad!* he thought. As he waited, his hackles rose, and suddenly he was very, very angry.

Omar scooted over till his head was close to Rogelio. "Look, these guys won't shoot," he whispered. "Let's just get up. I'll go get the pistol, and you get the *cutacha*.[6] They're going to kill—"

"Hey, what's going on?" the guard robber hissed, aiming his gun at Omar. "You shut up if you know what's good for you!"

"I'll shut up when I feel like it!" Omar barked back. "And if you want to shoot me, just go ahead!"

Omar nearly got to his feet, but two things held him back. If he got up, they would probably start shooting, and they would start with his dad. He also heard Rogelio whimpering beside him, "Omar, please shut up. They're going to kill us all."

But Omar still had the last word. Lying on the ground, he snarled, "If you think I'm afraid of you, guess again."

Fermín was able to convince the robbers that he truly had spent all the borrowed money on cattle. So they brought him back and ordered him to lie facedown again. By then the food was ready, and the nervous ladies served the wicked men coffee, tortillas, beans, cheese, and sour cream. The men on the ground wisely held still.

Suddenly the robbers were ready to leave. They all gathered in the yard by the prostrate men. "Everybody get inside!" the leader commanded.

So they did.

"Close the door and cut off the lights!"

They heard the shuffle of footsteps as the highwaymen left. "Where's that pistol?" Omar hissed.

Fermín held him back. "Wait," he whispered anxiously. "I think there's one guy out there yet. And let's be careful. These men are too well-armed to mess with."

Suddenly the air smelled strongly of kerosene, and the next thing they knew, the kitchen, a separate building from the main house, lit up in flames.

"Let's get that fire out!" Omar yelled. Not fearing the robbers, he made a dash for the kitchen. Fortunately, the fire was feeding on the kerosene

---

6   *Cutacha:* a special machete for fighting, sharpened on both sides and with a sharpened point like a sword.

only—the board walls were not burning. The flames were doused quickly with water from the barrel in the corner of the kitchen. Then they all went back into the house and locked up.

The day after the scare, Fermín lost no time. He borrowed an assault rifle and acquired a large quantity of bullets. He gave Omar some clear instructions about protecting themselves. And he moved to Regadío for good.

Still only fifteen, Omar was again forced to take his father's place as the man of the house. But what kind of man was he becoming?

As soon as Fermín left for Regadío, Omar got to work. He perched an old empty metal barrel in the corner of the living room and filled it with sand.

"This," he told his mother and siblings, "is my war trench. See, back here behind the barrel I have enough room to hide. From here I can easily see both the front and back doors. As soon as those good-for-nothings come through either of those doors, I'll blast them with this gun. I don't care if there are fifty of them—they all have to come through one of the doors. I will get them all, and they can't get me!"

During the next several weeks, the nights were terrifying for Miriam. She was as much afraid of what her son might do as she was of the robbers themselves. Omar had taken the responsibility of guarding the family, and every night he made sure everything was prepared. Then he would go to sleep with the gun by his bed.

Every evening Miriam imagined what would happen if the robbers ambushed them again. She knew that Omar would not open up the house and would certainly shoot anybody who dared invade their territory. So after Omar was asleep, Miriam would slip into his bedroom and snitch the gun and hide it. Since the robbers never came again, Omar never woke up to find his gun missing. After a month of no robbers, their fears subsided and life slipped back to normal.

One good thing that kept Omar's life exciting was Golondrino. He rode the horse daily, and the two of them blended well as horse and trainer. Omar taught Golondrino to obey him like a pup. Whenever Omar dismounted and wanted Golondrino to stay put, all he had to do was give a little jerk on the bridle, and Golondrino wouldn't move until Omar called him.

One day Omar left Golondrino outside of Grandma Ester's house in Regadío. After he was seated in the living room, visiting with the folks and enjoying a cup of coffee, he hollered, "Golondrino!"

To Omar's delight and everyone else's shock, Golondrino walked right into the living room looking for his master.

Omar grew more and more involved with a gang of about a dozen rowdy youngsters. More and more, the group relied on Omar for leadership. Only one thing could come from such a situation—plenty of trouble.

9

GROOMING THE NEIGHBOR'S HORSES

THE MOONLIT NIGHT seemed almost as bright as day. The two brothers slipped off the main road and sneaked through the fields. They flushed out a nighthawk, and it flew ahead of them in quick zigzags. Omar walked along nonchalantly, followed by Milo, now ten years old.

In the moonlight, Omar found the two horses he was looking for—two handsome paints, one red and white and the other a roan with several white splotches. These two horses were the pride and joy of Miriam's uncle Gustavo and his oldest son Donald.

"Okay, Milo," Omar commanded. "I'm going to rope these two beauties. You help me corner them if they start running."

Fifteen minutes later, Omar had both horses tied to the fencerow. Now it was time for the grooming. "Okay, I'll cut off these horses' tails and manes." Omar chuckled. "And you hold the hair. We can't let it lie here because then they'll know where this happened and maybe figure out who did it."

Omar pulled a knife from his waist and began to saw off the first fancy horse's tail. Then he whacked off its lovely mane. By the time he was done, the two horses looked a fright, even in the moonlight. Milo's arms were loaded with horsehair, and Omar felt triumphant about his revenge.

This drama had begun when Donald, Onel's older brother, had started sneaking around Omar's house trying to court fourteen-year-old Jáqueling on the sly. Omar hated the man for being such a chicken. Why didn't he just come over and ask Miriam for permission and date her openly?

One day he caught Donald down by the creek that ran between their houses, snitching a chance to talk to his girlfriend. Jáqueling and Cándida were out among the trees near the creek, cooperating with the sneaky plan. Omar hollered, "Donald, what do think you're doing down there, sneaking around our creek?"

Donald was afraid Miriam would hear Omar's brash accusation. "What do you care?" he yelled back. "Mind your own business, you little brat!"

"This *is* my business!" Omar screamed, picking up a rock. "I'm the man of the house over here since my dad left. And you know Dad doesn't want you seeing my sister!"

When stones began whizzing through the air between the two cousins, the girls fled. But before anyone got hit, Omar's anger overtook him. Turning as if on a dime, he stopped throwing rocks and made a beeline for the house. As he passed his mother, who was coming to investigate, he hissed, "I'm going for the gun to shoot Donald! He's trying to sneak a talk with Jáqueling again."

Miriam's blood ran cold. She hurried on to Gustavo's place to warn him. Donald had already fled for the house.

"Look, Gustavo," Miriam gasped. "Omar's in a rage. He just ran for his gun. He wants to shoot Donald!"

"What did Donald do?" Gustavo asked anxiously.

"He was down by the creek watching for a chance to talk to Jáqueling," Miriam explained, her eyes as troubled as the sky before a storm.

Gustavo acted quickly. Omar's gun was a borrowed one, since Fermín, once more needing money, had sold all the guns he owned. Instructing Donald to keep well hidden, Gustavo raced to the gun owner's home. He begged the owner to go immediately to Omar and demand that he return the borrowed gun.

In a matter of hours, the gun owner approached Omar. "I need my gun back. My friend showed up and he wants me to go deer hunting this evening."

Of course, Omar smelled the rat, but he gave the gun back, saying in his heart, *I'll still get even!*

That same evening Omar sidled up to Milo and whispered, "Come help me with a secret mission." Milo, always ready to follow Omar on any adventure, agreed. "Go hide the lariat in the weeds up the road a ways," Omar ordered. "Then do just what I say."

Omar stuck a knife in his belt. After dark, he and Milo went to while away the evening with friends at the tiny village between Naranjita and Regadío. As soon as the moon was out, the time was ripe. Omar and Milo walked toward home till they reached the site where the lariat was hidden. Then Omar told Milo to tie the lariat to his ankle.

"We can't afford to let any passerby see that we carry a lariat," Omar explained, "or tomorrow they'll know we were the culprits. So tie the lariat to your ankle and walk behind me till we're far away from any people."

After Omar had sheared the fancy horses, he led Milo over to a rock wall. He searched in the moonlight for a hole among the rocks. Before they headed for home, they stuffed all the hair into the rocks, leaving no evidence for anyone to discover.

Miriam thought Omar and Milo had acted a bit strange before they left that evening, and even stranger when they came home, but she didn't voice her suspicions.

The next day, however, when everybody found out that Gustavo and Donald were furious and too embarrassed to ride their bedraggled horses to town, Miriam marched over to her uncle's place again. "Omar is the guilty one!" she moaned.

"I already guessed that," Gustavo huffed. "But how can we prove it?"

"Omar won't talk," Miriam admitted, "but if I can get Milo alone, I think he'll confess."

But Omar kept Milo close by his side most of the day. Since Fermín had made Omar the boss of the farm, and since Miriam dreaded conflict, he managed to keep Milo busy till evening. He knew he couldn't afford to let his mama get hold of Milo.

But Miriam eventually discovered the truth. Milo denied everything when his mama questioned him. But Miriam saw in his eyes that he was lying.

She gave Milo a lashing that he would never forget, and then Milo confessed everything. Of course, Miriam told her uncle the truth that same evening.

Gustavo took quick action. The next day he and Donald traveled to Regadío and later to Estelí on their second-best horses.

That afternoon Fermín showed up at the farm with a slip of paper and a troubled expression. "I have a citation to the police station in Estelí," he announced to Omar. "They're asking me to come in with you tomorrow morning. What's going on?"

Omar told his father the whole story.

"Serves the old hound dogs right!" Fermín sneered, giving vent to his malice for Miriam's relatives. "I've always told you they're scoundrels."

Fermín paused, and Omar could see the hate in his eyes. Why did Fermín detest Miriam's family so much? Much later, Omar would understand that Fermín's hate was simply because Miriam's family was against him and complained about how he treated Miriam. The problems all pointed to one cause: Eva.

Fermín scratched his chin thoughtfully. "Even so, we'll have to show up at the police station in Estelí, or we'll land in more trouble. Let's head out tomorrow on the 7 a.m. bus, so we can work on this before Donald and Gustavo get there."

To Omar's surprise, when he and Fermín arrived at the police station, he was roughly separated from his dad. Because Omar was still a minor, they couldn't put him in a cell, so they took him into the back and locked him up in a big room. Omar felt lost.

With Omar locked up, Fermín realized they were in serious trouble. He knew his brother Bato was back from the United States again, so he walked down the street to his house. Since Bato managed to keep the police on his side by throwing parties and inviting them to drink, he could get away with practically anything.

As soon as Bato stepped into the police station, the atmosphere changed. Pointing at Fermín, Bato said, "This man is my brother, and it's my favorite nephew you've locked up." The police were agreeable when Bato sweet-talked them into leniency with Omar and his ruffled father.

"We'll let the youngster go soon," they promised.

Meanwhile, Gustavo and Donald arrived for the citation. When they had all been gathered in a special room in front of the investigating officer, Fermín looked Gustavo in the eye. "What do you want for those junky manes and tails?" he sneered. "I'll pay whatever you charge."

Omar watched Gustavo's face closely. His eyes were sad, not angry. "I'm not asking for pay, Fermín. Money won't put the manes and tails back on my horses. What I'm asking for is peace."

Donald sat there smoldering while Omar smothered a grin.

Fermín was quiet, his face like glass. He didn't answer.

"All I'm asking is that we get along, Fermín. We're not only neighbors, but also relatives. I asked for this meeting so we could make peace."

Unfortunately, peace was as far away as Antarctica, and the atmosphere just as cold.

The officers took Omar back to his room, and Fermín and Gustavo went to the secretary's office to sign papers. Gustavo signed that they turn Omar loose with no charges. Gustavo and Donald left, but Fermín waited for his son.

At 1 p.m., Omar was released. Fermín and Omar didn't talk much as they traveled back to Regadío on the bus, but Omar knew that as far as Fermín was concerned, he was free to keep tormenting their neighbors.

In some ways, Miriam was proud of her oldest son. He took the responsibility of the farmwork seriously. Since Fermín had moved to town, Omar took good care of the livestock as well. Keeping order at home was another thing that Omar took seriously—too seriously, in fact. At sixteen, rash and outgoing, he was not always wise in what he allowed and disallowed. He often clashed with his sisters, but Miriam felt helpless to intervene, because Omar had his dad's support. When Omar demanded something unreasonable, his excuse was, "I'm only obeying orders."

One morning as Omar wolfed down his breakfast of rice and beans, tortillas, and two fried eggs, Miriam watched him thoughtfully. What bothered her most was Omar's increasingly violent responses when things didn't go his way. It seemed that he feared neither God nor man—maybe not even the devil.

Miriam's heart trembled as she thought about Omar's future. Recently, he had been going to parties and drinking heavily, and his violent fits were escalating daily. But Miriam still loved her son, and she breathed an anxious prayer, *God, please take care of my son.*

As soon as Omar had eaten, he slipped out to tackle the work that needed to be done, Milo tagging behind. Miriam returned to patting out tortillas, but the worry didn't go away.

The week wasn't up before a terrible incident confirmed Miriam's worst fears. Omar and his rough gang of buddies traveled to Regadío one evening for what they called fun. Omar, wearing a knife at his belt, rode Golondrino proudly. His sharpened *cutacha* in its sheath was tied at his horse's side, right under the stirrup.

At dusk they rode up to Grandma Ester's place where the gang often hung out. Reining in their horses and hooting and howling as usual, they noticed a batch of Regadío boys standing along the street, smoking and jeering. Among them was Chepe, looking very angry. Omar knew why.

Chepe stepped forward. "Hey, Omar!" he shouted. "You've been messing with my girlfriend. We'll settle this issue tonight."

Before Omar could respond, the oldest Naranjita gangster jumped in. "Chepe, settle that with me, okay. Omar's still a youngster, but I'll take you on."

Everyone was surprised when Omar interrupted, his voice cold. "Ruben, don't worry. Leave Chepe to me. I'm not afraid of him. He's angry because his girl likes me. I'm ready to settle with him right now. Alone."

Chepe had gone too far to back out now. Striding toward the Naranjita gang, Chepe barked, "Okay, Omar and I are going to fight this out, and nobody meddles in!"

"And nobody meddles in!" Omar echoed. He flung himself off Golondrino, and on the way down he jerked out his *cutacha*.

Chepe came boldly, thinking that this was going to be just an ordinary fistfight. When Omar burst out from among the pack of horses, Chepe caught the gleam of the blade. But it was too late to run. Chepe dodged as Omar thrust his *cutacha* toward him.

The *cutacha* missed Chepe's torso, but sliced his shirt and nicked his side. Chepe leaped back, then raced back to his buddies on the sidewalk. "He cut me with his *cutacha!*" he cried.

In an instant, the Naranjita boys dismounted and began collecting stones to defend themselves. Omar headed toward Chepe again, but suddenly, a little woman burst out of the shadows.

Raising her hands high, she fearlessly stepped between the two. "My boys, don't you dare be hurting each other like that! What a shame!"

It was Grandma Ester.

Chepe and his buddies turned and fled down the street, and the Naranjita gang remounted their horses.

As Omar leaped onto Golondrino, he remembered what had happened thirteen years before when Grandma Ester had pled for Felipe. Grandma Ester had done it again! *I was going to kill Chepe, but she stopped me*, Omar realized, trembling. This time *she* had been *his* guardian angel!

10

THE MAKING OF A MONSTER

OMAR'S EYES SMOLDERED as he clenched a leather bridle in his fist, ready to punish his two sisters cowering in the corner. He had them trapped.

Even as he raised his arm to begin lashing them, he remembered that just the week before, his dad had flailed the girls in exactly the same way. *I'm becoming just like my dad,* Omar realized. But at that moment, he didn't care.

The week before, a photographer had wandered into Naranjita, going from house to house and offering his services. "In exchange for a down payment, I'll take any photo you ask for," he promised. "A month from now, I'll come by again to deliver and to charge the balance."

The smooth-talking photographer had no trouble convincing Omar, Jáqueling, and Cándida. The girls, being at the age when looking pretty mattered, were soon dressed and ready to pose in some new look-alike clothes their mother had bought for them. Omar wore his new cowboy hat, his best clothes, and his rust-red leather vest. The older children even persuaded little Melvin and Alvaro to pose.

Everything about the photos had seemed grand until Fermín stopped by later that day. Little Melvin, all excited because photos for his poor family were such a rare treat, had blurted out the whole story. Fermín had flown into a rage. "What a crazy waste of money for your vanity!" he shouted, hunting for the bridle. Then he had lashed the girls.

Left to right: Jáqueling, Alvaro, Cándida, Melvin, Omar.

Fermín didn't even ask if Omar had been involved in the photography business; he was afraid to touch his older son anymore. Fermín's unreasonable outburst angered Omar, but he didn't say a word.

Now the same two girls were not cooperating with Omar's demands, and he was even angrier than his dad had been. Omar didn't understand himself. Why was he so angry all the time? But right now he was too angry to figure it out. He raised the leather strap and started to flail.

Just as he struck Jáqueling, Miriam burst into the room. "No, you don't, my son!" she cried, stepping between Omar and his screaming sisters. "These girls are human beings—they are not beasts! And you are Omar Montenegro, not Fermín Montenegro."

But Omar's rage had made him dangerous, and he forgot to respect even his mother. First, he kicked her, and then he pushed her across the room, pummeling her with his fist. Miriam slammed against the wall and crumpled to the ground, weeping and heartbroken. Omar fled, shocked at what he had done.

He wasn't surprised that his mother went to the police station in Estelí that same day and showed them her black and blue marks. She had never involved the police before, but this was enough. The violence in her home had to stop.

Again, the police extended a citation for Omar, and Miriam brought it home. But the citation was not only for him—it also included Fermín. The next day, Omar and Fermín went to the police station again.

"Omar has become impossible at home," Miriam explained, tears streaming down her face. "But it's not his fault. His dad is ruining him." Then she told the investigator about Fermín's wild ways, his hatred for her relatives, and his brutal treatment of her and the children over the years.

Fermín sat with a face of stone, although his mouth curved in a little smirk. He did not say a word. Omar also said nothing. However, he knew that his mother was telling the truth.

After Miriam had spewed her frustrations, the investigator turned to Omar. "We do have a prison for minors," he warned. "You'll end up there if you don't mend your ways, boy." But most of his words were for Fermín. Again, Fermín refused to speak.

For a while, things seemed to return to normal at home. Apparently, Miriam believed the situation would improve. However, Miriam's family did not intend to let it go.

The following week, Omar went to town to buy supplies for the farm. As he rode past a bar on his way home, he heard a gruff voice from inside. "Aha! So there you are! Today we'll find out if you'll learn to respect your mother or not. Today I'm going to teach you a lesson!"

The angry voice belonged to his mother's brother Saul, an ex-military man who had recently moved back to Regadío. Thick-chested and tough as nails, he was respected by everyone. And right now, he was probably half drunk.

Fear leaped into Omar's heart. He spurred his horse and fled down the rocky road toward Naranjita.

Jerking out his *cutacha*, Saul leaped onto his own horse and galloped after Omar. But Omar had two things in his favor: his horse, Golondrino's mother, could run like the wind, and Omar was as light as a feather. Saul was bigger, and his horse a notch slower. The horses flew down the rocky road, heads stretched forward, their shod hooves clattering. Saul shouted over the noise, and Omar heard every word.

Saul denounced Omar as a horrible piece of humanity. He berated him for the awful things he had done to his mother and sisters. "What you need is a real man to set you straight! If I get my hands on you, I'll give you a beating you'll never forget!" Saul also yelled out plenty of ugly words about the irresponsible Fermín. Omar knew that Saul's words were largely true, but as he raced ahead, his hatred for his uncle increased a hundredfold.

When Saul realized he was falling behind, he shouted, "I don't want to ever see you in Regadío again!"

Omar hollered back, "I'm going to meet you again, sometime later!"

When Fermín came to Naranjita, Omar didn't tell him about Saul, but he watched for a chance to sneak his dad's pistol. *If I can get the pistol, I'll ride into Regadío and shoot my uncle,* he plotted.

A few days later, someone told Fermín how Saul had insulted his son. Furious, he rode to Naranjita and asked Omar for the whole story. Omar spared no details, including what Saul had said about Fermín.

"You and I will go to Estelí tomorrow!" Fermín declared. "I'm going to buy you a pistol so that crazy family learns to leave you alone." They found a secondhand pistol, a semi-automatic Russian Makarov. "It's quite expensive, but it will meet your needs," Fermín explained.

Omar nodded, cradling the pistol in his hands. "Now we go buy ammunition." Fermín smiled at his son.

"Sure thing!" Omar cheered.

"Now, listen to me," Fermín explained. "Don't go looking for Saul or for any of Miriam's relatives. Wait till they come bother you. If Saul tries any more tricks, empty this Makarov into him!"

But Omar was thinking, *Dad, if you only knew. I'm not waiting for Saul to come to me. He already did. I'm going after him as soon as I have a chance!*

"Omar, don't ever let anyone run over you again!" Fermín finished.

The ugly, warped message sank deeply into Omar's vulnerable, already violent heart, and it would be many years until it was erased from his mind. What would hold him back from becoming a monster? Poor Mama. She was in for a long rough haul!

"I don't ever want to see you in Regadío again!" Uncle Saul had said. But the very next day Omar, dressed in his best, was riding Golondrino toward Regadío. *Saul is going to see me,* Omar thought. *He'd better watch out.*

There was nothing unusual about Omar riding into town—but this was the first time he had come armed. *If Saul sees me,* thought Omar, *I'll make him notice me. I'm carrying my own pistol out in the open. Just like my dad!*

Omar passed the bar at the entrance of town; Saul wasn't there.

But as Golondrino trotted up Main Street, Omar saw what he was looking for. A few houses down from Grandma Ester's, two men stood in a doorway talking. One was a man named Naftalí; the other was Saul.

Adrenaline rushed through Omar. He glared at Saul as he rode past without a word. He saw recognition in Saul's eyes.

Omar tied Golondrino to a sapling in front of Grandma Ester's house, dismounted, and headed toward the two men who stood stiffly in the doorway, eying him. He intended to say several words to the man he hated before he pulled his gun.

But before Omar opened his mouth, Naftalí exclaimed, "Saul, that boy's armed!"

Saul whipped around the corner and disappeared into the house. Omar swore in disgust. *That chicken!* he jeered inwardly. *I expected he'd stand up to me.*

"Hey, I came to talk to you!" Omar yelled from the sidewalk. "Are you scared?"

After that, Saul carefully avoided his nephew. Omar soon saw that his uncle wanted to avoid an armed confrontation. Seeing that Saul didn't really want to hurt him, Omar's heart softened, and the crisis subsided. However, the fight with Miriam's family continued to burn.

Doña Chepa, Miriam's biological mother and Omar's grandmother, had moved with her husband René to a farm a few miles from Regadío. Chepa was angry to learn that Omar was after her son Saul, and she determined to set the young man straight.

A few days later Omar was sitting in Grandma Ester's kitchen, waiting for a bite to eat. Suddenly he heard a commotion in the front room. What a bustling and clatter of women's voices! Omar jumped to his feet.

What Omar saw next almost made him laugh. His two grandmothers burst through the door. Grandma Chepa was brandishing a huge stick and screaming, "Where is he? I hate that devil. I'm going to bash his head in!"

Grandma Ester hung onto Chepa for dear life and retorted, "Come on, Chepita, you don't want to do that. He's your grandson—your own flesh and blood."

"I don't care who he is. He's stalking my son Saul to kill him!"

Omar slipped around the corner and ran out to the street. The last thing he wanted was a fight with Grandma Chepa; like Saul, he disappeared till Grandma calmed down.

Once again, Omar's guardian angel, in the form of Grandma Ester, had intervened.

Omar was glad his mother considered Grandma Ester her real Mimita, and not the feisty little Chepa who had abandoned her children for René so many years ago. Though he usually had nothing against Doña Chepa, he liked Doña Ester so much better, and so did the rest of Regadío.

Omar sprinted toward Golondrino. He grasped the saddle horn and, as lightly as a cat, leaped into the saddle without grazing the stirrups.

Touching the Makarov at his waist, he squeezed his legs, which was a signal that Golondrino understood. In a flash, the two were gone with a clatter of hooves and a cloud of dust.

Omar sensed that his life was spiraling down, down, down with reckless speed. At just sixteen he was already feeling the cruel kickbacks from his own pride and sinful violence. If following his father's footsteps was indeed his goal, he was starting to reap the same bitter harvest Fermín had been reaping for years.

Only one sweet ray shining through the darkness made Omar smile. Her name was Daisy. True to her name, she was a bright, sweet flower that made him dream lovely dreams in spite of his moments of violence.

Daisy Blandon lived just a mile from Omar's home. Agustín Blandon's homestead lay up a steep hill near the rocky, dusty road. Don Agustín had a whole row of rowdy children, but two of them had caught Omar's attention—Daisy, because she was pretty and would make an ideal wife, and her older brother Norbin, who liked Omar's sister Cándida. So Omar became the means for Norbin to contact Cándida, in exchange for Norbin helping Omar to see Daisy. It was a handy setup.

During Omar's last year in Naranjita, he courted Daisy on the sly. Daisy was a shy girl, only fourteen years old. Several times Omar offered to elope with her, but she was too afraid of Omar's angry father—and of Omar himself. She had heard rumors that Omar was flirting with other girls. Although this was true, Omar liked Daisy best, and she was the only one he really considered marrying. But he was having a hard time convincing her.

Old Agustín was slow in allowing Daisy to date Omar, but he didn't mind that Omar came over during his free time. So Omar visited Daisy's home almost daily, and even though it wasn't supposed to be public knowledge, they *were* courting.

Now, as Golondrino's hooves ate up the miles to town, Omar rode lightly in the saddle, dreaming. *If Daisy and I could get together, we could make a home where there is love—not like my home now where everybody fights all the time.*

Tears welled up in the young man's eyes. His yearnings were almost more than he could stand. It wasn't fair that his home life was so horrible. If only he could find a good wife like Daisy and raise a happy family!

But Omar had another ambition even more compelling than winning Daisy. *Before I marry Daisy and settle down,* he vowed, *I'm going to the United States to make money. Just wait and see. I'll make my dreams come true.*

11

MILKING THE FARM

THE BLACK NARANJITA dirt, mellow and moist after the first rains, glistened in the sun. A pair of oxen panted, dripping with sweat as they pulled the wooden plow down the last furrow. Omar led them out of the field, unhitched the plow, and led the oxen back to the house. There he unstrapped their yoke and loosed them into the pasture across the road from the five-acre plot.

"Girls!" Omar called as he stepped inside. "Time to go plant those beans."

As he drank the glass of cool water that Jáqueling handed him, Omar reminded his siblings of their plans. "We're going to make a little extra cash to buy things we need. Since Dad's not helping anymore, we have to do something. We're going to all pitch in and plant beans now since it rained. Then we'll divide the cash out evenly at the end."

The three sisters who were big enough to help were delighted. It wasn't only that having some spending money was attractive, but also the fact that Omar was warming up to them instead of fighting.

Miriam was happy too. Maybe Omar was finally seeing how wrong he had been in always taking Fermín's side. Omar had been showing more kindness to her and the girls. Something good was happening.

Six of them worked at planting beans that afternoon—Omar, Jáqueling, Cándida, Ninozca, Milo, and even little Melvin. Omar explained how to drop three seeds into the furrows every six inches. They all listened well and followed his example. "Milo and Melvin," Omar announced, "you'll also get your share once the harvest is in. That's if you work hard like you are today. There's a lot of work in planting and harvesting five acres of beans."

The siblings chattered among themselves as they planned what they would do with the money, and Omar smiled as he listened. Even though his family had been through hard times and often fought like cats and dogs, he still loved his brothers and sisters.

Evening was creeping up on them by the time Omar straightened up from dropping bean seeds into the rough furrows. Wiping the sweat from his brow, he shared some of his worries with his sisters. "Girls, we will all have to work hard to keep food on the table from now on. Not only has Dad stopped helping buy groceries, but he's also milking this farm of its profits. Yesterday was the second time he took a cow to sell to pay some strange debt he owes in Regadío. This is getting bad!"

The girls nodded, glad to be taken into Omar's confidence. "If Dad keeps on doing this," Omar grumbled, "we soon won't have any cattle left, and we won't be able to sell cheese. I'll tell you the truth, girls. The whale who's swallowing up all of Dad's income is Eva!"

As they resumed their bean planting, Omar declared more cheerfully, "At least Dad won't get this bean money. We do the work, and we get the profit!"

One day Omar was having fun down by the sugarcane mill, which, unlike the abandoned mill at Regadío, was still used at times. One of the bulls being fattened for the market seemed extra tame. So Omar named him El Bandido[7] and sat on him regularly—not riding him like he and Onel often did the wild steers, hanging on to the bucking creatures like rodeo riders. Maybe he could train the placid bull to ride like a horse.

Omar saddled the six-hundred-pound animal and placed a bridle on his head. Then, quirt in hand, he mounted his dusky-colored steer. The men

---

7   El Bandido: the Bandit.

working at the sugarcane mill watched and laughed as Omar rode around on the bull.

After Omar discovered that he could actually steer the bull, and that it drew so much attention from his friends, he got another wild idea. *I'm going to ride this bull over to see Daisy!*

"Milo," Omar barked, "get on Golondrino and follow me. We're going on a special errand."

Minutes later, Omar and Milo were riding down the road. Their strange procession sparked a lot of attention. Even Don Agustín joined the crowd in his front yard as they laughed and cheered for the two clowns.

Daisy soon brought out a drink for the two riders. Omar dismounted, and they all visited by the front porch. While the boys sipped their drinks, Omar watched his girlfriend with admiration. She wore her black hair loosely draped over her slender shoulders. But what he liked best was the way her lips puckered in an endearing way every time she smiled. *Someday she'll be my wife,* Omar thought.

Little Mario was sizing up the bull. "Could I ride him?" he asked innocently.

"Sure!" Omar answered, winking at Daisy. "Tame as a kitten!"

Warily, Mario edged up to the bull. As he lifted his left leg, trying to find the stirrup, Bandido kicked, catching Mario in his middle and sending him sprawling. As the bewildered chap got to his feet, the crowd roared with laughter.

"Well, the truth is," Omar explained, "that Bandido is a one-man bull. He kicks others flat every time. But watch me."

Omar scratched Bandido all over, and the bull loved it. Then he took the stirrup and mounted. Bandido held perfectly still. "You just have to have the right touch," Omar bragged. "Bandido and I get along well, don't we?" He laughed, whacking the bull on the hump and again catching Daisy's eyes.

I'm getting along great with my Daisy, Omar rejoiced, as he wheeled the bull around and started out the lane. *By the way she looks at me, I can see she loves me too! Just maybe my dreams will come true in that cute young girl!*

As Milo and Omar rode away, the whole gaggle of children followed, hollering and cheering. But just as they started down the steep hill on which the homestead was perched, Daisy's little brothers sicced their pack of scrawny hounds on Golondrino and the bull.

Golondrino kicked up his heels and galloped ahead, but the bull started bucking as he ran. "Stop!" Omar screamed. "Cut it out, you rascals!"

But it was too late.

Staying on the bucking bull should not have been a problem—Omar was used to riding bareback on calves that bucked harder than Bandido was bucking now. But Omar generally rode loosely and lightly on Bandido, and he hadn't bothered to cinch the saddle. Now, as the bucking bull stampeded down the hill, the saddle slipped to the side, and Omar fell onto the rocky road.

Before the naughty boys could flee, Omar was up off the road in a rage. Daisy, who had stayed back at the house, was out of sight. Before the boys understood how angry Omar was, he used the quirt on two of them, making them howl in pain.

Omar jumped on Golondrino with Milo, and they led the bull home.

"Those crazy kids! That bull could have killed me! And I think I disjointed my thumb," Omar fussed, nursing it. "Bandido will probably never let me ride him again. At least I was able to strap a few of those rascals!"

"They'll probably go tell Daisy," Milo ventured.

"I don't care," Omar fumed. "They deserved it!"

The next two months were very full for Omar. The beans grew nicely, and it rained enough that everybody expected a good crop. Between riding Golondrino, courting Daisy, and taking care of the farm, it seemed as if Omar was always busy. So, when a letter came to Estelí announcing that Bato was coming back after six months in the States, Omar was ready for a break. "I'm going to Estelí for several days, Mama," he announced. "Don't worry. I'll be back soon."

Estelí was having its annual fiestas, and Bato's invitation was timed just right. Omar was excited as he packed his bags. *But I won't tell Mama or she'll worry. I wonder if I'll ride a bull during the rodeo.*

In Regadío, Fermín met Omar, and they traveled to Estelí together, Fermín on Califa and Omar on Golondrino. Several other friends rode with them. The year before, Omar had gone to the fiestas with friends, but his father hadn't gone along. During the rodeo, volunteers were encouraged to ride the next bull. Omar's buddies had challenged him. "I bet you could ride that bull and win," they had cajoled.

Omar had ridden enough steers at home that he knew he was good, so he had accepted the challenge and won. But when he got home, he had not told his dad; he was afraid that since he was only fifteen years old, Fermín might not approve.

One day Fermín and Omar had been in the corral, treating the cattle, when a wild young heifer tried to jump the fence.

"Omar, would you dare ride that heifer?" his dad had asked suddenly, an odd look on his face.

Omar had looked at his dad carefully. *Is this a test? I bet he knows what happened last week, and when I say I can ride, he'll beat me.*

However, taking the risk, he bragged, "Sure. I could ride that critter."

The next thing Omar knew, his dad had expertly roped the heifer. Then he snagged her up to the corral fence, and Omar helped him put a flank strap on her. Smiling, Fermín challenged, "Here's your ride."

Omar already had his spurs strapped onto his cowboy boots. The heifer crouched, trembling from head to toe as Omar walked up to her. In one quick jump, Omar was on the heifer's back, his right hand tightly wrapped onto the flank strap. With his left hand he jerked off his hat as he yelled, "Turn her loose!"

Fermín had jerked on the slip noose, and the heifer bounded out of the corral, bucking as she tried to get rid of the tick on her back—the tick called Omar Montenegro. Though she put on a great show, flinging herself across the fields, it did no good. Omar waved his hat to an invisible audience and applauded himself as he rode the heifer to the ground.

He hadn't known what to expect when he got back to his dad. *Will he beat me?* Omar wondered.

But his dad was waiting for him with a proud expression. "Son, I can't wait till next year. You're going to ride in the rodeo, and you're going to win!"

Now, a year later, the fiestas were going strong. Would Omar get to ride a bull in the rodeo again?

That first evening, they all met in Bato's nice house in Estelí. To Omar's surprise, his cousin Andrés was there—the one who had beaten a drunken Fermín four years before, and whom Omar had threatened to kill when he grew up.

Andrés had traveled to the United States with Uncle Bato and worked for several years. Now he was back on a visit. Time heals hurts, and boys do grow up. Andrés was friendly to his younger cousin, and Omar decided to let bygones be bygones.

Uncle Bato had married Delilah, a friendly young woman from Costa Rica. She took special interest in Bato's family, serving them as if they were her own relatives.

Uncle Bato and Delilah had a beautiful baby girl named Sheila, and Omar enjoyed his little cousin. Her innocent smiles reminded him of the family he dreamed of having someday. He wished he could be daddy to such a sweet little girl. Delilah's twelve-year-old sister Pearl was also visiting, and she soon warmed up to Omar.

Omar felt his face glow when Fermín told Bato and Andrés all about Omar's riding the wild heifer. "That's great!" Bato gloated. "We'll find you a good bull tomorrow in the rodeo, and you will ride." Fermín agreed.

"But don't drink, Omar," Bato admonished. "Never drink before you ride a bull. That could cost your life. You need all your wits and then some to tackle a bull. So, we'll party tonight, but no liquor. Then after you ride, we'll celebrate!"

A dozen or more horseback riders from far and near gathered in a wide-open field beside the high-walled corral. The frenzied bulls milled around in a small corral next to the chute.

Omar galloped across the field on Golondrino, throwing his hat off right in the middle. Then he rode back at breakneck speed, lying low in the saddle. Just as he swept past the hat, he leaned way over. Hanging down lower and lower, he snatched up the hat and reseated without Golondrino slowing his speed. Wild cheers rose from the onlookers.

Omar rode the first bull released from the chute, and the crowds went wild again. Though hardly anybody knew the upstart from Regadío, they would someday. His fame would go far and wide as the rider from the boonies who never trained professionally but rode the worst bulls with the agility of a monkey.

That night they celebrated hard and long, and the next day Omar traveled to Regadío, suffering a huge hangover. He felt empty and he cringed when he thought of some of the things he had done the night before. *I sure hope my mother and my girlfriend don't find out how I acted,* he lamented.

Bato and Andrés had filled Omar's head with vain ideas of what he could find in Los Angeles: women, money, and fame. Omar was becoming obsessed with the thought of living in the United States. *Someday,* he vowed once again, *I'll live in that dream city!*

The bean field glowed with a yellow hue in the afternoon sun. Omar and his brothers and sisters sweated as they pulled the ripened plants. It was backbreaking labor, but the joy of their anticipated pay spurred them on. They would let the beans dry in the hot Naranjita sun. Then they would thresh them, and they would have their hard-earned cash in hand.

"These beans look really good!" Omar bragged, straightening his aching back. "I expect we'll get at least fifty hundred-pound sacks."

The girls straightened up too and beamed at their big brother. If Omar was happy, they were happy. His optimistic confidence filled them with hope. "Maybe we'll finally have some spending money." Ninozca sighed. "We just never have any money anymore."

"That's the truth!" Omar grimaced. "You heard that Dad took another cow the other day, didn't you? It's only a matter of time till this farm will be wiped out of cattle. Dad never has enough money—it's all drained on Eva."

"Isn't there something we can do?" Jáqueling protested, throwing a dirt clod at Terry, the dog that lay panting among a cluster of bean plants.

"Not really," Omar admitted. "Mama doesn't want to stand up to him. She hates fights. As long as she isn't ready to fight back, it's a lost cause. Now, if he would cross *my* path, I sure wouldn't let him run over me. However, the cattle aren't mine. They're his. But since Mama has helped him so faithfully all these years, the cattle are hers just as much as his."

They were all agreed. As the sun went down, Omar's heart was sad. Life just wasn't fair at all.

A week later, the beans were all harvested, forty-eight sacks stacked in a corner of the little living room. "We'll keep four hundred pounds to eat," Omar decided. "The rest we'll sell, and then we'll divide out the cash between all of us."

"Yes, Omar," Miriam answered appreciatively. "This is timed just right. We need so many things, but since Fermín never helps anymore . . ."

"And there are hardly any cows left to give milk. You're right," Omar agreed. "It's timed just right."

The next day Fermín arrived with a pickup driver he had hired in Regadío. As he breezed into the house, smiling cheerfully, Omar felt suspicious. *Dad never comes to the farm in a vehicle. He must be up to something weird.*

Omar watched his dad closely as Miriam offered Fermín a plateful of food. Fermín took time to eat, and the pickup driver was served too. While they ate, Omar walked out behind the house, feeling apprehensive. *What does Dad want this time?*

Then everything happened fast. Omar came in the front door to find his dad pulling sacks of beans down from the stack and hauling them out to the pickup. "What are you doing?" Omar demanded, glaring at Fermín.

"I came for the beans," Fermín spat out, his lips tight. He threw one sack to the side. "This one is for your work in the bean field—so you can have beans to eat this year."

"No, Dad! You—you can't do that!" Omar stuttered, stepping closer.

"Who said I can't?" Fermín sneered, his eyes as hard as glass. "Son, you forget that this is my farm. I'm still the boss here. You just get out of my way and mind your own business!"

So this had been his dad's plan all along.

Omar felt like beating his dad up right then and there. But he couldn't make himself do it. Instead, he turned on his heel and walked down to the creek to cool off. But it didn't work. His anger grew by leaps and bounds.

I've been deceived! Omar told himself. *I've always been on my dad's side, but now I see the truth. My father is a low-down skunk, and my mother is the one who's been suffering all these years. Oh, how I hate that man!*

After Omar heard the pickup leave, he marched back up to the house. When he stepped inside the living room, he found his mom and sisters crying softly. He was so angry that he didn't say a word. He just grabbed the lone sack of beans, threw it onto his shoulders, and strode out of the house.

"What are you doing, Omar?" Miriam asked.

"I'm dumping these beans into the creek!" Omar yelled. "If he took the rest, he can have these too."

"No, Omar," Miriam pled. "Let's at least have something to eat for the next month. If you throw them away, we'll go hungry."

After some coaxing, Miriam finally convinced Omar to not pitch the beans. Like an old man carrying a heavy load, Omar slowly returned to the house. The weight of his feelings was much heavier than the hundred pounds of beans.

After dumping the sack onto the ground, Omar told his mother how wrong he had been all these years, taking his father's side against her. "How have you put up with this beast for so long?" Omar raged. "He has beaten you countless times. He's held a gun to your head. He's threatened you, and you don't fight back."

"What would it have helped?" Miriam sighed. "He's much too strong for me."

"We worked so hard for those beans!" Omar fumed.

Omar's siblings stood around, watching their brother rave. The more Omar stewed, the more his anger grew. "Mama, if that beast ever comes back to this house while I'm here, tell him what you think of him. Insult him like he deserves. Call him everything you can think of and remind him of all the evil he's done against you and the family. I'll be right here. If he dares to touch you, here's a son who won't allow it anymore. Do you hear? He'll never touch you again, as long as I'm around!"

12

LOVE GONE COLD

THE MORNING WAS crisp and clear, without a cloud in the sky. A torrential rain the afternoon before had washed the valley clean from the accumulation of dust the dry season had left behind, and the thirsty black soil had drunk its fill. A dozen scissor-tailed flycatchers crisscrossed the salmon-colored sky, their long tails streaming after them.

But the beauty of the morning was lost on Omar, who was out doing the early milking. He was too busy pondering the troubles in his family. Life was so unpredictable! Fermín had come to the farm the day before and had stayed the night. Omar's dad, who had been his hero for so long, had let him down cruelly with the bean-growing project, and now Omar detested him.

When Omar strode to the house for breakfast, he had barely stepped inside when he saw that something was wrong—very wrong! Fermín stood in the living room, his eyes like coals of fire. Miriam hurried out of the bedroom, her eyes red from crying. Jáqueling, her face as pale as a full moon, was wringing her hands and crying.

"It looks like Cándida left during the night," Fermín spat out the words. "And Jáqueling claims she knows nothing about it."

"Her best clothes are gone," Miriam whimpered. "I'm sure she left sometime during the night."

"With that dog, Norbin!" Fermín snarled, his lips trembling with rage.

Omar was silent. He didn't know anything about Cándida leaving the night before, but he wasn't surprised. He had seen it coming.

Fermín was angrier than Omar had ever seen him. This was his first daughter to run away from home. But this time, Omar loathed his dad's wrath, even as he realized how similar his own temper was.

Fermín motioned to Omar to follow him outside. "Go bring Cándida home, Omar. Do whatever it takes," he ordered grimly, glancing at the pistol at Omar's waist. "I can't go right now—I'm so angry I don't trust myself. It's better if you go. Just make sure to bring her home—and quickly!"

Omar walked out the door without saying a word. As he headed down the road, his quick mind schemed up a plan that wouldn't go against his dad's orders and might work out great for himself. He smiled to himself. Here was his chance!

Fifteen minutes later, as he strode into Agustín's yard, he had perfected his plan. Norbin was already up at the sugarcane factory, getting ready for the day's cane pressing. Agustín was out behind the house, milking his cows.

The first person to come out to meet Omar, smiling timidly, was Daisy. Cándida was right behind her. Omar saw that Cándida's face was pale; otherwise, she seemed cheerful. "Is Dad angry?" she asked anxiously.

"Actually, he wasn't too mad," Omar said nonchalantly, smiling sweetly at Daisy.

Daisy returned his smile, her lips puckered in her permanent little pout.

"He went to town soon after we discovered that you were gone. I think he had an errand to do," Omar lied. "Mama was pretty sad, but she was getting over it too. Actually, she thinks the best thing would be for you to come back right now while Dad's gone and get all of your clothes. Dad will be mad if you keep any connections with home. He's okay if you move over here, but you'd better stay away for a while."

"You mean, I should go get my clothes right now?" Cándida hesitated. "I'm scared."

"Right, that's what Mama said," Omar answered. "See, it's safer. Take Daisy with you so Mama doesn't scold you too much. I'll be there to help too."

Cándida and Daisy ran back into the house to give Miriam's message to Daisy's mother. *Will she agree to the plan?* Omar wondered.

This is taking too long, Omar thought anxiously as the minutes dragged by. *Please hurry up, you girls!* He feared that his dad would be coming in a minute, too angry for his own good. Would Omar's plan flop?

His plan was simple. If Omar took the girls home, Cándida might run if she saw her dad. So Omar planned to tell the girls the truth just before they got to the house. Then he would turn to Daisy and persuade her to come in and make herself at home.

Depending on the girls' reactions, Omar realized he might have to use force to show them they had no other choice. Omar thought he could make Daisy feel at home very soon, and they would live happily ever after.

But Omar's bold plans died suddenly.

Before the girls appeared, Fermín came galloping in on Califa. Omar wasn't sure which was foaming most, the horse or the man.

Fermín didn't say a word. He didn't ask where the man of the house was or whether he had permission to go inside. He simply jumped off his horse, jerked his *cutacha* from the sheath, and stomped into the house. Before Omar knew what was happening, Fermín marched back out, a weeping Cándida in tow.

To Omar's horror, his dad started to beat Cándida with his *cutacha* as soon as he was off the porch. Holding her firmly by the arm with his left hand, he used his strong right hand to flail her. *Whack!* Omar winced, imagining the sharp pain as the flat of the blade seared the flesh of her back.

Fleetingly, he considered rushing up and ripping the *cutacha* away from his dad. *It's not right that he beat her like that!* he fumed.

The second time the blade came down, Cándida raised her free arm in defense. The blade struck her arm at an angle, cutting deeply into her forearm. Blood spurted in every direction.

Fermín stopped, shocked at what he had done. Then he shoved Cándida, yelling, "Walk ahead of me. Go home immediately!" He jumped on Califa and followed Cándida up the road.

Agustín's family, who had been watching, turned and fled to the house. They understood that Fermín was crazed with fury and might do anything. But Daisy's mother stayed in the doorway.

Defeated, Omar turned to follow his dad home. In the distance he could see Cándida trotting ahead of Fermín as fast as she could. What would happen when they went past the sugarcane mill, and Norbin saw his girlfriend bleeding?

Fermín and Cándida had barely disappeared around the corner when Omar got his answer. Six pistol shots rang out loud and clear in the bright morning air.

Omar froze.

Daisy's mother screamed, "Fermín killed my son!"

Omar sprinted out to the road. Just before the flat place that ran past the sugarcane mill, he heard a shout. Agustín had been watching the whole scene, wisely staying out of it. But now he was running down the hill, brandishing his *cutacha*. "If Fermín killed my son, he can kill me too. But first I'm going to give him a taste of this *cutacha!*" he raved.

Feeling responsible to protect his dad, Omar hollered at Agustín, "Whoa! Where do you think you're going?" He pulled out his pistol. "You aren't going anywhere except home. Go back where you belong!" To prove he was serious, Omar shot his Makarov twice into the air.

The shots took the wind out of Agustín's sails, and he turned to go home. Omar ran on.

Arriving at his own house, Omar found Fermín shouting orders while Cándida sat in a corner, weeping and clutching her bleeding arm, a tendon hanging from the gaping wound. Jáqueling and Miriam were beside themselves. The smaller children cowered in the corners, eyes wide with fear.

Fermín screamed at Miriam, "Bring some water to wash her up, woman! Hurry, bring a towel to wrap up the wound. Jáqueling, get some clothes ready for her—we're taking her to a doctor. Omar, you change clothes too. You're going along. Milo, you get three horses ready."

Any minute, Fermín knew, Agustín and Norbin could burst into the house, and then blood might really run.

A half hour later, Omar, Fermín, and Cándida rode away from the farm, leaving a weeping family behind. Milo was riding behind Omar, clinging desperately to him and hiding his fears.

After they were safely on the road toward Regadío, Fermín told Omar what had happened at the sugarcane mill. Norbin had seen Omar and

Fermín go down to their house. Then he had seen Fermín coming up the road with Cándida trotting along ahead of him, clutching her bleeding arm. He had yelled out angrily at Fermín, but before he had a chance to dash toward them, Fermín was already shooting.

"Norbin ducked behind the mill's gearbox and disappeared," Fermín asserted, riding stiff and tall in the saddle. "I emptied my six-shooter, but I don't think I hit him. The nerve, trying to steal my daughter!"

Omar added his two bits to the story, bragging how his two shots into the air had sent Agustín back home.

"I heard the shots," Fermín acknowledged. "I was wondering if you killed him. If I had already cut my own daughter, why in the world wouldn't I kill those wretches? At least now they know who they're meddling with."

Cándida didn't say a word while they derided her boyfriend and his family.

"Look, Omar," Fermín planned. "We'll catch the bus at La Comarca, and Milo can lead the horses back home. We'll go to a clinic in Estelí first; then we'll have a talk with Bato. Maybe he can help us avoid some trouble. But meanwhile, when people ask what happened, we'll say you were cutting sugarcane with a very sharp machete. Then Cándida reached down to pick up a stalk just as you slashed. Okay?"

Omar nodded, but his thoughts boiled. *What a rat! Dad loses his temper and gets himself in trouble. Then instead of facing his crime, he lies out of it by blaming me!*

At the clinic, while Fermín lied his way out of his angry deed, Cándida fainted. The nurses quickly picked her up and wheeled her away. An hour later she was back and ready to go, her arm stitched up. Fermín paid the bill and led the way to Bato's house.

Bato ushered them into his nice living room and invited them all to take seats. Fermín told him the whole story, truthfully this time. But he forgot to tell about Omar's shots.

Bato looked at Omar thoughtfully. "Give me your pistol," he said.

Puzzled, Omar handed it over.

Bato smelled the end of the barrel. Then, nodding, he declared, "You also shot your pistol, son. Why did you shoot?"

Fermín quickly filled him in.

"Well." Bato gravely considered their options. "Fermín, you'll need to stay away from Regadío for a while. I suggest that all three of you go to our sister Amanda's place at La Trinidad. You'd better hide out there for at least several weeks. It won't be safe for you to go to Regadío soon, much less Naranjita. Okay?"

Fermín and Omar both nodded.

"As far as the police, I'll go take care of that right away. Don't you worry a bit."

The sad trio headed for La Trinidad on the bus, about forty minutes south of Estelí on the Pan-American Highway. Bato went straight to the police station. Omar never found out exactly what Bato did there, but when Agustín and his tribe came out to testify and to prosecute the Montenegros, they weren't able to accomplish anything.

Fermín was restless in La Trinidad, so after several days, he returned to Regadío, leaving Omar and Cándida with Amanda. Several weeks later Fermín came to get Omar and Cándida, whose arm had healed by this time.

Omar wondered what had happened during the three weeks he and Cándida had been away from home. On the bus ride home, the truth slowly came out. Fermín had sold the farm in Naranjita, bought a smaller place closer to Regadío, and moved the family into a tiny house. He had also sold several cows to pay for all the costs. "Things are getting tough in Regadío," Fermín complained. "It's getting harder and harder to make a living. And your mother is becoming harder and harder to get along with."

While the bad news unfolded, Omar determined not to say a word to his dad, though he was furious to know the farm had been sold. He swallowed deeply and listened some more—until Fermín complained about Miriam. "Stop complaining about my mother!" Omar snapped. "She's a lot better person than you are."

At that, Fermín quit talking, so Omar turned his face to the window and stared at the bone-dry countryside flying by. Sadness clutched at his heart as he realized that most of his dreams for Regadío and Naranjita had vanished in just three weeks. Daisy would probably never be his. After such a horrible confrontation between the two families, how could she ever look at him again?

The happy family Omar longed for seemed further away than ever before. Omar sighed to himself. His whole family had broken hearts. What little unity and love they had shared before was now shattered. Ever since the bean ordeal, Omar had realized clearly how his dad was ruining the family. *I hate that man more than I've ever hated anybody before,* Omar seethed.

Only one dream remained to make him feel that life might still be worth living—Bato's idea about Omar joining him in the United States. His uncle's words rang in his ears: "Omar, someday you'll live in LA. You'll have money, and you'll be famous. You'll have everything you want. That's the life for you!"

Why not make Bato's dream come true? First I'll go to Costa Rica so I can make enough money to go to the United States. I'll convince Onel to go with me, and we'll experience the adventure of our lives in a country I've heard so much about. I'll follow my dream, Omar vowed. What was left to live for in Nicaragua?

By the time the bus dropped off Omar, Cándida, and Fermín, his decision was made. He couldn't wait to get back to Regadío to find Onel and start making plans.

13

VAGABONDS

A BLOODRED SUN was setting on a pair of weary vagabonds trudging down the Pan-American Highway in Costa Rica. The two boys wore black army boots, their bill caps were turned backward, and they carried packs on their backs. They had walked twelve miles that afternoon.

"Hey, there's a checkpoint up ahead," Omar warned, pointing to a little building beside the highway. "Should we try to avoid it?"

"Naw," Onel drawled, "we have our permits and our visas. We're fine."

Minutes later a burly policeman hailed them and asked for their papers. Omar and Onel pulled out the little yellow permits they had been issued at immigration in Managua the day before.[8] The Costa Rican embassy had also stamped their permits with the visa they needed to work in the country.

"These permits don't have their border stamps," the guard barked. "Didn't you get them stamped at the border?"

"Yes, we did!" Omar said. "On the Nicaraguan side."

"But you didn't get them stamped on the Costa Rican side," the policeman growled.

"No," Omar answered. "We didn't know we were supposed to."

"How did you get across?" The guard frowned.

---

8   At that time, Nicas didn't need a passport to travel to Costa Rica. All they needed was a permit.

"Crowds of people were milling around, so we just walked across," Omar answered nonchalantly. "Didn't we?" He turned to Onel.

Onel nodded. "No one told us we had to have our papers stamped again. We had our visas."

The burly policemen threw back his head and laughed. "Listen to this," he hollered to his buddy standing in the door of the little station house. "These stupid Nicas just walked across the Costa Rican border and didn't get their permits stamped!"

He turned to the boys again. "Sorry, but you have to go back to the border to get those permits stamped. I can't let you through here."

Omar and Onel groaned inside. Not only had they failed to get their permits stamped at the border, but they had also run out of money that very morning. They had walked all this way from the border, stopping to ask for work at farms along the way. There had been no work so far. Now they were stuck at the Santa Cecilia entrance.

"Come on," Omar pleaded with the guard. "See how late it is? We're tired from walking all afternoon. Plus, we don't have any money to go back to the border."

"How come you're traveling with no money?" The policemen glared at them through the slits of his half-shut eyes.

"We're going to visit my relatives in San Jose. Look." Omar pulled a little paper from his pocket with an address scribbled on it. "We plan to hitchhike to San Jose."

The two boys pled for mercy, but the guard staunchly held his ground. Finally he sighed wistfully, eyeing the boys' boots. "I really like your army boots. We can't get them here in Costa Rica. I sure wish I had a pair."

Omar grinned. "You can have my boots if you let us go."

The policeman beamed. "Let's make a deal. Give me your boots and your watch, and I will not only let you go, I'll also help you find a ride to San Jose."

Omar hesitated. Two years before his dad had given him a good quality Seiko watch that he cherished. But faced with this crisis, he suddenly lost his love for the watch. Snapping it off his wrist, he said, "It's a deal!"

No sooner had Omar given the policeman his watch and his boots and put on a pair of cowboy boots he had along when a truck drove up to the checkpoint. The policeman asked the truck driver if the two boys could ride along. He agreed to take them as far as Alajuela.

As the truck gobbled up mile after mile of asphalt and climbed the mountain, Omar and Onel made small talk with the driver. Then they hunched down on the seat, trying to sleep. But tired as Omar was, sleep seemed even further away than Regadío and his family. His thoughts spun around and around. At last he dropped off for a short nap.

After leaving La Trinidad a few weeks before, Omar hadn't gone back to Regadío. He happened to meet Onel in Estelí and had invited him to Bato's house to make plans.

The problem was that Onel was only fourteen, and a person had to be seventeen years old to get a travel permit to Costa Rica without a parent's signature. Of course, Onel would never get his dad to sign, but Omar's scheming brain found a solution. He had a seventeen-year-old cousin in Estelí named Yasick. Omar convinced Yasick to loan his birth certificate to Onel for several days.

The birth certificate didn't have a photo, and Onel convinced the officials that he was Yasick. Once the boys had the permit with Onel's photo on it, stamped with the Costa Rican visa, they gave the birth certificate back to its owner and hit the road. As they traveled, Omar practiced calling Onel *Yasick*.

Onel had sold a heifer that his dad had given him so he would have money for the trip. But now, after their business in Managua, paying for their visas, bus fares, and taxis, as well as buying meals and sleeping in a hotel, they were broke. That worried Onel, but Omar was confident that they would easily find work in Costa Rica.

It was close to midnight when they arrived at Alajuela, and their new friend asked, "Do you have a place to stay?"

The boys shook their heads. "We've never been to Costa Rica before, and we don't know anyone."

The driver passed the airport and swung onto the exit to Alajuela. "I'll take you to the police station where you can find a safe corner to sleep," he suggested.

Omar and Onel looked at each other grimly. They didn't have their permits stamped, and the police station was the last place they wanted to go. *We'll make out somehow,* Omar thought.

At the police station, the kind driver offered, "I'll run in and talk to the officer on duty and tell him your predicament. I'm sure they'll take care of you."

As the driver disappeared into the building, Omar hissed, "Yasick, let's get out of here!"

Jumping out of the truck, the two boys sprinted around the truck and across the parking lot. They vaulted over a low wall and penetrated the dense coffee patch on the other side. They sat down and held their breaths. The cloudy night was very dark with no trace of the moon or stars.

When they heard voices in the parking lot, the two nervous boys got the giggles. Holding their sides in laughter and hissing at each other to shut up, they heard the perplexed driver talking to the policeman. "That's strange. Just a minute ago they were here in the cab of my truck."

"They must have run," the policeman responded.

"I suppose so," the driver agreed lamely. "I just wanted to help them."

"My guess is that if they ran, they weren't up to any good." The policeman chuckled. "Probably best, if they were a pair of Nicaraguan delinquents. They're probably a kilometer away by now, still running."

Omar and Onel buried their faces in their backpacks, choking back their laughter. Finally the truck drove off, and the policeman returned to his station.

Omar and Onel were exhausted. They curled up in their thin blankets on the damp, hard ground. Before dozing off, Onel whispered, "Omar, weren't we supposed to find work easily in Costa Rica?"

"I don't know," Omar snapped. "But I'm telling you, Yasick, I haven't been this hungry in a long time!"

Onel agreed. "That enchilada we had at the border this morning barely covered the bottom of my belly. I'm starving too."

"Maybe tomorrow we'll find work." Omar yawned. "Shut up and stop complaining. I want to sleep."

When Omar awoke, the coffee patch was lightening up slightly. He shivered in the cold morning air. He was just ready to wake Onel when he saw something through the coffee bushes that made his hair stand on end.

Omar shook Onel gently and whispered, "Yasick, we're right next to a ritzy house!"

Onel popped up, wiping the sleep from his eyes. Omar pointed to the well-kept yard surrounding a stately house. When a big man stepped around the corner, carrying a shotgun, they ducked low.

"It's the rich man's bodyguard!" Omar hissed. "Let's get out of here!"

Slipping like weasels through the coffee patch, the boys jumped over the low wall again and hit the road, hoping the policeman hadn't seen them.

The two Nicas were oblivious to the impression they made—two young squirts in long-sleeved checkered shirts walking along the busy highway. But they were in good spirits.

Suddenly Omar yelled, "Lookie, Yasick. There's our breakfast!" He darted out onto the highway, dodging the traffic. Smack on the yellow line lay the biggest muskmelon the boys had ever seen. Omar snatched it up and raced back to the side of the road. The fruit had apparently fallen off a loaded truck. It had burst open and the top half was gone, but what was left was good enough to eat. Gleefully, Onel pulled out his little pocketknife, and Omar cut the piece of melon exactly in half.

Laughing, the two boys ravenously slurped their unexpected breakfast. "This is the best melon I ever ate!" Omar exclaimed, juice running down his chin. "I'm sure it fell off the truck just for us!"

"Me too!" Onel wiped melon juice from his mouth with the back of his hand. "I never before ate a melon, seeds and rind and all—but this is the best melon ever raised!"

On the road to San Jose, the boys walked past dozens of businesses. "Let's stop and ask for work," Onel suggested.

Omar was doubtful. "I don't think they'll give us work at fancy places like these."

"We could at least try."

So Omar led the way toward an impressive shop advertising tires, tire repairs, and automobile parts.

"Maybe they'll give us work fixing tires," Onel whispered hopefully.

By the time they reached the counter, Omar was shaking in his boots. This was a much fancier shop than he had ever seen before. Mustering all his nerve, he asked for the boss.

A big man stepped out from his office. "What do you want?" he boomed.

"We're wondering if you might have work for us," Omar stuttered, staring down at his cowboy boots.

"How old are you?" the man asked. He eyed the two boys from head to toe.

"I'm nineteen," Omar lied, trying his best to smile.

"I'm seventeen," Onel announced, stretching to his full height.

The big boss shook his head. "I didn't know that Nicaraguans age so fast," he said, trying to hide a grin. "I don't have any work for kids."

Out on the road again, Onel announced, "We need to wait till we get to a farm to ask for work. I think these people can tell that I'm only fourteen and you're just turning seventeen."

"You're right," Omar agreed. "If we can't find work on a farm, maybe we should try the banana plantations down in Limon.[9] They say it's easy finding work there, and the pay is good. Don't you worry, kid, we'll find work sooner or later—we will."

At the entrance to San Jose, Omar and Onel were amazed to see an overpass—a high narrow bridge for people to walk across instead of fighting the traffic in the street.

Onel, keenly feeling hunger pangs, noticed the tip of a watermelon vine peeping through the weeds and grasses in the empty lot near the bridge. "Omar," he whispered, "I'm going to explore. Make sure the coast stays clear."

He disappeared into the high grass. Very soon he popped back out, triumphantly carrying a small watermelon.

Turning their backs to the hordes of people going up and down the steps of the overpass, the boys used Onel's knife again and whacked away at the watermelon. "At least it's pink!" Onel crowed, devouring the sloppy fruit. When the watermelon was gone, including the rind, they both wiped their sticky hands on their pants. Omar belched. "So, that's not too bad, is it? Muskmelon for breakfast and watermelon for lunch!"

Onel was holding back his snickers again. "And who knows what we'll have for supper?"

---

9   Limon: a port city on the east coast, about seventy-one miles from San Jose.

Around noon, the boys found themselves somewhere in the middle of San Jose. They gawked at the huge skyscrapers, something they had never seen before.

"What I don't like," Onel groaned, "is what happens to my nose every time we go past a restaurant. The smells almost kill me!"

"No, the worst is that we're lost!" Omar retorted.

At a food stand, Omar ventured to ask, "Señor, where is this?"

"This is Central Park," the man answered, eyeing them suspiciously.

"Which is the road that takes you to Limon?" Omar asked.

The man gave them directions, and they hurried on, block after block, till they came to an immense bus station. A bus was leaving right at that moment with a plaque on the front saying, "Puerto Limon."

Omar groaned. "He sent us to the Limon bus station. He didn't realize we don't have any money."

A well-dressed man carrying a briefcase strode out of the bus stop. Omar accosted him, "Where is the road to Limon?" he asked boldly.

The man looked warily at the two vagabonds. "Go three blocks this way till you come to a main road." He pointed. "After you get to that road, take a right, and it will be about five miles till you get out of town."

After the man left, Onel laughed. "Well, that sure was encouraging, wasn't it, Omar? Just five more miles. As if it were only five blocks!"

"Let's hurry!" Omar snapped. "We want to get out of this horrible city before dark!"

Out in the country, Omar had a sudden idea. "You know, Yasick, we need to hitchhike. My sore feet are killing me! If we don't get a ride, we'll never get to Puerto Limon."

But after an hour of thumbing, they were ready to give up, until a snazzy white Toyota pickup squealed to a stop. Delighted, Omar and Onel hopped onto the back. Soon the sky turned black, and the driver stopped and invited them to take the back seat inside the cab.

The driver was a fine-looking man with a thick beard and white skin like Omar's. His wife was pretty, and they were both friendly. "I saw it was going to rain, and I didn't want you to get wet," the man said. "Where are you headed?"

"We're on our way to Puerto Limon, looking for work," Omar answered.

"You wouldn't have some work for us, would you?" Onel blurted.

"No, I don't," the man answered. "I do have a farm, but I have enough hired help right now."

Darkness caught up with them suddenly in a mountainous area, and then the storm raged in earnest. The windows of the vehicle soon fogged over as rain slashed at them, whipping down from the steep crags hanging out over the road.

Suddenly the Toyota plunged into total darkness. Were they driving through a deep canyon, or what? Then Omar's eyes focused, and he poked Onel. "This is a tunnel, man!"

When they burst out the other end, Onel sighed in relief. "I wasn't sure what was happening," he whispered. "I've never been through a tunnel before!"

"Me either," Omar admitted. "But I've seen them in the movies. We went right through that mountain."

An hour later the driver announced that he was going only as far as the city of Guapiles. "That's fine," Omar assured him. "Drop us off there."

"Where do you want to get off?" the driver asked. "I don't want to drop you off in the rain."

"Just anywhere," Omar answered nonchalantly. "It doesn't matter. We'll make out." *But please, not to the police station!* he screamed silently.

"I'll leave you here at this bus stop," the driver decided, pulling over.

The two boys piled out. Thanking the driver, they huddled in under the roof of the little lean-to.

The bus stop seemed abandoned at that time of night. They had walked for hours, and now all they wanted to do was sleep. Looking around, Omar muttered, "You know, Yasick, we won't find a better place than this bus stop to spend the night. If we go anywhere else, we'll be soaked in this rain."

It was dry back in the lean-to, and Omar and Onel pulled out their blankets. "Muskmelon for breakfast. Watermelon for lunch. So, what was going to be for supper, Yasick?" Omar asked.

"Thin air!" Onel snapped.

Omar chuckled as he disappeared into his blanket and fell asleep immediately.

But Onel pulled out his little pocketknife whose blade was a scant two-and-a-half inches long. He clutched it in his hand as he tried to sleep. If someone attacked him, he would use his knife! He thought about home and his mom's wonderful cooking. What was he doing here in this detestable country, starving? Maybe his cousin Omar had reasons to seek a new life, but Onel had been perfectly content at home.

Onel sighed, realizing he had made a huge mistake.

14

THE CRAZIEST ANGEL

THE CRUEL RAYS of the afternoon sun smote the two travelers, and the asphalt seemed to smoke like the barrel of a hot pistol as they inched along. Omar's steps were especially slow and measured—he was almost done in.

The night before, they had camped beside a river amid a cluster of trees. When Omar had managed to jerk his cowboy boots off his swollen feet, he understood why his feet hurt so much. "Look at this, Yasick," he said to Onel. Blisters the size of silver dollars decorated his feet—one on the ball and one on the heel of each foot.

Onel shook his head. "Sorry, man!" he muttered. "That does look bad. You should have given that policeman your cowboy boots instead of your army boots!"

"No wonder I can hardly walk anymore!" Omar cried.

In the morning they had bathed in the river and washed their clothes before heading down the road again. Omar laughed to imagine how they looked from behind, each with a pair of wet blue jeans hung on their backpacks to dry. But neither of them cared anymore how they looked. They just concentrated on putting each foot ahead of the other and tried not to dwell on food—food they didn't have.

Their diet hadn't improved much. In Central American culture, helping oneself to fruit is not considered stealing; therefore, fruit became their main food as they traveled through Costa Rica. Guava became a daily staple. Several times they downed some oranges they picked from trees along the road, or found a sugarcane patch and helped themselves.

The day before, the travelers had snitched a cluster of coconuts hanging out over a low wall surrounding a fancy house close to the highway. Omar had whacked the thick stem with Onel's little knife and thrown the cluster over his shoulder until they were safely away from the house. Then they both sat down beside the road and cracked the coconut hulls against the asphalt. They ate the white flesh until their stomachs bulged. Then they cut the rest of the meat into little squares and stuffed them into their backpacks.

Coconuts were easy to find along the roads, and they were the most important part of Omar and Onel's diet during those grueling days. They drank from creeks or cut holes in coconuts so they could drink the milk.

The sun glared on them with extra ferocity as they approached the Limon flats. Omar groaned, walking slowly. "I think we're getting close to the banana plantations. I don't think I can make it much farther. I think my blisters burst, because now my feet are burning."

When they noticed a well-kept farm along the highway, Onel suggested, "Let's stop here and ask for work. Maybe we'll have some luck."

They walked in the long lane and found the owner. "Come back next week," was his discouraging answer.

Next they took a side road that led them deep into the banana plantations. For miles they walked along a gravel road, flanked on both sides with acres and acres of green banana stalks. Each individual hanger was dressed in a bright blue plastic bag to keep off the insects.

They finally arrived at the headquarters nestled among the bananas. At the main office, the clerk looked at the two boys as if they were crazy. "We're full. No work."

In the parking lot, the two weary adventurers met another traveler—a large strongly built man with a bushy beard. His sandals were in shreds, and his clothes looked even worse than Omar's and Onel's. "I'm from Panama, and people told me that anybody could find work at the banana plantations." He sighed. "But there's just no work these days. I've been walking from place to place looking for work for a week. Today I'm giving up."

By late afternoon Omar and Onel had walked for what seemed like miles. Suddenly, Omar turned and looked back down the straight road. As far as the eye could see was a sea of green banana trees, sprinkled with blue. When he looked ahead, it was exactly the same. "Yasick," he groaned, "I'm done. What do you say? Is there any use?"

Onel stepped off the road and sat down on a rock. He sighed. "If that big fellow from Panama can't find work, why should we kids do any better? Let's go home!"

Omar found a stump to sit on, and the two boys sat in silence. Onel cupped his face in his hands and looked as if he were ready to weep. "Omar, I can't help but remember my mama's big hot tortillas with a chunk of cheese and a bowl of sour cream."

"Add a cup of coffee to that list," Omar said, laughing suddenly, "and we'd be in paradise instead of this horrible country called Costa Rica! Let's head back. If we hurry, we might be able to make it to that river where we slept last night."

The next day was just as discouraging. Omar and Onel walked along the highway, thumbing for a ride, but with no success.

It took the boys two days till they finally reached the mountain where they had been given a ride. They slept at the same stations they had on the way down, averaging thirty miles a day. They stopped asking for work— they were simply too tired to walk in the long lanes to the various farms along the road.

By now Omar and Onel understood that the Ticos were not hiring them because they were Nicas, and besides, they were too young. All they wanted to do now was get to San Jose and find Delilah, Uncle Bato's Costa Rican wife. During her stay in Estelí, Delilah had given Omar a little piece of paper with her address in Costa Rica. Omar still had that scrap of paper in his wallet, and now it was his last hope.

He and Onel were starving now. After almost two weeks on their fruit diet, they had lost so much weight that they looked like walking skeletons.

As they climbed the long mountain, they watched the sides of the road like hawks.

Once Onel pounced into the grass beside the road and retrieved a bottle of Coca-Cola that still had about two ounces of fluid in the bottom. Gauging the amount carefully, he drank exactly half and passed the rest to Omar. Omar gulped it down eagerly, then flung the empty bottle over a bank into the deep green jungle below. "If that wasn't two weeks old, it was nothing!" he grumbled.

That day Onel spotted a ripe cluster of tiny bananas, shining yellow from the jungle. "Lookie! Ripe bananas!" He jumped down over the bank.

"Those wild bananas are no good!" Omar yelled after him.

Undaunted, Onel hauled at the dry leaves alongside the stalk, bringing the hanger down to head level. With his little Barlow, he slashed off the stalk. He hauled the little hanger up to the highway. "If you don't want any, Omar, all the better for me!" Onel grinned as he jammed the first banana into his mouth.

Omar also peeled one of the chubby little bananas and stuffed it into his mouth. To his surprise, the flavor was pleasing and sweet. But the fruit was so full of tiny seeds that it was like eating sand.

The two fellows devoured the bananas as they walked, spitting out the seeds.

Then Onel had a scary thought. "Omar, how are we going to get back through that tunnel?"

"I don't know," Omar mumbled, sucking at his next banana. "Didn't it have a walkway for pedestrians?"

"I didn't see any. How can we walk through there in the dark and not be hit by cars? I think I'd rather climb over the mountain than risk it."

"We'll cross that bridge once we get there," Omar philosophized. "I mean, we'll go through that tunnel."

Suddenly a semi came barging past, creating a fierce wind that jerked at Omar's shirt and hair and almost knocked him over. Omar fussed, "Man! I wish these guys would have a little mercy on us."

To the boys' surprise, the semi slammed to a stop ahead. Adrenaline surged through Omar, and he sprinted eagerly toward the truck. The driver had jumped out and was throwing things into the back of the cab. He was motioning and hollering, "Come on, come on. Hurry, jump on!"

Running the risk, the two fellows scrambled up into the cab. When they came face-to-face with the skinny middle-aged driver, Omar tried not to stare. The man's long hair looked as if a whirlwind had arranged it. He wore huge sunglasses that covered half of his face. His beard and mustache needed attention, and his teeth were almost as yellow as the wild bananas they had just finished. He wore shorts and a sleeveless T-shirt, revealing arms and legs covered with tattoos. But most outstanding was his immense bulbous nose.

"Welcome on board, my comrades!" he shouted, his voice grating like metal on metal.

Perched in the middle of the wide seat, Omar eyed the man carefully. "Thanks for giving us a ride," he said, but he wondered, *What will we do if this crazy man attacks us?*

"Look, fellas," the man prattled, bouncing on the seat. "My full name is Andrés Alberto del Carmen Andino Madrigal. But don't bother remembering it. Everybody just calls me Pinocchio. You don't have to ask me why.

"And listen, I didn't give you a ride because I'm a good man," he rasped, smiling widely. "I gave you a ride because I need you. I'm almost shot."

Omar and Onel watched the man intently, saying nothing.

"You see, I didn't sleep a wink last night." Pinocchio cackled. "I've been partying down in Puerto Limon for the last two days, and I've hardly had any sleep. I have to have this load in San Jose by tonight. Otherwise, I'd be parked beside the road somewhere, snoozing."

The semi topped a hill and began zooming down the other side. After they roared over a narrow bridge, Pinocchio pulled the truck over onto the shoulder. As an abyss opened its gaping mouth to receive them, Omar and Onel gasped, leaning away from the valley below.

But Pinocchio pulled the semi back onto the road just in time to fly up the hill beyond. He was cackling extra hard now, and Omar and Onel stared at him, shocked at the strange man's deadly sense of humor.

"Do you understand now why I need you? Look at the chasms all along this highway. Now, look at me," Pinocchio ordered once he had the semi under control again. He pulled his glasses away from his eyes and pushed his battered face toward the boys. "Do I look fit to drive?"

Omar laughed nervously. The man's face was frightful. His bloodshot eyes told Omar that he was either stoned on drugs or suffering from a huge hangover. Probably both! Dark half-moons hung under his eyes as though he hadn't slept in a month. *This is going to be a wild trip!* Omar realized.

"That bank right over there is where I smashed on my last trip," Pinocchio bragged, pointing. "Fortunately, I wasn't going too fast. That really woke me up."

The boys looked at each other soberly. What had they gotten themselves into?

"I saw how tired you guys were coming up that hill," Pinocchio continued. "So, you need me and I need you. We'll get along great!"

Omar and Onel spent the next half hour listening to their new friend talk about his wild life. "I believe in living it up," he explained. "That's my god!"

That's pretty obvious! Omar thought.

Several hours later Pinocchio's need was confirmed. They had talked themselves out, and everything grew quiet except for the purr of the motor. When Pinocchio started falling asleep, even Omar's shouts didn't seem to wake him. At one point, Omar reached over and turned the steering wheel to save them from running into another bank. Then they roared through the tunnel, and that seemed to wake Pinocchio. Later, as the semi rolled into San Jose, Pinocchio asked, "Where do you want to go?"

Omar fished out the little paper with Delilah's address on it.

"Oh, Heredia! That's not far," Pinocchio said. "After I drop off my load, I'll run you over there and make sure you're okay. But look, I'm not supposed to haul hitchhikers, so I'll drop you off at a corner before I get to the warehouse. Then I'll come back and pick you up again."

Sure enough, the afternoon was still young when Pinocchio came back, driving only the cab. In a matter of minutes, they were taking the many curves to Heredia at breakneck speeds.

By now Omar and Onel were enjoying their host. In spite of his erratic behavior, he had a big heart. Soon they were cruising through the residential area of Heredia, taking the curves gracefully.

"I don't think I can drive up that street with this rig," Pinocchio decided. "So I'll drop you off right here. Just go up that street till you find the house number."

Omar and Onel piled out of the truck and thanked their new friend profusely.

Pinocchio laughed. "Aw, that's nothing. Remember, you helped me too." Then he roared away.

Omar and Onel looked at each other, grinning. Onel broke the silence, "That man is crazy! But he sure did give us a lift, didn't he?"

Omar chuckled in answer. "If it weren't for him, we'd be walking through that tunnel about now, dodging cars. I'm sure he's the craziest angel I've ever seen!"

As they ambled along, watching the house numbers, Omar groaned. "I'm starving!"

Suddenly the number D27 glared at them in gold letters from above the door of a nice clean house. Omar hesitated. What if Delilah didn't live here anymore?

He led the way as they slipped through the front gate and strode nonchalantly to one side of the house and sat on the nicely mowed lawn. There they took their backpacks off and waited to see what would happen. Two young people that Omar didn't know came in from the street and entered the house. As they passed, they stared at the two boys. *Now we're in trouble,* Omar thought.

When the young people opened the door, they were received by Pearl, Delilah's little sister, who caught a glimpse of Omar sitting out on the lawn. Delilah later told the boys how Pearl had run up to her, exclaiming, "Delilah, there's a man sitting out in the yard. He looks just like Omar!"

"Can't be!" Delilah scoffed. "Omar is far away in Nicaragua."

But Pearl hauled her sister over to the window and pulled back the curtain. Omar recognized the young face staring at them. Then he heard her clear, childish voice ring out, "See, I *told* you it was Omar!"

That's when Omar jumped up and sprinted toward the door. There he met Delilah, carrying her little girl Sheila, and Pearl, who welcomed him with a hug and ushered the boys into the house.

In the spotlessly clean, well-furnished living room, Omar and Onel wondered how they must appear to the gracious lady who had welcomed them in. The fronts of their pant legs were crusty and stained from rubbing their juicy hands on them. To hide their dirty pant legs, both boys sat down and leaned forward, elbows on their knees.

Innocently Delilah asked, "Have you eaten lunch yet?"

Omar looked over at Onel. "Well . . . not really, I guess."

Delilah instructed her maid to fix some food, and Omar told her about their adventures and how the Ticos refused to give them work even though they had lied about their ages. "We traveled far and wide, Delilah, and didn't find any work. So I remembered that when you were in Nicaragua, you invited me to come see you someday. Remember, you gave me that little piece of paper with your address. That's what saved our day."

The smells wafting out of Delilah's kitchen were making Omar dizzy with hunger so that he could hardly keep up his end of the conversation. If only this woman knew how long it had been since they had eaten real food, she'd tell her maid to hurry!

Delilah smiled at Onel. "What do you like best about Costa Rica?" she asked.

Totally unprepared for the question, Onel stuttered around, drawing a blank about anything good in Costa Rica.

Delilah smiled broadly. "I'm sure what you liked best was the food, right? Isn't Tico food just the best in the world?"

Onel almost burst into tears. He felt like shouting, "And how could I know if I never had any, ma'am?" He was just a fourteen-year-old kid, missing his mama. If this woman didn't hurry up and give him some food, he was going to start bawling!

Eventually Delilah ushered them into her lovely kitchen, but the boys didn't notice her nicely varnished cabinets or her tile sink. It was what was on the table that mesmerized them—a big bowl of rice and beans, a plate of fried plantains, cheese, a bowl of sour cream, and a big stack of fresh tortillas!

Was Delilah finally catching on to how hungry the boys were, or was it providence that made the women exit the kitchen right away? The boys didn't know, but Onel did find that Tico food was the best food in the world!

If Delilah hadn't guessed before, she surely must have caught on when she found every bowl completely licked clean. Where in the world had two boys tucked away that much food?

Delilah showed the boys which room they could sleep in and where the shower was. The boys never told Delilah how much they suffered the rest of that evening. During their much-needed showers and later, rolling around on their beds, they suffered acute stomach pains. They were just not used to food anymore!

When their bellies had finally calmed down, they talked and laughed, reliving their adventures. "I thought finding work in Costa Rica was going to be easy," Omar confessed. "But now we know it's not true. We need connections. And that's exactly what we have here. Delilah's brother told me that tomorrow he'll take the day off to help us find work. This is what we should have done when we first got to Costa Rica."

Onel was barely listening as he lay with his head plastered onto the softest pillow he had ever experienced. Before either of them could think of anything else to say, they were fast asleep.

15

MONEY-MAKING MACHINE

A LOVELY MORNING dawned on Heredia as if blessing Omar and Onel with special joy after their terrible trip. Golden sunshine splashed down upon the happy land. Bright skies hosted a flock of fluffy clouds that bounced like sheep ahead of the dancing breezes. The clay-colored robins, Costa Rica's national bird, seemed to be trying to outdo each other, trilling their melodies.

But what Omar and Onel liked best that bright morning was breakfast—rice and beans with eggs and tortillas, washed down with wonderful cups of black coffee.

"I had no idea food could be so good." Omar sighed as he pushed away from the table.

"Yeah," Onel drawled. "It was almost worth it to starve for two weeks so we could enjoy food so much again."

That same day, Delilah's brother took Omar and Onel to look for work. All day they drove around Heredia, but found nothing. For two days following, Omar and Onel went out themselves. Still nothing.

The next day, Onel told his cousin, "Omar, I'm heading home. You can stay if you want. Here everybody works except you and me. That's not a problem for you, because you have connections with these people, but I don't. I told Delilah's brother I wanted to go home, and he gave me money for the bus fare."

Omar understood. Though he would miss Onel, he knew he couldn't keep him. The next day they parted ways, Onel with a lump in his throat and Omar with tears in his eyes.

Omar enjoyed the children at Delilah's house. He couldn't help but notice how innocent and pure little Pearl's eyes looked. *Someday I want to have a little girl like that,* he thought. *A family of my own and a little girl as friendly and as sweet as this one.*

But as he bounced baby Sheila on his knee, his heart ached. So far, Bato had not been mentioned. Had his uncle abandoned this child, along with her mother, as he had done to many other women in the past?

One evening Omar sensed Delilah looking at him as if she wanted to talk. After putting Sheila to bed, she broached the subject. "Omar," she started cautiously, "your uncle Gilberto married me when I was in Nicaragua last year, and I learned to love him. He knew that I had a house and a job here in Heredia, so he told me to come back home, promising he would come to live with us later. I call him regularly, but he always gives reasons why he can't come quite yet. Tell me the truth, Omar. What's going on?" Worry was written all over her face.

Omar hesitated. He wanted to protect his uncle, but this good woman deserved the truth. "I'm sorry, Delilah," he answered. "I'll tell you the truth. Bato will never come back for you. He's a trickster. His marriage with you was his third one. But that doesn't mean you're only his third woman—he's had dozens already. He's probably back in the United States with a new woman by now. I really am sorry."

I pity little Sheila most. Omar sighed. *That little girl's daddy will never be the daddy she needs.* But hiding the truth wouldn't help a bit.

The black stallion lifted his head high. He pranced in a circle around Omar, who was holding the lead rope in his left hand and a buggy whip in his right hand. As the horse came around the circle, Omar followed slowly, always facing him. Then, at a light jerk on the rope, the horse swung in and pranced up to Omar, stopping directly in front of him.

Omar stroked the horse's sweaty forehead, talking to him gently. The horse tossed his head, flinging his mane in the wind. *So much like my Golondrino.* Omar smiled. *Oh, how I love this job!*

After a little break, Omar commanded the stallion to go, giving the whip a flourishing snap. The horse plunged the opposite way, trotting grandly, white flecks of foam breaking out on his black hide.

After a week of looking, Omar had found a job helping a horse trainer on a rich man's ranch. Not only was Omar enjoying working with horses, but he was watching the trainer and learning new things. Every day, after eight hours of light work, Omar went back to Delilah's place to eat and sleep. It was almost too good to be true, but Omar was finally earning money.

Nicas working on the horse ranch were required to have their legal papers up-to-date. So when Omar's monthly permit ran out, he borrowed money from the ranch owner and went back to Nicaragua to get his passport. It took two weeks—longer than he had expected. By the time Omar returned to Heredia, the ranch owner had hired another man.

Though devastated, Omar would not be deterred from his dream of earning money in Costa Rica so that he could go to the United States. So he spent another week looking for work.

Delilah had another brother who worked with a company called Yuca Tica in the Guapiles area. When he came to visit his sister, he heard about Omar's dilemma. "What in the world?" he exclaimed. "You can't find work here? Just come with me, and I'll set you up in no time." And he did.

On the yuca plantation, Yuca Tica provided rows of tiny rooms for their workers. Omar's room was just big enough for a single bunk bed and a place to turn around between the bed and the wall, and he shared it with another Nica named Fedrico. The workers ate at the mess hall where the company provided food.

Fedrico was a good listener, and Omar was a talker. He often talked to his roommate long into the night, not even sure if Fedrico was asleep or awake. Omar pitied Fedrico because he generally spent all of his money the same week he got paid. But they got along well and often worked together on the plantation.

Omar soon made friends with Romo, another Yuca Tica coworker who was honest and helpful. Romo had a bank account in United States dollars. Every payday, after Omar took out what he needed for the next week, he gave the rest to Romo. Romo converted Omar's savings into dollars and deposited it into his account. He always gave Omar the receipts so Omar could keep track of how much Romo owed him.

The new job gave Omar an outlet for his boundless energy, and he began saving in earnest for his big dream of going to the United States. Soon, nothing mattered to Omar except for work, work, work. Working gave vent to years of pent-up feelings. When the rancid bile of anger threatened to choke him, he tried to alleviate the pain by working like a madman.

One day when the Guapiles sun was beating down ferociously, Omar and Fedrico were cleaning one of the ditches between the yuca fields. The ditch was overgrown with high grass and elephant ears. While Omar slashed at the weeds along one side of the ditch, Fedrico came along behind, macheting the other side. Once more, anger churned in Omar's gut, and he took it out on the weeds.

His bitter thoughts centered on his father Fermín. *I wonder if my dad hasn't sold my Golondrino. He's probably sold my saddle too and spent the money on Eva. Daisy will probably never be mine because of my angry father.* But what really scared Omar was that he was becoming more like Fermín Montenegro every day.

"Omar, slow down!" Fedrico yelled. "I can't keep up. You're killing me! What do you gain by working so hard?"

"So we can finish quicker and go rest," Omar yelled back, sweat streaming down his face. "When I work, I *work!*"

The Yuca Tica company contracted out most of their work. For example, if a man were slashing weeds from a field, he was paid so much per row or per quarter hectare. Omar often did double the amount of work other men did, and this irritated his fellow workers. If a few exceptional workers got so much done, the foreman would start being harder on the slowpokes. But Omar didn't care.

That's why Fedrico was complaining now. But Omar was remembering the horrible day his dad had sold their beans. As he came to a section of the canal where the weeds were higher and denser, instead of slowing down, fury took over and he began slashing and throwing weeds aside like a tiger.

Once I get to the United States, I'm going to make money. Lots of it. I'll send money to my mother, but I'll never send my father a cent!

Fedrico stopped to sharpen his machete. He watched Omar tearing at the tall weeds like a powerful machine. What was eating at that man?

As Omar fumed, a stack of elephant ears and grasses piled up around his feet. Then his machete got wrapped up in a tangle of morning glory vines. Suddenly Omar let his machete drop. Bending over, he grasped the pile of weeds and threw the whole tangle into the ditch. The angry motion caused his feet to slip. Cursing and swearing, he slid down into the bottom of the ditch, falling on top of the weeds he had just cut.

Feeling foolish and still angry, he climbed back up the bank to find his machete. Fedrico had stopped working and just stood there, gaping.

Omar barked, "Did you like the free show?" Then grabbing the machete, he resumed his slashing.

The next day a large crew was macheting a huge yuca field, for which they would be paid by the row. When Omar reached the end of his first row, he was so far ahead of the rest that he couldn't even see them. So he took the next row back.

When he met his fellow workers, who had stuck together working at the same pace, Omar finally stopped for a breather. The others were standing among the waist-high yuca plants, nonchalantly sharpening their machetes.

One of the Tico workers, whom everyone called Tepesquintle,[10] was watching him closely. "Omar, we have a question for you," he said. "Why do you work so hard? You never drink or party with us. You don't even have a girlfriend. What are you saving all your money for?"

Omar smiled a little and answered quietly, "I'm saving money to go to the States."

The Ticos laughed as if they had heard the funniest joke of the year. Even Omar's fellow Nicas were grinning.

---

10 Tepesquintle: paca, a medium-sized rodent that the Ticos hunt to eat.

"*Where* are you going?" Tepesquintle asked again, winking at his buddies.

"I'm going to the States once I save up enough money," Omar said, his hackles rising.

"He's going to the United States," Tepesquintle hooted, bending over laughing, "but he doesn't even know his directions. He came south when the States is to the north."

"This Nica probably can't even read," another Tico mocked. "And he thinks he's going to get a visa to the United States?"

Omar bent over his row, hiding his red face as his machete started flinging like a machine again. *Right swing. Left swing. Right swing. Left swing.* Weeds flew as Omar chopped them off level with the ground. His anger boiling dangerously, Omar finished his second row before his buddies had done their first.

That evening Omar, hot from the day's work, sat out on the porch that ran all along the front of the shacks. Fedrico was inside lying on the bed, pouting because he had just been fired for drinking too much. Everyone had been down to the mess hall for supper, and it was soon time to turn in.

Omar was feeling homesick and a little guilty. He'd been working for two months and hadn't called his family once. Surely Onel had told them how they couldn't find work, and Miriam was probably worrying about him.

But I have my own set of worries, Omar argued. *I'll let them take care of themselves—just like I take care of myself.*

Then he noticed Tepesquintle leading a bunch of fellows across the yard toward him. Omar's sharp ears picked up Tepesquintle's quiet comment, "And he's also a loner."

Suddenly Omar was wary.

"Look," Tepesquintle began, grinning maliciously. "These fellows didn't believe me when I told them you were going to the United States. They want to hear it from your own mouth. Tell them, where are you going once you get some money together?"

Omar coldly returned their stares and answered distinctly, "I'm going to the United States of America. The reason I came here first is because I needed work to make money for the trip. That's why my bank account is growing, and you guys who carouse every night are blowing your money faster than you make it. You'll never get anywhere."

The rowdy fellows didn't hear all of Omar's speech because they were laughing too hard. But when they saw that Omar's anger was rising, they turned and left, still cackling. "That Nica sure is crazy!"

A new fellow, Pedro, was given Fedrico's bunk. But because Fedrico didn't know where to get another job, he stayed around. He had to sleep on the floor, and Omar started paying for his food so he wouldn't starve.

When Yuca Tica threw its annual party, providing food and liquor for the occasion, about three hundred men gathered around the mess hall. This time Omar went along and allowed himself to splurge.

One thing Omar *had* been buying was clothes. Like his dad, Omar walked with the bearing of a king. He wore gleaming black cowboy boots and an expensive gold watch. When he smiled, he flashed a row of flawless white teeth. More and more Omar found himself dressing in black. Did the black clothes somehow symbolize the blackness in his heart?

When the company party dispersed at midnight, Fedrico was too drunk to walk, so Omar asked Tepesquintle to help haul him back to the bunk rooms. Pedro and several others followed, all of them at least partly drunk. As soon as Fedrico was lifted off the ground, dangling between the two taller men, he started complaining. "You're hurting me!" he bellowed, squirming madly.

Tepesquintle and Omar paid no attention and just dragged him along, laughing at him. "You're bumping me!" Fedrico screamed again.

Tepesquintle and Omar tossed Fedrico onto Pedro's bed. Omar stepped to the door, laughing and joking with his friends. But the angry Fedrico reached under the bed where they stored the sharp machetes. He jumped out of bed and charged.

Omar saw the machete coming and even through his drunken stupor, he realized it would catch him before he could dodge it. He jumped at Fedrico, grabbing his arm. The machete grazed Omar's face, cutting him slightly on the forehead, but he didn't even feel the cut. He wrenched Fedrico's arm and brought him to the ground with a crash. Placing his knee on Fedrico's chest, Omar shouted, "So this is the way you pay me back for being kind to you, you dog!"

Then Pedro hollered over the din, "Omar, this afternoon we found Fedrico going through your stuff looking for money." As Pedro's words sunk in, Omar reached up to wipe his face and discovered, to his horror, that his hand was bathed in blood.

Crazed to a frenzy, Omar reached under the bed for a weapon. The first thing he grabbed was one of the knife files he used to sharpen his machete. Raising it high over his head, Omar brought it down toward Fedrico's chest with all his strength. But before he plunged it in, a guardian angel grabbed his hand.

"No, Omar!" Tepesquintle hollered. "Don't kill him. He's drunk!"

Tepesquintle was not only quick, he was also strong. As he grappled with Omar, Pedro and another fellow dragged Fedrico out into the dark. "Get out of here if you know what's good for you," were Pedro's parting words. "Omar will kill you!"

They never saw Fedrico again.

"Here come the guards!" Tepesquintle shouted. The crowd quickly dispersed.

The next day as Omar worked, hot and angry, he thought about his life. *This is getting bad,* he realized, whacking viciously at the weeds. *I would've killed Chepe that time with the* cutacha *if he hadn't dodged. I would have shot Saul if he hadn't run. I would have shot Donald if Gustavo hadn't connived to get the gun back to its owner. And last night I would have killed Fedrico if Tepesquintle hadn't grabbed my arm. Why do I get so uncontrollably angry?*

If something didn't change, Omar feared it would be only a matter of time until he actually did kill someone.

When Omar was fired that evening because of the fight with Fedrico, he was neither surprised nor totally disappointed. The receipts in his billfold showed that he had saved a little over one thousand dollars in six months, all safe in Romo's bank account.

16

LAST STRAW

THE NIGHT WAS very dark as Fermín stepped up to the door of the shabby brick house and knocked. Miriam opened the door, holding up a small lamp so she could see who her visitor was.

"What's up, Fermín?" Miriam asked quietly, staring at him. It was unusual for her ex-husband to stop in late like this. Something was wrong.

"Don't you see who came?" Fermín asked, glancing out at the street.

"Who came?" Alarm touched Miriam's voice.

Fermín pointed toward the dark street. "It's your son."

Miriam swung the light off to one side. Then she saw her son, dressed totally in black, standing in the shadows.

With a wild cry, Miriam thrust the lamp at Fermín and rushed out onto the street. "Omar!"

Omar seemed stiff and cold in her embrace. Miriam couldn't see his expression in the dark, but she didn't feel any warmth in her son's response. And he was so thin.

Weeping, she complained, "Omar, why did you do this to us? We haven't heard from you for a year. I've been so worried about you. We didn't know if you were dead or alive!"

CHAPTER 16

Omar struggled with conflicting emotions. His mother was in his arms, weeping. The father whom he hated stood in the shadows, his face cold. His brothers and sisters whom he had loved, but now felt estranged from, were quickly pouring out of the house onto the street. Omar's chest felt numb. How was he supposed to feel? It seemed pointless to attach to anyone, since he would soon be leaving anyway.

"It will be so nice to have you back," Miriam murmured as she led Omar into the house. The children followed, and a surge of tenderness warmed Omar's heart.

Fermín's voice cut into the night, "Omar isn't coming to stay, Miriam. He's got everything ready to go to the States with his uncle Gilberto as soon as he can."

"That's right," Omar echoed. "I'm just coming to say goodbye."

Miriam's heart, which was already breaking, sank further. What would happen now to her wild son? He was only seventeen.

Fermín left. Everybody knew where he was going. Omar shrugged.

After the family was together in the house, Omar caught up on the news from Regadío. Soon after he had left for Costa Rica, Cándida had eloped with Norbin again, only this time they went far away to a city several hours north of Regadío, where Norbin had relatives. Jáqueling had shacked up with her cousin Donald, but under pressure from Miriam, they got married soon afterward. Fermín continued living with Eva.

Miriam fixed food for Omar, and his siblings stared as he wolfed it down. Then he told them stories about his adventures in Costa Rica.

"You can sleep in the boys' room," Miriam offered.

Milo, Melvin, and little Alvaro were all growing up fast. After the lights were out, Omar had a whispered conversation with Milo, who was sharing the same bed.

"What happened to Golondrino?"

"Dad sold him soon after you left."

"What about the saddle?"

"He sold it too."

"Are there any cows left?"

"Not one. Dad spent all the money from the farm deal and everything else that we owned—except this house that he gave to our mother."

"I knew it," Omar hissed. "I hate that man!"

The horrible truth was the last straw. He had nothing to live for here; he would leave as soon as he could.

"What about Daisy? Is she still in Naranjita?"

"Yes, but they say she's getting married any day now to a fellow from Estelí. They're making wedding plans."

"Do you think she still likes me?" Omar ventured.

Milo didn't know.

Omar lay in bed for hours before falling asleep. His mind raced from scene to scene as he relived his past. So many hurts!

Upon arriving back in Nicaragua, Omar's first stop had been in Estelí. He was delighted to find Uncle Bato at home. Not only that—Bato was eager to help him get to the United States. Bato located a coyote[11] in Estelí who promised to take Omar to the United States for four thousand dollars. The coyote wanted two thousand dollars as a down payment and two thousand once he had delivered Omar safely to Los Angeles. Bato, who was planning to fly back to the United States within a week, and Andrés, who was back in the States, promised to loan Omar the last half once he arrived.

Omar debated about going to Regadío before he left. He wanted to look up his girlfriend, but he wasn't sure about facing her family. Then Fermín had dropped in and found Omar in Bato's living room visiting with Bato and his new mistress.

Surprised to see Omar, Fermín immediately put on a sad face. "Oh my, Omar! You've made the family suffer so."

Omar wanted to shout back, *Who made the family suffer? Who but you?*

"Look." Fermín's tone was wheedling. "Now that you're a man, I want to start a butchering business with you in Regadío. We'll buy cattle and sell them and butcher on the side."

Again, Omar felt like screaming, *Your business deals never work. I don't want to have anything to do with you!* Instead, he just glared at his father. "I'm going to LA, Dad. Uncle Bato and I have everything arranged."

Bato broke in and confirmed the plans. "Yes, we even have the coyote hired and ready. Omar will be okay, Fermín. I'll be there next week to help

---

11   Coyote: person who smuggles Latino citizens into the States to work as illegal immigrants.

arrange things. Andrés is already there and promises to help. Our sister Yolanda is living there and promises Omar room and board."

"But your mother is so sad." Fermín looked over at Omar again. "You need to at least go say goodbye. We all feel hurt that you left and didn't let us know what was going on for a year." Finally Omar had consented to go to Regadío, but he vowed to not let his mother sway him.

Milo was fast asleep by now, but Omar's mind kept on traveling. He had complied with his dad's suggestion to come to Regadío to say goodbye to his family. He had one more plan he was eager to carry out, but it would have to wait till the next day. His burning question demanded an answer: *Does Daisy still love me?*

The next morning Omar borrowed a horse and rode off for Naranjita. Though he had revealed his mission to no one, everybody guessed his intentions. Miriam's heart filled with dread. What would happen in Naranjita?

The news of Omar's arrival flew immediately to all the corners of Naranjita. Soon Onel showed up to see his old friend, and Jáqueling and Cándida came to see their long-lost brother. As soon as possible, Omar pulled Cándida aside, hoping she would help him set up a meeting with Daisy.

Cándida told Omar the truth. "Daisy is engaged to a man from Estelí named Walter. When her dad heard you were in the area, he sent Daisy off to her aunt in Estelí right away. He's afraid you'll try to contact her."

"So Daisy is heading for Estelí?" Omar was incredulous. Maybe if he hurried, he could catch up with her. Saying quick goodbyes, he galloped out the lane.

But by the time Omar got to Regadío, Daisy had already left for Estelí on the bus. He stopped and said a quick final goodbye to his family. Then he took the next bus to Estelí.

He went straight to Daisy's aunt's house. How pleased he was to find his flower outside with one of her cousins! She had matured and was prettier than ever. He gave her a quick hug and said, "Daisy, I've come to take you with me."

Daisy blushed deeply. "I-I can't," she stammered. "I'm engaged to get married."

"That doesn't matter." Omar gave her his sweetest smile. "Our love was real, and you'll never forget me."

"But—" Daisy hesitated. "You went away and my family wanted me to marry Walter. Now I'm engaged."

Omar sensed that Daisy was wavering. "We need to talk," he announced. "Alone."

"I can't," Daisy answered, her face full of worry. "If my dad finds out that I talked to you, he'll beat me."

"Nobody needs to know," Omar insisted. If he could just get this girl alone, he was sure he could convince her easily.

"Where could we go? If the people of the house see me, I'm in big trouble."

"Look, I'll leave right away before they see me. Take this cousin with you and walk down to the corner. I'll meet you there."

Daisy finally nodded her agreement, but her eyes were full of fear.

Out on the street, Omar flagged down a taxi and directed the driver to park at the corner. While they waited for Daisy, he gave the taxi driver clear instructions. Then he crawled into the back seat. When the girls came, Omar motioned to the cousin to jump in the front. Then he motioned to Daisy to join him in the back. The taxi driver turned up the music.

Daisy was harder to convince than Omar expected. She had too many fears. *Wait till we get to the park,* Omar thought. *Once we're alone, it should be easy.*

He had instructed the driver to take them to a romantic park beside the lake. Once there, Omar ushered Daisy out and told the taxi driver to take the cousin back where he had picked them up.

Soon Omar and Daisy were strolling around the park with other couples who were enjoying the evening breezes. But Daisy's response was discouraging. Someone had told her about Omar's plans to go to the United States.

"I know you're leaving, Omar," Daisy cried, wringing her hands, "but you can't take me with you if you go illegally. I still love you like everything, but I can't believe in you."

"Listen carefully," Omar urged. "It's true that I have everything ready to go to the United States. But I haven't paid the coyote. This has been my plan all along—if you go with me, I'll drop my trip to the States, and we'll go to Costa Rica instead. I have all kinds of connections there. I have a job whenever I want one. We'll make a happy life together there. I'm not that set on going to the United States. But I am set on marrying you!"

Omar's charms and sweet words didn't convince the young girl. He was serious about dropping the trip for Daisy's sake, but he finally gave up because he saw she didn't believe him. That hurt.

Suddenly Omar was done. He hailed a taxi and told the driver where to take Daisy, who was crying softly now.

"Goodbye, Daisy." His voice was bitter. "Since you refuse to go with me, I leave for the United States very shortly. Go marry your man and see if you'll be happy."

The parting was worse than sad. Omar's last Nicaraguan dream died on that gloomy afternoon.

But the worst was still to come. Before Omar left Nicaragua, he heard the news. Agustín had followed Omar to Estelí. By the time he got to his sister's place, Daisy had disappeared. Agustín knew she had left with Omar, and he had paced the floor until she came back. When Daisy crawled out of the taxi, her father had not listened to the truth. Instead, he beat her mercilessly.

That night Daisy had contacted Walter, her fiancé, and asked him to come and get her. As they left, Daisy carried along the bruises of her father's brutality.

The next day Miriam showed up at Bato's place in Estelí, worried sick. She had heard the rumors flying thick in Regadío. "Omar, please don't mess with that family anymore," she advised. "We've had enough trouble with them. Please forget that girl and go to the United States as you planned."

"Yes, Mama." Omar sighed. "You wouldn't have had to come all the way to Estelí to tell me. You're right. Daisy dropped her wedding plans because that brute Agustín beat her. She eloped with her man. It was never meant to be with me." He grimaced, pounding one fist into his other hand. "Next week I'm off to the United States. Please don't worry about me. I'm big enough now to take care of myself."

Miriam started to cry, partly out of relief and partly because she was losing her son whom she both admired and feared. In spite of all the suffering she had already gone through because of her firstborn son, she still loved him. And now he was leaving—would she ever see him again?

17

THE COYOTE'S TRAIL

THE TALL MEXICAN immigration official smirked as he scrutinized Omar. "So, I'm supposed to believe you're a Mexican traveling north on some errand, eh? That's asking a lot of me, son."

Omar squirmed.

"How much will you turn loose? Or do you want to go back into your cage?"

"I don't have any money," Omar lied. "How can I swing a deal with you if I have nothing to offer?"

"I'm supposed to believe that too?" The official chuckled. "Man, you're a stupid kid. If you use your brains and turn some dough loose, you're good to go. Otherwise, you go back to the cage, and tomorrow you head back the way you came. That's how we do things in Mexico City."

The cowboy boot on Omar's right foot almost burned his crossed leg as he slouched in his chair, pretending innocence. Inwardly he trembled. What if the Mexican official frisked him and found the money he had hidden between the double layers of his leather boot, as the coyote had instructed? He didn't want to lose several hundred dollars.

The coyote Uncle Bato had found for Omar had gathered a group of eight Nicas at a friend's house in Estelí where he always started his trips. The eight spent the night there, catching some sleep after receiving detailed instructions for the journey.

All went well at first. The first day the group took a bus to San Salvador, where they all slept in a nice hotel. The next night they slept in Guatemala, close to the Mexican border. Again the coyote had chosen a fancy hotel.

The next morning, the coyote had divided them into smaller groups. The border crossing into Mexico was crucial, and security would be tight.

"Look, Omar, you'll do better traveling by yourself, so I'm going to send you ahead," the coyote told him. "Since you look Mexican, you have a good chance of slipping through the border at Ciudad Hidalgo. The others I'll send by twos, and I'll follow a day or two later. I have things to take care of here."

Everybody had agreed to the plan.

"If you get caught, Omar, call your aunt Yolanda in LA. I'll also be in touch with her. If they deport you, find your way back to this hotel and stay until you get further instructions."

Back in his cell in Mexico City, Omar had plenty of time to think. *I won't give that official my money,* he vowed. *I'd rather suffer the consequences.*

Omar's cell had a little window facing the street. All night long he sat on the floor, scared that some Mexican official would come in to strip him for his money or steal his boots or beat him.

Morning dawned bright and clear, but Omar was tired and almost sick with worry. What would happen next?

The answer came quickly. A bus with armed men at the doors roared past the cell window. A dozen Latinos were leaning out of the windows, hollering. "Going home! Going home!" they chanted.

A half hour later Omar was on that bus with the rowdy crowd. The last thing he wanted to do was to go home, but at this point he had no other options. *Sure enough, I'm being deported,* he groaned as the bus roared through Mexico City, heading south. *I wonder where the coyote and the rest of the group are.*

The driver dropped off the deported Latinos at a border crossing many miles to the east of where Omar had crossed the day before. Omar felt lost, but by asking, he found his way across Guatemala to the same hotel, only to discover that the coyote had left that morning.

So Omar found a public phone and called Yolanda. He told her to ask the coyote what he was supposed to do next. Yolanda relayed the coyote's message the next morning. The rest of the group had made it to Tijuana and were ready to cross the border into the United States the next day. "The coyote says you should bus back to Nicaragua. He'll take you with the next group two weeks from now."

Omar didn't like this answer, but having no other options, he headed back to Nicaragua and started preparing for the next time around. He avoided Regadío and Estelí, staying with relatives elsewhere.

Two weeks later Omar went through the same process with the same coyote but a new group of six Nicaraguan traveling companions. This time, after passing through Honduras and El Salvador, the coyote stayed with the group and accompanied them in crossing from Guatemala into Mexico at La Mesilla.

Then, instead of heading northwest toward Mexico City as they had the first time, they took a bus that swung northeast toward the Yucatán. The coyote didn't tell the group what he planned. They just followed quietly, trusting their lives into his hands.

Since getting through Mexico was actually trickier than crossing the border into the United States, the coyote had chosen a route that was less risky than traveling through Mexico City. The plan was to head northeast to Merida and fly from there, first to Mexico City and then on to Tijuana, where they would cross into the United States.

Omar was surprised when the coyote took a bus off the beaten track, ending up at an immense lake called La Angostura. "What's going on?" he asked.

The coyote laughed. "Oh, don't worry! We're just avoiding checkpoints, that's all."

He ushered the group onto an old wooden boat equipped with a high-powered motor. Minutes later a long-haired stranger with the look of a mafioso was speeding them across the lake.

The scenery was beautiful and the ride glorious. But Omar felt uneasy when he noticed that only several inches of boat sat above the surface of the water. It seemed that at any minute, the whole lake might flood into the boat. Not only that, but the old rig leaked badly. The driver pointed at an old bowl lying on the bottom of the boat and barked, "Time to start bailing!"

The coyote took his turn first. Then Omar bailed as hard as he could, trying not to look at the little edge whizzing along, almost kissing the water's surface. He would be lucky to get out of this alive. But the mafioso was grinning, and the coyote seemed at ease. So maybe they'd be all right.

Eventually the group did arrive safely at the other side of the lake. There they caught another bus, still heading northeast. This route avoided checkpoints and brought them all the way to their destination.

The coyote had clandestine connections in Merida. Within twenty-four hours, each one of the group had Mexican citizenship cards.

"Now you're 'true' Mexican citizens!" the coyote bragged. "But please be careful and talk as little as possible around the officials. You sure don't talk like Mexicans—you talk like Nicas!"

Though nerve-racking at first, after Merida every time Omar was stopped or questioned, all he had to do was show his card and he was waved through.

Boarding the plane in Merida was a thrilling, new experience for Omar. He was tickled to get a window seat some distance from the rest of his group. After takeoff, he drank in the fascinating sights from his window—fluffy white clouds below him, roads like ant trails, vehicles like toy cars, and houses like building blocks. He just couldn't stop looking.

As the plane landed in Mexico City, taxied up to the gate, and finally came to a complete stop, Omar saw how everybody jumped up, grabbed their handbags, and got ready to exit.

But when he tried to do the same, the seat belt jerked him back. Frantically he tried to unbuckle, but he didn't understand how it worked, and he was too proud to ask for help. As people began to exit at the front of the plane, Omar tried to slip out of his seat belt. It was a good thing he was skinny!

He had partly squirmed out of his predicament when a man standing in the aisle noticed his problem. Hardly suppressing his grin, he said, "Just a minute, young man. I'll help you." Reaching down, he gave the buckle a little twitch, and Omar was free.

"Thank you!" Omar spluttered, hoping no one else had noticed his embarrassment.

At airport immigration in Mexico City, Omar took the line for Mexican citizens as the coyote had instructed. Mindful of his Nicaraguan accent, he avoided talking any more than necessary. Everything went well.

Aboard the next plane, Omar wisely figured out first thing how the seat belt buckle worked. He thoroughly enjoyed the second flight—especially the sandwich and drink served by the flight attendant.

The coyote had warned them that security would be tight in Tijuana. Omar trotted ahead of the rest of his group and got into the line for Mexican citizens, hoping that this time he wouldn't get caught and left behind as he had two weeks earlier.

The immigration officer took Omar's new card and looked him over intently. "Where are you from?" he asked brusquely.

"Merida," Omar answered, keeping a cool face.

"Your destination?"

"I'm staying here in Tijuana. My uncle lives here."

"What's your uncle's name?"

Omar popped off the fictitious name he had chosen in anticipation of this question, but the official looked suspicious. "Step over into that room," he barked.

Omar's heart sank. *Here I go again! They got me, and the rest will get through again without me. I should have stayed with them.*

In the little room, Omar discovered that two officials were questioning another person who wasn't cooperating. One of the officers asked Omar, "Where are *you* going?"

Without speaking, Omar showed him the Tijuana address that he carried on a piece of paper.

Distracted by the other problem, the official nodded, and Omar walked back out of the room to join the crowd in line for the immigration booths. To his horror, he was just in time to see his whole group, including the coyote, being ushered by policemen into another room. *They got them!* Omar exclaimed to himself. *And this time I'm the one who's free!*

He couldn't leave without the group, but he slipped out of the airport building and stepped out into the lawn. He found a thick bush and plunged the satchel containing all of his belongings deeply into its branches. Then he crouched down, hoping he'd be taken for a tramp who needed to rest.

What in the world would he do now? He was in Tijuana, but far from safe.

Finally Omar got up enough nerve to go back into the airport to use a pay phone to call his aunt Yolanda.

"Just lay low," she advised. "As soon as the coyote calls me, I'll let him know where you are."

How is the coyote going to call Yolanda if he's in prison? Omar wondered. She sounded so sure that everything would be all right. But what if the whole group got deported?

Two hours ticked by slowly as Omar sat low, hugging his bush. He was just about to go inside to call Yolanda again when a van drove by. That was nothing new—vans had been roaring by all evening. But wait! The side door of this van was open, and as it slowed to a stop, Omar could see it was packed full of people. A stranger hung halfway out the door, beckoning to him. "Hurry! Hurry up!" The tone was low but urgent.

Frightened, Omar almost ran in the opposite direction. But then he realized these people weren't officials in uniform—they were dressed like civilians.

He retrieved his satchel and darted toward the van. He saw the coyote ducked low behind a seat, motioning for him to jump in. So Omar did. The van door slammed shut, and the driver zoomed out of the airport area. As they zipped down the streets of Tijuana, the passengers were all quiet until they arrived at a house in a residential area. The vehicle stopped abruptly, and everybody was ushered into a spacious living room.

Omar soon learned that the coyote had bribed the officials so they would allow some of the group to call relatives in San Diego, just across the border from Tijuana. Then they had waited until the van from the United States side arrived with a few of the relatives, who knew all the tricks to the trade. They quickly made a deal with the officials and slipped the group out the back of the airport. The coyote had called Yolanda, who told him where Omar was waiting.

As the relatives from San Diego mingled with the group at the house, Omar was surprised to see other Latinos there. They seemed to be waiting on the same thing as his own group. Omar could also see that the coyote was relieved. He had done his part successfully and would now hand the group over to another set of coyotes.

Soon a tall heavily built man stepped into the living room. He wore expensive clothes and lots of gold jewelry on his wrist and neck. He smiled and boomed, "Who do we have here?"

He looks like a Nica, Omar thought. He was astonished to learn that this man, whom everybody called The Boss, was originally from Estelí. Nobody knew his name, but everybody jumped to his tune.

The coyote gathered Omar's group and handed over all their documents and information. The Boss asked some questions, then explained, "You are now delivered into my hands. Say thank you to this coyote. From now on, do exactly what I say, and everything will be all right."

It was a little hard to say goodbye to their special coyote, also from Estelí. He had been a shrewd leader, and he had also become their friend. Now he would head back south to pick up another load, and Omar and the rest of his group were at the mercy of this powerful lion of a man whom Omar feared from the first sight of him. "We'll be crossing the border tomorrow," The Boss assured them.

The next morning, The Boss arrived with a large battered work van. He got the group together. "There's room under the back seats for you to curl up," he explained. "Once we're ready to go, get under the seats and don't dare move till I let you know we're safe on the San Diego side. No talking, no sneezing—nothing. Since they know me so well at the border, they don't usually check my vehicles. But if they do happen to look inside the van, it's got to be quiet and look empty, okay? No heads sticking out or legs sprawled around."

After the men squeezed under the seats, someone threw boxes, plastic bags, and other trash between the seats to cover their hiding places. Then the van roared off. The van started and stopped a lot in the next forty minutes. Fifteen minutes into the trip, Omar began to feel cramped from being curled so tightly under the seat. By the time The Boss pulled into a closed garage and opened the van, he was so stiff he could hardly walk.

"Welcome to the United States of America!" The Boss said as the men crawled out.

Omar and his buddies looked at each other and grinned. *That was easy! A lot easier than I expected.*

They were ushered into a large house where many other Latinos were lying low. Armed men guarded the closed doors and heavily curtained windows. They could use the bathroom if they needed to, but otherwise they were to remain sitting on the floor.

As the evening progressed, a man came in from the garage and announced, "The group that goes to Miami..." He called out a list of names, and the people slipped into the garage and were gone.

When the names for Omar's group were called, they were ushered into another van and told to just squat or lie between the seats. Once more, junk was thrown in to hide them. Finally, Omar was able to find a comfortable position so he could sleep.

Before he dozed off, he whispered, *Finally, Los Angeles, here I come!*

18

TACOS MEXICO

AN UNNATURAL SILENCE shrouded the room, and thick curtains and dim lighting gave it an eerie feel. Heavily armed men were stationed at the two doors, and dozens of Latino men and women either sat on the floor or stood against the wall. Their faces showed the strain of the long risky journey from Central America to Los Angeles. Hunger pangs gnawed at Omar, who hadn't eaten a thing for almost twenty-four hours.

Several hours earlier, Omar and his Nica buddies had arrived at a safe house in Los Angeles. The van had slipped into a garage, and once again, a sliding door had concealed their arrival. The van driver hustled them through a secret hole in the wall into the large living room where they now waited.

Would life ever seem normal again? Omar sighed and hunched down, his back against the wall. Everybody in the room seemed restless, exhausted from traveling for miles and not sleeping properly for weeks. Omar was sick of his smelly clothes, the hunger pangs, and the constant fear. *I sure hope it's worth the sacrifice. Los Angeles will have to be good!*

Someone knocked at the front door, and the guard called, "Who is it? What do you want?" The guard grew jittery as the knocking continued, but he finally opened the door cautiously. It was The Boss, who stuck his head in and barked, "Omar Montenegro."

Omar crossed the room and followed The Boss to his limousine waiting outside. *What does this man want now?*

The Boss had come all the way from San Diego, supposedly to deliver Omar personally to his aunt Yolanda. But he had another idea in mind—he had singled Omar out for his shrewdness and hoped to persuade him to return to San Diego.

"I want to offer you a job, young man," The Boss proposed. "Many immigrants think life in the United States will be easy and they'll make a lot of money. But that's not true. It's not always easy to find a job, and everything is extremely expensive. Some of them get caught and deported."

Omar was noncommittal as The Boss drove him deep into a suburb called Huntingdon Park on the west side of Los Angeles.

"Working for me, you'll be safe. I have a house in San Diego, and another one in Tijuana. I cross the border whenever I want, and they don't bother checking me. Here even the government officials respect me." The Boss winked. "I know how to handle them."

Seeing that Omar wasn't convinced, he upped the pressure. "Working for me, you could eventually make $500 a day, either in Tijuana or San Diego, whichever you want."

But Omar didn't trust this man. *Anything would be better than slaving for this creepy man who acts like a king.* He wouldn't allow this coyote to derail his plan to join Uncle Bato in Los Angeles.

Just before Omar crawled out of the car, the Boss gave him his card. "I like you, man. If you ever get tired of life as a slave in LA, just give me a call. That's a standing offer."

Aunt Yolanda met Omar on the sidewalk in front of her rented house. She thanked The Boss profusely and handed him a wad of money. The Boss shook hands with them both and swaggered back to his fancy car.

His dad's sister was a feisty little woman, and she immediately began to give orders. First she showed him a tiny bedroom. "Here is where you'll sleep. Your uncle Bato will have the bed, and you'll sleep on the floor."

Shouldn't be bad. The carpet looks thick enough to allow a good night's sleep.

Then Yolanda showed him the shower. "My next recommendation is that you take a shower, because you stink!"

After his shower, Yolanda led him to the dining room table and motioned for him to sit down. Sitting beside him, she said, "The first thing you'll do here in LA is find work so you can pay off your debts." Pointing to a page in her little notebook, she barged on. "You owe your cousin Andrés five hundred dollars. You owe Bato five hundred dollars and your uncle Yico[12] seven hundred fifty dollars. They pitched in to raise the money I paid to the coyote just now."

Omar nodded.

"And," Yolando added, "you owe *me* two thousand dollars."

Omar flinched. *Two thousand dollars?* "Wh-what do I owe *you* for?" he stuttered, staring at his aunt.

"The collect calls you've been making the last several months," Yolanda snapped. "I kept track of every call. Here are the receipts. You were calling me all the time!"

Man, if I had known how expensive those calls were, I would have been more careful! Sweating, Omar agreed, "That's fine. I'll pay it all as soon as I find work."

"So it's a deal." Yolanda was smiling now. "I'll get all of your wages to start with. First comes the hundred dollars a month for your room and board. Next, you'll pay your debt to me—the others can wait. You see, I pay high rent for this house, and your payments help me make mine. If you need money to pay for your washing or to buy clothes, just ask me and I'll take it out of your wages."

After Omar had agreed to all of his aunt's demands, he asked feebly, "Aunt Yolanda, could I have something to eat? I'm starving!"

"Why, sure!" she answered, disappearing into the kitchen.

Looks like I'll have a tough row to hoe! Omar worried. It would take him forever to pay off his debts. Meanwhile, he'd have to live like a poor beggar.

That evening the Montenegro family got together at Yolanda's place to see Omar. Bato was there, the center of attention as usual. Uncle Yico, also living in Los Angeles, helped liven up the evening with his jokes. Andrés and his wife Deyania showed up too.

---

12   Yico: nickname for Fedrico.

Yolanda told all of them that they needed to help Omar find work to pay his debt to her first. Later he would pay the rest of them. Bato and Yico grinned knowingly. Although Yolanda had a job at a textile factory, she often complained about how tough life was for her, and she made sure they all paid her on time.

Andrés had a good job, driving a semi. Maybe someday Omar could pursue the same kind of work. Meanwhile, Andrés tried to help Omar find a job in construction. After a week with no success, they approached Bato, who was enjoying an evening cup of coffee in Yolanda's kitchen.

"Well, Yico and I are both professional night guards, but right now there's no work there," Bato mused. Then his face lightened into a grin. "But I have an old friend . . ."

When Bato grins, things happen. Omar chuckled to himself.

"My friend, Tony Moreno, is pure Mexican. He's a big shot now—the owner of Tacos Mexico."

Omar's interest was stirred. Several evenings before, Andrés had taken him out to eat at Tacos Mexico, where they had eaten the hottest but most delicious tacos Omar had ever tasted. He had immediately liked the bustling atmosphere at the restaurant.

"When Tony came from Mexico," Bato reminisced, "he was just a poor boy. But he had a tremendous determination to make a go of things here. Twenty-five years ago, he had only two restaurants in the city, and now he has at least fifty all over LA."

I have a determination like that too, Omar told himself. *I'll make a go of it here as well. But what makes Bato think I have a job with this big shot Tony?*

Downing the last drop of coffee, Bato grinned at Omar. "Tony owes me an old debt. I just never had the occasion to charge it. Maybe this is the time."

Omar watched Bato's face for clues.

"Years ago, when Tony was just getting on his feet," Bato explained, "we were friends. We'd drink together . . . go to parties together. I loaned him money many times and didn't charge interest. He always paid me back."

Bato jumped up from his chair and grabbed Yolanda's phone. Soon he was talking with his old friend. "Look," Bato said, "my son, who just came from Nicaragua, needs a job badly. What can you do for me?"

Oh, so now I'm Bato's son! Omar smiled. *I'll have to remember that and live up to it.*

Minutes later Bato got off the phone, exuberant. "You have a job, son! Tony's going to tell his manager, Javier, that you'll be at the Tacos Mexico just down the street, tomorrow at 8 a.m. You'd better be ready to move. Those guys hop, feeding flocks of people twenty-four hours a day."

Omar could hardly believe his ears. He was finally in the States, and he had landed a job the first week!

"You first work for free," Bato informed him. "They'll teach you every part of the job. Then once you can really be a help, they'll start paying you."

"That's fair," Omar agreed. "I'll do my best."

"You'll have to dress up to work there," Bato continued. "They provide the red cap and aprons with the Tacos Mexico's emblem on them. But you'll need to come up with a long-sleeved white shirt, black pants, and a red tie."

"But I don't have such clothes!" Omar complained, looking down over his T-shirt and blue jeans.

"I'll buy you two sets of clothes this evening," Bato offered. "I know you don't have any money yet, so I'll pay for them."

The next morning Omar presented himself at the closest Tacos Mexico a half hour early, dressed in his stiff new clothes. He waited on the porch, nervous but excited.

Soon a flashy convertible drove up, and out popped a small wiry Mexican with a big mustache. "Omar Montenegro! I'm Javier Cervantes." The restaurant manager smiled as he shook Omar's hand. "Follow me."

It was almost eight o'clock, time for the shift turnover. Javier gathered all the workers and explained, "New guy on the block." He beamed, pointing at Omar. "He's not just anybody—he's the son of one of Tony's best friends, and Tony wants him to learn everything there is to learn about Tacos Mexico's restaurants—I mean *everything*. His training starts here, today. This week, teach him every branch of the work except cooking and the cash register. We'll see what he can do."

He turned to Omar. "Look, young man, you start at the bottom. No pay. But if you learn fast, you'll get the minimum wage soon. And if you're *very* good, we'll promote you—all the way to the top!"

Everybody, including Omar, smiled in agreement. When Javier and the night shift left, the new shift of seven men dove into their work. Juan, another lively little Mexican who managed the restaurant in Javier's absence, ran the cash register. He fingered his huge curled-up mustache as he looked Omar over. "Let's get you a cap and an apron. Today you'll start cutting up vegetables in the kitchen. Cookie, you teach him how."

So the first thing Omar did was dice what seemed like tons of vegetables. Cookie taught Omar how to slice in thin, uniform cuts—fast and then faster. Omar learned rapidly. After the chopping, Omar mopped the floors, washed dishes, wiped tables, and washed the huge glass windows out at the front of the store. Worst of all was cleaning the bathrooms, but the cleaning boy trained Omar thoroughly. Again, Omar learned fast.

What Omar enjoyed most was eating the delicious food at Tacos Mexico whenever he got hungry. Juan had told him that he could help himself to whatever was on the menu. He experimented with various tacos made with specialty meats, burritos, quesadillas—all smothered in different kinds of hot sauces.

The customers also interested him. Most of them were Latinos, but all stripes of people came to try Tony's tacos—the rich aristocrats as well as the poor working class. The tacos were cheap, and the service was fast. Many returned again and again.

By the end of the twelve-hour shift, Omar's head was swimming, his feet ached, and he was so tired he felt as if he could flop down anywhere and sleep for a week.

But after three days of training, Omar's efforts were rewarded. At shift change on the fourth morning, when Javier breezed in to check on things, Juan said, "Javier, Omar has learned everything there is to learn on the first level. He learns fast. He's ready to make a wage."

"Okay!" Javier cheered, smiling at Omar. "As of today, Omar starts earning minimum wage. That's $4.75 an hour, Omar. You deserve it!"

That night, Omar had a little trouble dozing off. He was tired, but he kept thinking about what Javier had told him. He had done some quick arithmetic on the restaurant's calculator. Tacos Mexico paid its workers every two weeks. *If I work twelve hours a day, six days a week, that's* *seventy-two hours. If I get paid every two weeks, that's 144 hours. Multiply that by $4.75 an hour, and that's $684. If a dollar is worth 6.73 córdobas, that means I'll earn over four thousand córdobas every two weeks.* For a man fresh from Nicaragua, that was a lot of money!

Of course, for now he'd have to turn all of his wages over to his stingy aunt. That was a bitter thought. *But as soon as I can pay off my debts,* Omar determined, *she loses all of her rights over me, and that money will be mine! Then my life in the United States will really begin.*

The first two weeks on the job, Omar sensed a strange hostility from the other employees. He worked in all three Tacos Mexico restaurants in the area, and in each one, he got the dirtiest jobs, especially cleaning the bathrooms. His fellow workers mocked him, claiming that he wasn't Mexican but some counterfeit Nicaraguan, Honduran, or Salvadoran. They called him "son of Tony," and although they laughed as if they were teasing him, Omar knew that they really didn't like him. Even Juan joined in pestering Omar.

But whenever Omar was tempted to anger, he remembered Bato's strong words: "Omar, you have to behave at the restaurant. I don't want Tony to get mad at me. You can't let him down. If you get yourself in trouble, I'll be the one to suffer, and I'm the one who'll deal with you, okay?"

Omar had understood. So he determined to put up with the mocking and rejection until he could figure out why the others resented him. He knew that part of the problem was that they thought he was the son of Tony's best friend.

Not only was Omar learning fast, but he was also ascending fast—too fast for his envious fellow employees. Javier was already asking Juan to allow Omar to work the cash register, the highest position in Tacos Mexico, next to Javier himself. Nobody else except Juan was allowed the privileges Omar was given. Omar understood a bit of resentment, but why did it seem as if his coworkers feared him?

One day Juan questioned Omar about his connections with Tony Moreno. Omar told him the truth. "I never knew the man till now," he admitted. "I've only met him a time or two when he stopped by, always in a hurry. I'm working here because my Uncle Gilberto is one of Tony's old friends."

"We thought maybe you were Tony's spy," Juan informed him with a sly grin. "We were sure you were here to see if we behaved."

Omar laughed. "I have no interest in getting you people in trouble. All I want is a chance to work and make enough money to pay off my debts."

The very next day Omar caught Juan slipping some money from the cash register to one of the workers. The two looked nervous when they realized Omar had seen it.

"What's going on?" Omar asked.

"Look," Juan answered warily, "our wages here are way too low. Tacos Mexico is known to underpay their staff. So we have our ways of making a little extra money."

"And how do you do that?" Omar asked, feeling warm under his collar.

"I just sent that guy to buy disposable cups from the grocer down the street," Juan explained. "See, the restaurant keeps track of how many cups of coffee we sell by keeping close inventory of the special cups that have the restaurant's emblem on them. If we sell a hundred cups of coffee in their cups, then we have to have the money for that many coffees at the end of the day. But if we sell fifty cups out of regular cups from the grocery store, we don't figure that in. So, since the coffees cost a dollar fifty each, that gives us seventy-five dollars at the end of the day to divide up between us. Just little tricks to the trade." He winked.

Omar laughed, understanding the gimmick. "Man, you guys are slick! Just be careful and don't get caught. And please don't worry that I'll get you in trouble. I need money just as much as the rest of you."

The next day Juan gave Omar the first twenty-dollar bill that he hadn't earned. Omar accepted it, gloating that he hadn't had to beg the money from his stingy aunt.

From then on Omar felt part of the Tacos Mexico's employee family. It was amazing how much extra cash came along with his newfound acceptance.

19

EL MORENO

OMAR TOSSED THE bags of trash into the dumpster behind Tacos Mexico. He glanced up at the building across the street, curious about the activity he had seen there several times. Through the second-story windows, Omar could see people dressed in short white robes, exercising and doing stunts. The sign over the door read, "Martial Arts," but Omar didn't know what that meant. However, he asked a few questions and learned that what he was seeing was a karate class, that the classes were in Spanish, and that the students were mainly Latinos.

Omar had seen karate in the movies, and he had always admired the defense skills. So he signed up to take classes in the evenings, and he succeeded rapidly.

A distinct class of people frequented the restaurant at night. Most of them were Omar's age, nineteen or even younger. They dressed in expensive clothes and often wore black—especially black jackets. Their gold watches, bracelets, and necklaces fascinated Omar.

Cell phones were just coming into common use, and not everybody could afford them. But the Black Jackets, as they were called, apparently could; they proudly used cell phones everywhere they went.

The Black Jackets spent money recklessly when they came into the restaurants with their beautiful girlfriends, who also wore black jackets and black boots. How, Omar wondered, did the Black Jackets make all their money?

One evening near the end of his shift, Omar packed up several of his favorite meals to take home. Actually, since he ate at Tacos Mexico every day, he was starting to get tired of the food. But Bato and Yolanda would gladly trade some good old rice and beans for some spicy tacos.

Juan was turning the cash register over to the night cashier when several Black Jackets stopped by to pay. Omar shook his head at the exorbitant totals. After they left, Omar asked Juan, "Where do those dudes get their money?"

Juan laughed, twirling his mustache handles. "Well, son, they're in the business."

"What business?"

"Buying and selling cocaine."

"So that's easy money?" Omar watched Juan closely.

"You might call it that," Juan answered. "But it's not really so easy if you figure in the risks they run and the constant dangers they face. I don't want anything to do with it."

"What's the risk? Jail time?"

"Yes, that, but the worst of it is that these guys can't take anything off each other. The competition's fierce. They're always getting into fights, and too often, someone gets killed when they can't pay up. They handle big money! It's a dangerous life."

Omar walked the few blocks home, thinking hard. He was so tired of never having enough money. He'd have to check out these Black Jackets. He didn't want to work for The Boss in Tijuana, but maybe he could be a man like The Boss and work on his own in LA.

The next morning a large dark-skinned man entered the restaurant, a girlfriend on his arm. He was built like a bull with a neck like an ox. His sleeveless shirt revealed rippling muscles splattered with tattoos. Instead of ordering his food like the rest by pointing at the food in the buffet, he walked up to the counter and hollered directly in to the cook. "I want five tacos al pastor, two quesadillas, and a big bottle of Coca-Cola. That's to go."

While the big man waited, Omar watched him closely. *He acts like he owns the world,* Omar thought, feeling his hackles rise. Minutes later, the cook's helper handed the stranger a big bag of food and the bottle of drink. To Omar's surprise, the big man and his girlfriend left without paying a cent.

"What in the world is going on?" Omar asked Juan. "Why didn't that monster pay?"

"Oh, that was El Moreno,"[13] Juan answered lamely. "Nobody messes with him—he's mean. Javier says just to give him the food he asks for and avoid conflict. He comes to a lot of our restaurants, and everybody lets it go."

"Man, if I'd have the say-so around here, that would stop!" Omar fumed. "How can you allow such a bully to take advantage of you? I'm surprised that Javier doesn't make sure he gets dealt with."

"I guess *you* could tackle him?" Juan laughed, looking at Omar. "I would enjoy seeing the flea fight the elephant!"

Omar didn't answer, but he stored the incident in his mind. *If nobody else puts that man in his place, I will!*

One spring morning, Omar was working in the kitchen when someone cried, "Here comes El Moreno!"

Omar stepped out of the kitchen and waited behind the counter. Although he put on his coolest expression, his heart was pounding. He braced himself for what was coming.

El Moreno walked in alone, wearing his usual sleeveless shirt, head held high. As before, he barked at the cook, "Give me two tacos al pastor, a quesadilla, and a big bottle of Coca-Cola."

"For here or to go?" the cook asked uneasily.

"What are you thinking, man?" Omar challenged. "If you think this restaurant gives handouts to freeloaders, you're mistaken. In *this* restaurant, you pay like everybody else."

"And who are *you?*" El Moreno sneered, stepping closer and glowering at Omar.

---

13   El Moreno: dark skin.

"It doesn't matter who I am," Omar answered coldly. "What matters is that here in Tacos Mexico, we're tired of you coming in, acting as if you owned the place and not paying. Today this stops!"

El Moreno tried to stare Omar down as he sized him up. "You silly kid!" El Moreno bellowed. "Do you want me to haul you out to the parking lot? I'll show you that I do whatever I please."

When Omar sprinted around the counter, El Moreno charged. But before his huge fists hit anything, Omar jumped aside. With a blow to the jaw, he knocked El Moreno to the floor. When he rose with a roar, Omar again knocked him down.

Slowly El Moreno picked himself up and headed for the door. He turned to glare at Omar. "I'll be back!" he snarled.

"Omar, we can't let this happen again!" Juan implored after El Moreno was gone. "We need to keep the restaurants quiet and peaceful for the sake of the customers. Javier will not be happy!"

"Have you asked him?" Omar sneered. "I think he'd be happy to not have to feed that parasite so many free meals. I say this has to stop."

Some of the workers sided with Omar. Others took Juan's side. "El Moreno will be back," Omar reminded them. "That's why we all need to be prepared. We can't let him have his way. That bully has to be put in his place. I just hope he doesn't try something dirty like shooting me in the parking lot or jumping me with a knife."

For the next several days, Omar approached the restaurant carefully, standing at the street corner for a long time, watching, before he entered. All day while he worked, Omar was wary. He didn't trust El Moreno at all.

Javier and Tony both took Omar's side when they heard about the fight. Tony laughed and said, "Well, nothing like Tacos Mexico providing live entertainment while their customers eat!"

Javier, too, just chuckled. "If Omar wants to set that greedy fellow straight, let him," he told Juan. "It will help Tacos Mexico in the long run. If Omar has what it takes to stop the bully, give him room."

Three days after the first round, someone cried, "Here comes El Moreno!"

El Moreno walked into the restaurant, marched to the counter, and stared Omar straight in the eye. "I'm coming for you," he barked.

This time they landed in a tangle on the floor, but Omar had El Moreno's neck in a strangling chokehold. It took four men to pull Omar loose. Still lying on the floor, his face purple, El Moreno slowly got his wind back. Sluggishly he got to his feet and stumbled out of the restaurant, thoroughly humbled. From behind the counter, Juan and Omar watched him go.

"He'll never come back," Omar predicted, still pale from the fight.

The subdued workers congratulated Omar, sure that El Moreno would never bother any of Tacos Mexico's restaurants again.

They were right. Omar's reputation spread through LA's fifty Tacos Mexico restaurants with the slogan, "If you ever have any trouble with anybody, you can always ask Omar for help."

"What are you going to do with your first paycheck?" Bato asked Omar one evening. He knew that Omar had finally paid off his debts. "Are you going to celebrate?"

Omar didn't answer. He wasn't sure himself. He was just relieved that, finally, after eight grueling months, he was debt-free.

"If I were you," Uncle Yico suggested, "I'd spend an evening at the Macarena nightclub. So far, you haven't had much fun. All you do is work, work, work. It's time that changes."

"That's a plan!" Bato agreed. "Let's go Saturday night. We all have off this weekend."

Yico's woman had kicked him out for womanizing, so Yolanda had taken him in. Now he was sleeping in the tiny bedroom along with Omar and Bato. Being the oldest, Yico got the bed. Bato slept on the floor, with his head and torso inside the little closet in the corner. Omar slept in the small area between the bed and the door, but he rarely saw his uncles, since they both worked nights.

"I'll see if I'm willing to blow my wages in La Macarena," Omar answered. "I'll let you know."

I need to buy new clothes, Omar realized. *But I also appreciate what my uncles have done for me, and yes, I'm starved for fun. All I've done here so far is work. Why not spend my first money on some relaxation?*

On Saturday evening, Omar put on the best clothes he owned and borrowed a cowboy hat from Bato and a pair of snazzy cowboy boots from his cousin Andrés. He had cashed his check at a bank, so he had almost seven hundred dollars in his pocket. *Tonight we'll live it up!* Omar gloated.

Omar had done his share of partying in Estelí and Regadío, so he knew how to dance, drink, and carouse. But nothing he had experienced in Nicaragua had prepared him for the wild, immoral atmosphere in the La Macarena nightclub. After the night was over and he and his uncles were headed home, very drunk, Omar was much wiser in the ways of Los Angeles nightlife.

"Why didn't you warn me about what it costs to party in that place?" he spluttered. "When I went to pay, I owed over six hundred dollars! Now I have almost nothing left to show for my last two weeks of hard work."

Yico, eyes swimming from too much alcohol, just laughed. "That's how it is in these places. What did you expect?"

"I'll know better for the next time," Omar hissed, frowning deeply.

There would be many more "next times" for the young man experimenting with the world and its glamour. Omar determined he would be more careful so that at least his money would go a little further.

About three weeks after Omar's second round with El Moreno, he showed up again, accompanied by several friends. They went through the line ordering their food like everybody else, and the workers served them like kings. El Moreno seemed as subdued as a kitten, though he was a little pale—and he refused to look at Omar.

Would El Moreno actually pay his bill? To Omar's surprise, El Moreno came to the cash register and paid up, acting as if he had never seen Omar before. In return, Omar treated El Moreno like a fine gentleman he had just met. From then on, El Moreno was a regular, well-behaved customer at the Tacos Mexico restaurants. He and Omar even became friends of sorts.

Omar's place in the restaurant chain was firmly established. He had reached the top, surmounted only by Tony himself, and Javier, who was becoming his great friend.

But at home, Omar was tired of sharing the tiny bedroom, and he resented that Aunt Yolanda still tried to run his life. She constantly asked what he was doing and where he was going. She objected to his being out late at nights. When Andrés offered to find him a room elsewhere, Omar agreed.

Doña Flora, also originally from Estelí, rented Omar a room for the same amount he had been paying Yolanda. The friendly lady took Omar in as one of the family and shamelessly spoiled him. Her own children didn't resent her giving Omar so much attention, and Omar fit in as if it were truly his home.

But one thing didn't change. Doña Flora, even more than Yolanda, gave Omar unsolicited advice and scolded him for his wild ways and late nights. "It's just too dangerous, son!" she would admonish.

Neither did Doña Flora approve of Omar's many girlfriends. "That's not the way to live, son," she fussed. "All you do is hurt the girls' hearts. You need to find one girl, and then you need to marry her and be faithful to her." Omar knew Doña Flora was right, but he didn't accept her motherly advice.

After eight months he left, claiming that he had been asked to work at a restaurant in the other end of the city and needed to live close to work. He moved in with Carlos, a Mexican coworker. Newly married, Carlos had rented an apartment, and he offered Omar one room—again for one hundred dollars a month. Carlos was a native Mexican, helping the rest of his family come to the United States one by one.

The Mexican workers also began to accept Omar as one of their own. They invited him to their homes for holidays and birthday parties. Omar dressed like them and talked like they talked. He even ate what they ate, including hot pepper. Finally, Omar could pull off his identity as a real Mexican.

But in his heart, Omar was still a Nica and thought like a Nica. *I'll be a Nica till I die!* Omar vowed, grinning to himself.

20

THE YEAR OF GOLD

THE DINING HALL in Tacos Mexico was full and running over. Lively music filled the air. Omar's shift had just ended, and he had invited his friend and coworker Horacio to eat a taco with him before they headed home.

"Horacio," Omar addressed the tall Mexican sitting across the table, "if I would like to get into the business, how would I go about it?"

"So . . . you want to get into the business, eh?"

"I'm considering it," Omar answered slowly, looking around to make sure no one else was listening. He knew that Horacio used drugs, so he could probably give him some information.

"I used to work in the business full-time," Horacio told him.

"Why did you quit?" Omar questioned, watching Horacio's face closely. "Couldn't you make enough money?"

"No, it wasn't that. It pays well. But when I carry cocaine, I can't control my intake. I was killing myself with the stuff. That's why I stopped."

"But you still take drugs, don't you?"

"Yeah, but when I have to buy it in daily portions, I don't take as much. But since you don't do drugs, that part wouldn't be a problem for you."

Horacio offered to take Omar to meet a friend in Pasadena who could sell him his first batch for fifteen hundred dollars.

"Give me some time," Omar answered. "I'll let you know tomorrow. Thanks, Horacio."

After a night of little sleep, Omar called Javier and asked for the day off. He made arrangements to rent a small apartment just a block away. By afternoon, he and Horacio were driving toward Pasadena in the little maroon Datsun that Omar had bought from Andrés. Since Omar didn't have a driver's license yet, he had asked Horacio to drive.

Horacio had called Primo,[14] the cocaine dealer, to tell him they were coming. Primo invited them to take seats in his lavishly furnished apartment. Horacio introduced them and explained their reason for coming and how much Omar could buy.

Primo disappeared into his bedroom and came out carrying a small duffel bag. He extracted a glistening white wedge of cocaine and placed it on the coffee table between them. Reaching into the duffel bag again, he pulled out a little electronic scale. With a sharp knife, he expertly cut a piece from the end of the wedge. It weighed exactly two ounces.

"I get $20 per gram," Primo said. "At twenty-eight grams to an ounce, that's $560 per ounce. Two ounces are worth $1,120. And I guarantee that my product is 100 percent pure."

Omar handed over the money. They exchanged telephone numbers, and Horacio and Omar slipped out to the Datsun. Omar hid the little plastic bag holding the expensive snow under his seat before he crawled in. If the police would catch him with this little start, he would be in bad trouble. Since he didn't have immigration papers, they would surely deport him.

But I will not get caught! Omar determined. *In this cat and mouse game, the mouse is way too smart to let the cats catch him.*

On the way back to Huntington Park, Omar and Horacio stopped and bought a duffel bag, an electronic scale, and a bunch of plastic bags. Then they drove to Omar's new apartment. Once they were inside and had

---

14   Primo: cousin. The drug dealers use only nicknames, never their real names, nor do they give out information about themselves. Therefore, if they ever get caught, they can't tattle on each other.

locked the door and pulled the blinds, Horacio said, "I need a glass plate and a sharp butcher knife."

Omar brought him the items, and Horacio showed him how to make the grams go even farther, by turning a whole gram into three "halves." He shaved off little slices until the two ounces were a neat little mound of powder. With the knife, he picked up little piles of the white powder and placed them on the scales until he had a third of a gram. Then he scraped the powder into one corner of a plastic bag and tied a knot to hold in the powder.

"Twenty-eight grams to the ounce," Horacio said. "We produce three halves per gram. That's 84 halves, or 168 halves from two ounces. You're going to sell each gram for $40 and the halves for $20. When someone asks for a gram, just give them two of our fixed-up halves!"

Omar figured up on his calculator—$3,360. *That's making two hundred percent profit! My problems of always running out of money are over!*

Once the little plastic bags were all knotted and the duffel bag was bulging, Omar hid the paraphernalia in the closet under some boxes of junk. Then he asked, "And what do I owe you, my friend?"

"Just give me a couple of those bags."

And Omar had his first regular customer.

Horacio helped Omar make contacts, and he soon discovered that most of the workers at Tacos Mexico did cocaine on the sly. That's why their money never reached. Omar knew better than to sell on the job, so the addicts watched for him when he finished a shift.

But Omar sold most of his cocaine at the parties he attended at night, slipping a tiny plastic bag to a customer, while the customer slipped him a twenty-dollar bill. This could be done by a simple handshake, without detection. This had been going on all around him, Omar realized, and he had never noticed before.

Before the week was up, Omar asked Pepe, a fellow worker at Tacos Mexico, to drive him to meet Primo at a restaurant. As they ate, Omar whispered to Primo how much cocaine he wanted—five ounces. Later

Primo slipped out to his vehicle, pretending to get something he had forgotten. He and Omar met in the restroom to close the deal.

When they got home, Omar invited Pepe to help him prepare the little packages of death. Pepe, a tough Mexican covered in tattoos, was also a consumer, and Omar trusted him. Soon Omar invited Pepe, who was single, to move into his apartment, and Pepe started to work for him, dealing drugs on the side.

After a month of selling drugs, Omar was able to buy the things he had always dreamed of—the best clothes, black jackets, expensive cowboy boots, a newer car—and gold. Especially genuine gold. Omar wasn't satisfied till he owned a gold bracelet, a gold ring with a diamond, an expensive gold watch, and a gold necklace. He also bought a tiny .22 revolver. It was so small that it fit into his pocket, his belt, or his boots without leaving a trace.

Omar soon became well-known in the bars and dance halls in the Huntington Park area. He was handsome and self-confident, always smiling and flashing his snow-white teeth. And he had money. He especially enjoyed paying his friends' restaurant bills. Slowly his group of friends grew as he lavished money and attention on them. It was new and thrilling to Omar's flesh. The power he enjoyed, especially with the girls, made him dizzy with the glamour and pride of this world. His dreams were coming true—or so he thought.

For a whole year Omar lived it up, fearing neither God nor the law. Unchecked by either, he grew confident and bold. Why, then, did he still have times of feeling lonely and unhappy? Along the way, little warning signs caught his attention momentarily. But Omar did not heed these signals.

One evening Omar asked Pepe to drive him over to see his cousin Andrés, who had recently bought his own tractor trailer. Andrés owned and managed a route for a trucking company. Omar admired his cousin's success, and he secretly wanted to show Andrés that he was also making a go of it in LA.

Pepe stayed in the car, and Omar promised to not stay long. Andrés invited Omar in, but he seemed troubled. "Omar, I'm hearing things about you," Andrés said, looking his cousin over searchingly. "I don't like what I'm hearing."

Omar's guard went up. "What have you been hearing?"

"I didn't want to believe it," Andrés said, shaking his head, "but now I know it's true. Your fancy outfit and your expensive jewelry tell the whole story. You don't just *look* like a Black Jacket, you *are* one!"

Omar stood stock-still in front of his cousin, feeling hard and cold. He had not expected this.

"I warn you, Omar," Andrés said, as if he were scolding a youngster, "you don't want to go that route. It's a dangerous, slippery path."

"What do you care?" Omar sneered, turning on his heel. "I know what I'm doing. I'm making a lot of money, and I'm always careful."

Andrés followed Omar out into the yard. "Omar, think about your family back in Nicaragua. If they would know what you're up to . . ."

"Mind your own business, man!" Omar barked, turning toward his car. "Like I said, I know what I'm doing! Just don't meddle in my life, okay?"

As Omar marched toward his car, Andrés tried one more time. "Omar, I'm warning you. I'm afraid for your life! Think about what you're doing."

As Omar crawled into his car and fastened his seat belt, hatred for his cousin surged up inside.

Pepe was frowning deeply. "What was wrong with that man?" Pepe wondered as he started the car. He had his automatic pistol on his lap and was caressing it softly. "I could tell that guy was mad at you," Pepe said. "I was ready to blow him up if he touched you." He wasn't joking. This vicious man, who had maybe shot someone already, had become Omar's bodyguard.

Omar shivered. For a moment, he realized that Andrés was right—that he, Omar, was going the wrong way. His cousin's sad face nudged Omar's conscience. But he quickly pushed it aside. *I know what I'm doing, and no one will stop me from making all the money I want!*

The Tacos Mexico restaurant was almost empty. Omar's shift as a waiter would be over in two hours, but he was already wishing to get back to his apartment where he could relax. He wasn't getting enough sleep, and he was wired as tight as a fiddle string all day long and sometimes far into the night.

A clean-cut young Latino strode into the restaurant. He was wearing a long-sleeved white shirt and black pants just like Omar's. He had a neat short haircut, also like Omar. But whereas Omar's tie was red, this man's tie was black. Their eyes met twice as Omar served him, and they smiled at each other.

But Omar also noticed that the man was flabby; he must have been born into a rich man's home and never done a lick of work. *What do I have in common with that young peach?* Omar pondered. *He's probably some innocent kid raised in a religious home, and I'm a son of the devil. But it sure is interesting that we dress so alike.*

When Omar refilled the man's glass of Coca-Cola, he was startled to hear him ask in perfect Spanish, "Where do you live, sir?"

"Right here . . . in Huntington Park," Omar stuttered. "And you?"

"I live over on Florence Street. I decided to go for a walk this evening and ended up here. Where are you from?"

"I'm from Mexico," Omar lied. "I've lived here for five years."

"I was born here in LA," the newcomer answered.

After chitchatting and consuming his tacos, the young man paid his bill. He stopped by to shake Omar's hand before he left. "My name is Stewart," he said. "I'll stop by to see you again sometime."

Several evenings later, Stewart stopped in as Omar was going off his shift. To Omar's surprise, Stewart invited him to join his table and bought him two tacos.

"Why do you dress like you do?" Omar asked. "I dress this way because it's a rule for Tacos Mexico employees. But why do you dress like that when you're just out for an evening stroll?"

"I belong to the Mormon church," Stewart explained. "Just like your restaurant, our church has a dress code. I was born and raised Mormon, and I've dressed this way all my life."

"What's it like to be a Mormon?" Omar probed.

Omar found himself liking the innocent Mormon youth. He also found himself telling Stewart about his own sad childhood. Of course, the story developed somewhere in southern Mexico close to the Guatemala border in a place called Chiapas, not Regadío, Nicaragua.

When Stewart invited Omar to visit his church sometime, Omar promised to go with him. *Now I understand why this kid is so friendly. He's trying to win me over to this religion, and he really thinks I'm interested.* Though Omar had no desire to join his church, he did want to be Stewart's friend.

Stewart told Omar all about his church and what they believed. Before they parted that evening, he said, "If you come to our church, you might be able to find yourself a pretty Christian girl."

Omar almost snickered into his tie. If this young man only knew the kind of life Omar lived, he would know that Omar could have any number of pretty girls whenever he wanted them.

The evening was clinched when Omar also put out an invitation. "Stewart, I need to go see a cousin of mine in Pasadena. He's a great guy, and I promised to go eat out with him. I was wondering . . . would you like to go along?"

"Sure, I would love that." Stewart beamed. "Just tell me when."

"I lost my license recently," Omar lied, "so maybe you could drive my car for me."

"Oh no! We can go in my car," Stewart insisted. "And, of course, I can drive. What's your cousin's name?"

"They call him Primo, and he's a fine fellow." Omar chuckled. "I promised to pay the restaurant bill when I go, so that will also include yours."

The two young men who dressed identically each went home happy that night—Omar, because he anticipated a friendly, free trip to Pasadena to pick up more coke, and Stewart because he was sure that he was winning his friend Omar over to the Mormon church.

21

OMAR TO THE RESCUE

ONE NIGHT OMAR, Pepe, and Mosquito—another helper Omar had hired—were partying with a bunch of their friends at the La Macarena nightclub. When his cell phone rang, Omar quickly exited the dance hall to answer it. But the voice on the other end did not belong to a drug customer.

It was his aunt Yolanda, sounding very angry. "Omar, your uncle Bato is here at my house. He told me to call you. Come right away."

Then Yolanda hung up.

Omar hurried back to his friends. "I've got to leave right now," he barked. He left the nightclub as fast as he could, mystifying Mosquito and Pepe.

Omar revved the motor of the sports car he had recently purchased at the impounded car auction. The music throbbed and the tires squealed as he zipped out of the parking lot and onto the highway. Bato had been living in Chiapas in southern Mexico for about a year now. What could be wrong?

What Omar found on Yolanda's porch was pathetic. Uncle Bato, who usually held his head high with Montenegro pride, looked totally abashed. He leaned against the wall, his head hanging low, his face a mask. His duffel bag lay on the floor. Although it was barely eight o'clock, Yolanda's house was dark. The curtains were drawn, and the door was closed.

"Jump into my car, Uncle!" Omar said, grabbing Bato's bag.

Bato followed slowly and crawled into the front seat. This time Omar didn't turn up the music or squeal his tires. He just drove carefully and asked quietly, "Uncle, what's wrong?"

"Everything!" Bato groaned. "Everything! I'm sunk, son!"

"What happened?" Omar insisted gently. "Did somebody die?"

"No, but all of my financial endeavors back home did. I lost my shirt on my last effort to get something going in Guadalajara. My family is mad at me. Even after I helped them all and bought those city lots for them, they hate me. I'm totally broke. I had just enough money to buy my ticket back to the States, and I have nothing left. Now even my sister disowns me. She shouted at me this evening and refused to open up for me. So I begged her to call you."

Omar parked the car in La Macarena's parking lot. He turned slowly to Bato. "Uncle, what do you want?" he asked. "I don't like to see you so sad. You're usually the optimist—the happy one. I want to see you happy tonight."

Bato stared bleakly at his nephew.

"What more do you want?" Omar asked again, his voice sharpening. "You have all the money you need. You have an apartment. You have a car. You have all the food you want. Most of all, you have a friend! What more do you want? Now get a smile on your face, and let's go party!"

Slowly Bato understood. If Omar possessed all those things, then Bato, Omar's uncle, had them as well. Suddenly the dark weight seemed to lift, and Bato smiled faintly.

"What do you say, Uncle? Are we on to party tonight? Are you ready to go in with me and be happy?"

Bato nodded. To prove it, he jumped out of the car and strode into La Macarena with his head held high. He had regained the Montenegro stride that said, *I own the world!*

Omar and Bato and their friends partied into the night. When they got back to the apartment at midnight, Omar ordered the boys to empty out the extra room for Bato to use as long as he needed it. The boys would sleep on the living room floor.

Next Omar handed Bato the keys to his older car that he hardly used since he had bought the newer one. Last of all he handed Bato a handful of cash. "See what I told you!" Omar exulted. "You have everything you need as long as you're with me. You helped me get to the United States. It's my turn to pay you back. Now, get on with life."

"Thanks," Bato mumbled. Then they both stumbled to bed, seeking rest for their drunken bodies.

Sitting in the Mormon chapel, Omar tried hard to stifle his boredom. The book he had been given weighed heavily on his lap, and he tried in vain to understand what the speaker was saying. *I guess this is the price I pay for getting a free ride to Pasadena. Poor old Stewart thinks he's finally got me into the fold.*

The Mormon chapel was a large impressive building with spotless white walls. The aisles and the pews were padded with dark maroon carpet, and chandeliers dangled from high ceilings. A sprinkling of people had gathered for what Stewart had called a Bible study. But now, sitting there beside his friend, Omar wondered why they were studying the Book of Mormon instead of the Bible.

The well-dressed man at the pulpit was not an eloquent speaker. For Stewart's sake, Omar tried to get something out of the Bible study, but he really didn't get the point. While the speaker droned on, Omar recalled the happenings of the day before.

Stewart had driven Omar to Pasadena and back, and they had had a great time. Omar had warned Primo about the setup, so he and Omar acted as if they were old friends having a grand time at the Tortas Mexico restaurant. During a break, Omar met with Primo in the restroom briefly where Primo passed Omar a half kilo of cocaine, and Omar paid him for it.

Omar knew that he was taking advantage of Stewart's innocence, and he pitied him a little. When they got back, Omar was ready to be rid of Stewart, but he couldn't turn him down when he invited Omar into his house for a snack.

Omar had been to Stewart's house once before. He dreaded going there again, because he realized Stewart's mother was too smart to be deceived. Her expression when she looked at Omar was disdainful and distrustful.

After a half hour of tension, Omar suggested that they go watch TV in the little trailer house in the backyard where Stewart slept. On the way out, Omar stopped by his car and picked up the latest movie he had rented.

"How about watching a real thrilling movie tonight?" Omar suggested as he waved it at Stewart, revealing an indecent cover. "I rented this one yesterday, and we might as well watch it together."

Stewart's face turned red, and he shifted his feet uneasily. *It's against their beliefs,* Omar guessed. But Stewart made no protest, so Omar snapped off the lights and soon they were plunged into the dark underworld of a pornographic movie.

Omar's power over girls impressed his friends, especially his manager Javier at Tacos Mexico. Javier depended on Omar for access to the girls, and Omar depended on Javier to make sure his schedule at the restaurant was flexible.

Omar's job with Tacos Mexico was a cover-up for his real business, which was taking more and more of his time, and his nightlife was so taxing that every so often he needed a day to catch up with his sleep. So he would call Javier early in the morning, asking for the day off after he had been carousing and selling drugs all night. Javier never said no. Javier was aware of Omar's real business, and even though he himself wouldn't touch it, he tolerated it for Omar.

Every other Saturday, Javier would drive all over the city from one Tacos Mexico to the next, paying the workers. Omar followed right behind, charging the workers for the cocaine they had consumed.

One evening Omar's friend Carlos asked Omar to do a favor for his sister who had recently come from Mexico. She wanted to go see her aunt who lived in Long Beach. Omar was familiar with the area and was glad to do the run for them.

Carlos' sister chose the back seat, and Omar turned up the music and drove. More and more he was doing his own driving even though he still didn't have a driver's license.

Just a few blocks from the destination, Omar drove confidently, though slowly, through an intersection with a stop sign. He had the right-of-way.

Whammo!

Carlos' sister screamed as Omar's car jerked forward, rammed from behind. Another driver had ignored the stop sign and rear-ended them, but neither vehicle was going fast, so the damage was minimal.

The cops will be here in a minute, Omar realized, *and I'm loaded. I can't afford to stay around and let myself get caught.*

The tires squealed as Omar took off. His car careened down the block and whipped around several corners. Then he stopped abruptly, opened his door, and reached under his seat. In one swipe, he flipped his duffel bag into a culvert. Then he slammed the door and drove the two blocks to their destination. He could hear the sirens screaming as the police closed in.

Carlos' sister fled into her aunt's house just before the police cars surrounded Omar's vehicle, lights flashing. Omar couldn't hear a thing over the noise, but he knew what to expect.

When the police officers hollered at him to open up, Omar stepped outside with his hands raised. Several officers pointed their guns at him as he crawled out. One of the officers quickly frisked Omar. "Get onto your knees!" the officer barked.

Omar slowly got down on his knees as a helicopter closed in above them.

"Get your hands behind your back!" the officer snapped.

Omar cooperated, and they snapped handcuffs on him. Music from Omar's stereo continued to throb into the darkness. Meanwhile, several officers were combing carefully through his car. *They won't find anything,* Omar thought smugly.

When a black vehicle slipped onto the scene, Omar recognized it as the anti-narcotics vehicle. Several men dressed in black climbed out and led two German shepherds to Omar's car. Right away, the dogs found the spot under the seat where the drugs had been stored. Their barks clearly told the police officers the truth: This man is a drug dealer.

But Omar wasn't too worried. His LA cronies had taught him the slogan: If there's no proof, there's no crime. They might get him for running from the scene of the accident, but not because of drugs.

After what seemed like a long time, Omar was shoved into the back seat of one of the police vehicles, guarded by an officer on one side and a dog on the other. Omar held very still in the middle. As they drove along, Omar tried to talk to the policeman sitting beside him. "The accident wasn't my fault," he pleaded lamely. "The other vehicle jumped a stop sign and hit me."

"Shut up!" the policeman snapped. "You aren't supposed to talk in here."

The rest of the trip to the jail was made in silence.

Omar was amazed at the condition of the jail cell. *Not too bad,* he cheered to himself. *It would sure be worse if I were in jail in my own country!*

Two weeks and two trials later, Omar was found guilty of running from the scene of an accident and for not carrying a license. He was given the option of spending a year in prison or paying a $25,000 fine. Omar chose to pay, and he was released. They couldn't confiscate his driver's license because he didn't have one. They did impound his car, but Omar soon replaced it with a snazzy gray Nissan.

Omar invited Stewart for another trip to Pasadena, and Stewart accepted gladly, convinced that Omar really was concerned about his cousin Primo's loneliness. Of course, the real mission was that Omar picked up another pound of snow, at a much higher price than he had paid the first time.

In return for the jaunt to Pasadena, Stewart insisted that Omar go with him to a Mormon youth dance at a fancy dance hall. Only Mormon youth and the people they had invited could attend. Omar enjoyed dancing, and a few of the youth were Latinos like Stewart. Several of the attractive girls knew his language. The refreshments were superb, and Omar enjoyed the evening. Omar snickered to himself as they left the dance hall. *If Stewart only knew that this is the price I pay for his help in the narco-world.*

Without a doubt, Omar was making a fortune in his new business. He didn't really care how he made his money, who he used, or how he used them in the process. The consequences mattered little to him. He had taken the glamorous plunge, and so far, things were going fine.

Or so he thought.

22

MADMAN'S RETRIBUTION

THE SUN WAS setting over the ocean, giving its crashing waves a salmon-colored hue. Large black frigate birds wheeled above the beach, watching for any fish that dared venture into the shallow waters along the shore. The white beach, now reflecting pink, stretched out along the blue ocean as far as the eye could see. *That must be why they call this Long Beach,* Omar thought.

Omar and his buddies and their girlfriends had gathered along the beach to party that evening. Bato lounged beside Omar, a can of beer in his hand. Omar looked over at him and grinned, thinking, *I helped my uncle out and now he's back on his feet, making money like always.*

Bato had something on his mind. Turning to Omar, he asked, "Did you hear that Andrés wants to sell me his semi? I have a notion to buy it. What do you think?"

Omar, whose mind was on the party, answered casually, "Sure! Great idea. Andrés has done really well with trucking. Good solid investment."

Several days later Omar came home from Tacos Mexico to find Bato in a terrible stew. "What's wrong, Bato?" Omar asked.

"That devil Andrés ripped me off!" Bato's eyes were spitting fire. "I can't believe he would do that to me."

"How did he rip you off?"

"Well, he sold me that semi I told you about," Bato growled.

"What's wrong with that? Why aren't you happy about it, Uncle?"

"Andrés ripped me off," Bato repeated, slamming his fist onto the arm of the chair. "He went and bought a newer semi for himself. Here I thought if I bought the truck, I'd have a route and an established business. But Andrés pulled the wool over my eyes."

Omar listened carefully.

"Yesterday, after he gave me the keys and the title to the truck," Bato continued, "I discovered that he had ripped off all his business signs. He moved them over to his new truck and went right on hauling for his company. And here I am, stuck high and dry. I have no driver . . . no business . . . no route . . . no connections. All I have is that useless old semi."

"But isn't that the way the trucking business works?" Omar asked, perplexed. "You have to set up your own route and start your own business."

"I don't care how business usually works!" Bato bellowed, jumping up from his chair. "All I know is that Andrés ripped me off, and he's going to pay for it. Son, will you help me set something up to punish him? I'll provide the cash."

"I don't really know what I have to do with this," Omar answered. Even so, he hated Andrés—especially for preaching at him several months before.

"You don't know what you have to do with this?" Bato hollered, whirling around and facing his nephew. "Of course you do! Have you forgotten the day he beat up your dad? If somebody would have beaten my dad and then lashed me too, I'd never have let it pass!"

Omar backed off and went to hunt for some food in the refrigerator. But his hackles rose when Bato growled, "Omar, if I had vowed to kill someone someday, I sure wouldn't let it go!"

"Am I a god?" Omar countered. "What could I do to pay him back?"

"You have connections. You're in the business, and people like you always know someone who can do the dirty work."

Understanding hit Omar like a freight truck. He knew what Bato meant. He had nearly forgotten that long-ago episode, and he sure didn't need any trouble with Andrés—they had been friends for years now. Omar had come to think of that angry vow as a childhood stupidity. Still, it wasn't hard at all to relive the horrible day that Andrés had beaten up Fermín and then also lashed Omar. That painful memory and Bato's pressure took its toll.

Day after day Bato hounded Omar about taking revenge on Andrés. "If you're too chicken to settle up for what he did to you and your dad, at least be brave enough to punish him for me!" Bato protested. "I want to get rid of that rat. I can hardly take it when I see him driving around like a bigshot in his fancy semi every day!"

Omar began to scheme secretly. *I can take revenge for my uncle's sake,* he reasoned. *After all, Bato did help me come to the United States, and Andrés did deceive him, so that Bato had to sell the semi at a loss.*

Omar could plan the punishment, but he wouldn't be responsible to carry it out. He could hire the thugs, but they would be responsible for the actual crime. Soon Bato and Omar were deep into planning an assault. It would look as if thugs killed Andrés for his money—and he had plenty!

On the next trip to a restaurant in Pasadena with the unsuspecting Stewart, Primo and Omar again slipped into the restroom. Minutes later Omar left with two powerful weapons in his possession—a pound of cocaine in his duffel bag that would continue to ruin the lives of many addicts, and a phone number that had the potential to kill his cousin.

On the drive home, Stewart said innocently, "Omar, I noticed you have a new car. What happened to the old one?"

"Oh, it blew a piston," Omar lied, smiling at his friend. "So I sold it for a song and bought the new one you saw. Do you like it?"

"Yes, it's a very nice vehicle! I'm so glad for you." Stewart smiled. "Are you coming over tonight?" They were back at the Tacos Mexico where Omar had parked his gray Nissan.

"Nope. Not tonight. But thanks again for driving me up to Pasadena!"

"Sure! Glad to do it!" Stewart beamed. "Anytime. Just let me know. Will you be coming to church on Sunday?"

The two men stood toward the back of the Tacos Mexico parking lot, and Omar sized them up in the glow from the street lamps. The Latino was dark-skinned, medium-sized, and muscular—but what Omar noticed most were his hard eyes. Behind the Latino towered an ox of a man who made the dark-skinned fellow look puny. At least six feet tall, his huge arms and face were covered with curly yellow hair so thick as to resemble animal fur. The blond giant's eyes were as cruel as his buddy's—just maybe not as intelligent.

These fellows were genuine thugs, and Omar caught his breath. Did he really want to deal with them? But it was too late to back out.

Later that evening, Omar and the Latino met in the area where his cousin lived. They sneaked down an alley together, and Omar pointed out the apartment building with the red trim. "See that side door?" Omar said. "That's a hallway that's never locked. You can sneak in that door and go to the end of the hallway. Wait at that door. The man will open up just before 1 a.m."

The Latino was listening carefully.

"The man is a trucker, and he's planning a long run out of state tomorrow. He'll be alone, and his apartment will be empty. If you catch him as he leaves the apartment, the cash in the apartment is yours. And don't forget, he has a briefcase in there somewhere that might have as much as thirty grand. Don't open the briefcase. Bring it here. We'll open it together and split the loot fifty-fifty."

Returning to the place where they had parked their vehicles, Omar clinched the plan. "Look, I want you to beat the man up, but don't kill him." He was purposely not obeying Bato's last request: "Make sure to tell the thugs to kill him."

The Latino left, and Omar climbed into his car, wondering, *What have I done? How will this turn out? Poor Andrés. He hardly deserves it. But what's done is done.*

He pushed aside his qualms by putting his heart into the night shift for Tacos Mexico that evening. He smiled at the customers who came to pay, trying to act as if it were a normal evening. But it wasn't—far from it.

How would it go for Andrés? Would the thugs find enough money to satisfy them? Would they kill Andrés or leave him with some life? As midnight drew nearer, Omar's heart filled with dread. *What did I do to my cousin?* his heart asked over and over again.

At 1:30 a.m. Omar heard the short toot of the Latino's horn. Telling Carlos to watch the cash register, Omar sprinted out to the parking lot. Both thugs crawled out of the vehicle and met Omar in the shadows. Each carried a metal baseball bat. They told Omar that they had broken both of the man's arms and bashed in his head. But they had not killed him.

Omar was horrified to see Andrés' blood on both bats, and he realized that those same bats could bash in his own brains as well. He stared at the Latino's cloudy face. "Where's his briefcase?" Omar inquired nervously.

The Latino reached into his car and pulled out the briefcase that Omar had seen many times before. The last time he had gotten a glimpse of it, it had been full of cash. "Let's go inside to the restrooms," Omar suggested, looking around nervously. "I hate to take risks out here in the open. Meet you in the men's room."

Latino and Big Boy strolled nonchalantly into the restaurant and headed for the restroom. Omar followed minutes later. The Latino placed the briefcase on the floor. Then, lifting his foot, he slammed it onto the edge of the briefcase, breaking the latches. *He's done that before!* Omar realized.

Omar bent over and lifted the briefcase lid. To his horror, no cash was visible. He rummaged through the papers, ransacking the briefcase rapidly. Zero money!

"What's going on, bud?" the Latino growled. "You claimed there was a lot of cash in this briefcase. We ransacked the apartment, and all we found was one gold necklace. That's not what we agreed on, man."

Omar found himself trembling, but he steeled himself for what had to be done. "I know this guy was carrying big money recently," he explained lamely, shaking his head. "I can't imagine what happened to it. I was sure..."

"We don't do jobs like this for free," the man snarled. "You'd better hurry and dish out some cash, or else."

"Calm down, man," Omar hissed, hoping he sounded as tough as they did. "This was not intentional. I was sure he had money. But okay, he didn't. So, how much are you going to deal for?"

"Two thousand dollars," the thug answered. "That's dirt cheap for a dangerous job like that."

"Come on, give me a break," Omar begged, smiling wanly. "That necklace is worth a thousand dollars. I'll give you another thousand, and we'll call it a day. I've got to make a living too."

"Okay," the Latino croaked, looking over at his giant buddy.

The giant nodded.

Omar didn't have enough cash on him; most of his money was stashed in his apartment. So he slipped out and borrowed some cash from the register and took it back to the thugs. As soon as they drove off, Omar shook his head. *Those guys are crazy. I bet they'll be back to hassle me for more money. I wish I would have never had anything to do with those two devils.*

Omar called Bato and told him what had happened. "So Andrés didn't have any money in that briefcase!" Bato jeered. "Well, that's the thugs' tough luck, not our problem!"

Omar didn't bother to tell Bato that he'd paid them a thousand dollars. Obviously, Bato wasn't going to help pay for the crime; neither would he bear the blame for it. Bato was already laughing about what had happened, and the blame would rest on Omar.

As the long night passed, Omar was perplexed by how rotten this whole ordeal made him feel. He realized, with a twinge of relief, that he was not as calloused as his uncle. He still had a bit of conscience left.

How Omar wished he could go back and undo this chapter—that he had never agreed to participate in the crime. Though he might always claim he had taken revenge for his uncle, Omar would carry the load of guilt for the attack on a man who was better than both he and Bato put together.

23

A SINNER'S PAYMENT

EEEOOO . . . eeeooo . . . eeeooo. The wail of sirens pierced the stillness of the morning. People and police cars crowded around the apartment building with red trim, and ambulances rushed onto the scene.

On the outskirts, Bato and Omar stood watching. They had received a call a half hour earlier from Yolanda, telling them that people from the apartment had found Andrés half-dead in the hallway.

"We need to get to the scene of the accident immediately," Bato had rationalized, heading for the door. "They won't suspect our involvement if we show up with the rest of the relatives."

Omar's heart filled with dread, seeing the ambulances arrive. But it really hit him when he saw his cousin wheeled out on a stretcher. Even from a distance, Omar sensed that Andrés was dangling between life and death.

They must not have found Andrés till now, Omar realized. *He's been suffering alone almost seven hours. Poor man!*

"Got what he deserved," Bato hissed under his breath. "Exactly what he deserved."

But the worst was yet to come. Bato decided that to really cover up their tracks, he and Omar should go see Andrés at the hospital.

Walking down the hospital corridor, Omar could hardly believe how cold his uncle was toward his nephew. Bato seemed untouched by even a hint of remorse. By contrast, although Omar was trying hard to hide it, neither his heart nor his conscience were on vacation.

The waiting room outside of the intensive care unit was full of somber people when Bato and Omar entered. It seemed as if every relative and friend Andrés had in LA was there. Omar and Bato found seats. The atmosphere felt like a wake. No one said a word.

The door to intensive care opened and Aunt Yolanda came out, her face etched with sadness. "Do you want to go in?" Uncle Yico asked quietly.

Bato shook his head.

But Omar steeled his emotions and entered the room. Nothing had prepared him for what he found. Andrés' battered face was swollen and purple, and multiple tubes and wires ran from Andrés to the beeping, blinking machines that monitored his condition. Both of his arms were in casts. As Omar stared at his cousin, waves of pity, remorse, and pain swept over him.

By the time Andrés was aware of Omar's presence and opened his swollen eyes a slit, tears were streaming down Omar's face. Omar turned and fled. He stumbled through the waiting room, leaned his head against the wall in the hallway, and cried his heart out.

He didn't notice that Bato had followed him. As Bato walked past, he hissed, "Stop bawling, you crybaby! They're going to guess your involvement if you act like a woman. Let's get our hides out of here!"

Driving home, Bato exploded, "Why in the world didn't they kill the man?"

It took Omar weeks to get over seeing Andrés lying in that hospital bed, so battered up. Even when he heard that Andrés wasn't going to die, the remorse often hit him, dark and heavy. He could not shake it.

"Hello. Is this Stewart?" Omar spoke into his cell phone.

"Yes, it is," a hesitant voice answered from the other end.

"Look, this is Omar. Does it suit you to make another run over to Pasadena? Primo called me and would really like for us to come for another visit. He says he misses you."

"Well," Stewart answered lamely, "I'm not sure it's going to suit me this time, Omar."

Uh-oh! Somebody has finally enlightened my Mormon friend. He knows what's going on.

"Omar," Stewart stammered. "I sure hate it, but I don't think I'll be making these trips with you anymore . . . I—"

"That's fine!" Omar said. "Thanks a lot for being my friend."

"Will you come to our Bible study Wednesday evening?" Stewart asked weakly.

"No, I'm busy Wednesday. Thanks again for being my friend."

Omar sighed as he hung up. *That's goodbye to Stewart. For good.*

Someone had squealed. Now Omar would need either another driver or a source closer than Pasadena.

Omar made contact with Benjie the next day. Benjie worked in a distant Tacos Mexico, and Omar invited him to share a couple of tacos with him after the evening shift. Once they were engrossed in eating and talking, Omar asked Benjie if he knew of a wholesale source in the area.

Benjie lifted his eyebrows. "So! Pasadena is suddenly too far for you, eh?"

"Yeah, it's farther than I want to drive without a license," Omar admitted.

"Did you lose your driver, perhaps?"

Now it was Omar's turn to raise his eyebrows. "What do you know about my driver?"

"Stewart and I have become friends," Benjie explained, his eyes laughing as he talked. "He comes to this Tacos Mexico now and then. Did you notice that he doesn't come anymore to the restaurants that you frequent?"

Omar nodded.

"Stewart started telling me about his new friend over in Huntington Park. At first I didn't realize he was talking about you."

"What did he say about me?" Omar wondered. "Was it good?"

"Too good!" Benjie said. "When he mentioned Pasadena, I caught on. So I asked him, 'What's your friend's name?' When he said Omar Montenegro, I just about burst out laughing."

"What did you tell him?" Omar demanded.

"Don't get mad, Omar. I can't stand when others deceive me. So I told him the truth."

"What's the truth?" Omar insisted, glaring at his buddy.

" 'Ah, Stewart,' I told him, 'you're being duped. Omar is a friend of mine, and he's a cocaine dealer. He's been using you. He doesn't have a driver's license because he's here in the United States illegally. So he gets you to drive him to Pasadena, and on every trip he brings home a load of coke.'

" 'But how can he do that and I not find it out?' Stewart wailed. 'He seems like such a friendly chap!'

"So I asked him, 'Didn't you ever notice that Omar and Primo end up in the restroom together every time you have your party? Didn't you ever wonder why Omar always carried that brown duffel bag?' "

"Well, that's the last I'll see of our good friend Stewart," Omar said, laughing. "But at least I got three trips out of him."

"Yeah," Benjie agreed. Then he gave Omar the phone number of a dealer close to Huntington Park. "Be careful with this character. He likes quick, clean deals and no tricks. They call him Satan."

He must be like me, Omar mused.

Omar frowned at the cell phone in his hand and shook his head. Less than three days after he had paid the hit men for attacking Andrés, they were bugging him again. The Latino claimed that the mission had been very dangerous. He threatened that if Omar didn't come up with more money, things would get bad.

Omar entered into a terrific tug-of-war with the thugs. Omar stalled and the Latino threatened. Omar didn't bother getting Bato involved, knowing it would only anger his uncle. After a week of haggling by cell phone, they finally reached an agreement. Omar met the Latino in the parking lot and gave him another two thousand dollars.

Then, knowing he was taking a risk, Omar announced, "This is the last money I'll ever give you guys. Lay off, or you'll be in serious trouble with me."

The thugs stopped asking Omar for money, but a week later, they came back to extract a more horrible payment than money.

It was midnight and Tacos Mexico was almost empty. Only one couple was sitting toward the back of the restaurant, drinking Coca-Cola and eating tacos. Omar and another worker were alone, easily taking care of business at that hour. Omar had poured himself a cold drink and was feeling almost sleepy when he noticed the man at the table get up and head for the restroom.

No sooner had he closed the restroom door when the Latino sprinted into the restaurant and approached the counter. Glaring at Omar, he commanded, "Turn up the volume to the music. I have an account to settle with that fellow."

Omar would have loved to deny the request. He no longer owed the Latino anything. But fearing what the wicked man and his giant of a companion would do if he refused, Omar turned up the volume.

The Latino disappeared, and minutes later the loud music was shattered by a terrific crash. The thug leered at Omar as he ran past. The woman fled out the door with the thug.

What in the world had happened in the back of the restaurant? Omar didn't have long to wonder. In less than a minute, the midnight customer stumbled out of the restroom, blood streaming down his face. As the dying man passed the cash register, his glazed eyes briefly met Omar's. Then he staggered through the door and disappeared into the dark.

Omar shuddered at that glance of death. Once more his long-dormant conscience kicked in, and horrible feelings washed over him.

What have I done? Omar asked himself, burying his face in his hands. *Though I didn't participate, I helped kill that man. I think that look will haunt me till the day I die.*

As soon as the wounded man left, Omar and his fellow worker sprinted into the restroom. Clearly, the victim had been battered over the head with the heavy porcelain toilet lid, which lay broken on the floor.

Turning to the fellow worker, Omar pointed his finger at his face and hissed, "You didn't see anything happen in Tacos Mexico tonight, okay? Neither of us did. We don't want any trouble for the restaurant, so we're not going to tell a soul. You go back and watch for customers, and I'll mop up the blood."

It took Omar a long time to clean up all the blood in the restroom and the trail out through the restaurant and on into the parking lot. By the time the hour was up, nobody would have guessed what had happened. But the horrible scene was etched deeply into Omar's heart.

Several hours later, the rescue squad wailed into the parking lot across the street. Soon the cry went up, "Somebody killed a guy in the parking lot across from Tacos Mexico."

Nobody ever found out what the crime was all about. Only Omar, his fellow worker, the Latino thug, and his wicked girlfriend knew the horrible truth that the crime had been committed in the restroom of the Tacos Mexico on Pacific Boulevard.

The next day Omar knew he had to get some sleep. He hadn't slept right for days, and he couldn't go on like that indefinitely. So after a shower and a snack, Omar headed for his bedroom.

Bato had recently moved out, and the two cronies who still shared the apartment with Omar were on the day shift. Omar was glad to be all alone. Maybe, just maybe, he could get some sleep.

But Omar lay wide awake for a full hour, his thoughts in turmoil. Although he now had plenty of money, women, and so-called friends, he was still a very lonely man.

He had no close friends. Yes, Carlos and Javier were great to hang out with, but he never had heart-to-heart talks with them. Even Omar's girlfriends didn't know the real Omar, nor did he really know them. They were just strangers who, like Omar, were seeking fun things to do together. They walked into his life and then back out again.

As Omar stared at the ceiling, trying to figure out his life, he finally acknowledged the truth: *Even though I have all these things that I used to yearn for, I'm not happy.*

If Omar had been totally honest, he would have also confessed that his involvement in damaging people's lives through drugs, his wild immoral flings, his part in the attack on Andrés, and now his part in killing the man in the restroom also added to his burden of unhappiness. No man who lives in sin can be happy, but Omar didn't realize that yet.

When the turbulent thoughts brought on a headache, Omar finally jumped up and took some pain pills. Then he dressed and headed for the bar. *Maybe after I drink for a few hours, I might be able to sleep,* he fussed. *If not, I'll call Javier and tell him I won't work tonight. I have to get some sleep!*

Drinking at the bar, Omar could put on a front, but the deeper search for happiness would only intensify.

Oh, happiness, where are you? was the cry of his heart.

24

IN SEARCH OF A GEM

TACOS MEXICO ON Pacific Boulevard was jam-packed. The workers were scampering like ants, taking care of the rowdy crowd. The usual pop music was playing in the background. But after a while, Omar became aware that a catchy, nostalgic piece of music was changing the atmosphere.

Working at the cash register, Omar soon spotted the girl who was deliberately manipulating the mood of the evening. She was hanging around the jukebox, selecting song after song to her own liking. Each song seemed to be exactly what Omar would have selected.

The girl was pretty and petite. She wore her waves of ebony hair down over her shoulders, and her pastel lavender gown clung to her figure, giving her the look of an Egyptian queen. She wore very little makeup and no jewelry. Suddenly Omar felt an urge to talk to the beautiful girl who liked music.

"Carlos," Omar whispered, "watch the cash register a bit. I want to talk to that girl by the jukebox."

Omar approached the girl quietly. She was obviously a Latina—probably Mexican. Her skin was flawless. At just the right moment, Omar said softly, "You like music, don't you?"

Mildly surprised, the girl looked around quickly. Her white teeth flashed as she smiled at him. But what struck Omar most were her large green eyes. Never in his life had he seen such beautiful green eyes in a Latina face.

Still smiling, the green-eyed girl answered in a melodious voice, "I sure do love music! It's one of my passions."

"I love music too," Omar said, smiling.

He could tell she didn't mind his advances. She was neither too timid nor too assertive. She stood, relaxed, facing him as a friend. As she listened to the song she had selected, Omar felt free to continue his attentions.

Omar grinned at her. "Since you and I both love music, maybe we should see each other again sometime. I would love to take you out so we could learn to know each other."

The girl smiled again, as if approving of his boldness. Her chuckle told Omar that he was making a little progress in winning her confidence.

"Who are you with?" Omar asked politely, glancing around the dining hall.

"With my brother and his wife." She smiled and pointed to a table in the corner where a Mexican couple was quietly enjoying their tacos. They were watching Omar and the girl discreetly.

"What's your name?" Omar asked, stepping a little closer.

But the girl only gave her head a coy little shake, letting the flick of her hair give the answer, *Not yet, bud.*

Omar tried his best to get at least a little information from her, but he wasn't successful. Though she enjoyed his attention, she wasn't ready to reveal any part of her heart. Giving up momentarily, Omar told her that he hoped to see her again and returned to his station.

Though Omar didn't talk to the girl again that evening, he watched her for the rest of the hour. She did take time to eat an order of tacos, but she kept control of the jukebox, and the music she chose spoke volumes to Omar about what kind of girl she was.

Omar caught her glancing at him every now and then. When she and her companions came past to pay their bill, she looked Omar squarely in the eye and gave him the sweetest smile he had received in a long time.

Would he ever again see the girl who loved music? He felt as if a little piece of his heart had gone along with her. *If I ever have a chance, I'll learn to know that lovely girl,* Omar vowed. *I think we would get along very well.*

And so the green-eyed girl became the centerpiece in Omar's pursuit of happiness.

Los Lidos Concert Hall was a lively, upbeat place, and it was becoming one of Omar's favorite hangouts. His merchandise was in great demand there, and he enjoyed the type of people who frequented the place—upstart movie stars—because he also dreamed of becoming a Hollywood star someday.

Los Lidos gave opportunities for any of these dreamers to ask for the mic and go onstage to show off their abilities. The crowd applauded those who did well and booed those who didn't. The professionals among the audience were ready to whisk off those with the most potential and make sure they got to Hollywood. Many a famous actor had started on the stage of the Los Lidos Concert Hall.

One evening Omar and his coworker Pedro walked into Los Lidos and headed straight for the dance hall. "Let's dance a few pieces to work up an appetite," Omar suggested, "then we'll stop to eat once we're good and hungry."

Suddenly Omar stopped in his tracks. Across the room he saw the lovely girl who had caught his attention at Tacos Mexico a month before. "Pedro, wait!" Omar hissed. "I see my long-lost friend I told you about— the girl with the green eyes. Ah, finally I found her!"

But the next moment Omar was disappointed to see a man leading the girl onto the dance floor. In a short time, she was lost among the sea of dancing couples. *I'll wait,* Omar decided. *I'll find her later, and she'll be mine!*

Omar soon picked out the girl's table, where he recognized her brother and his wife and another fellow enjoying a meal in the dining hall. So he chose a table close by. As soon as the music stopped and the dancing couples returned to their places, Omar watched for his chance.

Just as the green-eyed girl parted ways with the man she had danced with, Omar stepped up beside her and took her gently by the arm. He whispered, "I found you again!"

The girl swung around and blushed when she recognized Omar. "How did you find me?"

"Ah, it's called luck," Omar answered. "I told you I'd find the gorgeous girl who loves music. So here we are, and I want you to spend the rest of the night with me," he murmured.

She nodded her agreement.

Omar steered her toward an empty table at the end of the dining hall, and they took seats. Minutes later he went with the girl to meet her relatives, and she told them she was going to spend the evening with Omar.

"Look, all the bills tonight are on me," Omar announced, smiling broadly. "I like to spend money on friends, so live it up! Ask for anything you want."

Pedro was forgotten, and so were the girl's trio of relatives. The evening was theirs to enjoy. Again, Omar was surprised and pleased at how easily he and the girl could communicate. They felt comfortable together, and Omar began dreaming of this girl becoming his for good. But even though they enjoyed the night immensely, dancing, eating, and visiting, Omar could not get any personal information out of her.

By two in the morning, the girl's brother started showing signs of impatience, and Omar became desperate. "Look," he said, "I've enjoyed this evening so much! I can see we both enjoy each other's company. We have to get together again! May I have your phone number?"

"I don't have a phone," the girl answered simply. "And we don't have a phone where I live either."

Omar quickly jotted down his cell phone number and handed it to his new friend. "Look, Tacos Mexico is having a grand Christmas party at the end of the month. I want to invite you to join me as my honored guest. Call me so we can make plans."

The green-eyed girl nodded.

They were walking toward her relatives' table now. "Where do you live?" Omar asked desperately. "I don't even know your name!"

But the girl laughed at Omar, clearly indicating that she was glad to be his friend, but not ready to give him any personal information yet.

"Here, take my extra cell phone so you can call me," Omar insisted, handing her a phone.

She shook her head. "I have your number. I will call you," she whispered, patting Omar's arm and smiling sweetly.

"May I take you home?" Omar pleaded, clinging to her arm.

Again the girl shook her head. "Not this time. I'll go home with my brother."

Omar paid all the bills, realizing that the girl he was infatuated with was departing again without leaving a trace. How could he be sure she would call him?

Suddenly Omar had an idea. He quickly found Pedro. "Go track that girl!" he hissed. "Don't let her know you're following. But don't you dare come back here without finding out where she lives." He handed Pedro his car keys and ushered him out the door.

An hour later Pedro was back, grinning widely. "I got it! It's just over on the other end of Huntington Park."

Omar grasped Pedro's hand and thanked him. "Tomorrow morning you're taking me to look her up. But for now, let's go home and get some sleep."

The short night seemed endless to Omar, but he did sleep a little. Knowing that the girl had also gone to bed in the wee hours, he waited till late morning to go see her. Pedro drove his own vehicle, and Omar followed. Once they arrived at the house, Pedro returned to his apartment.

Omar was surprised to find out that his new girlfriend lived in a shabby house in a poor neighborhood. *No wonder she doesn't want me to find her,* he assumed.

Omar knocked boldly on the door, and a short slender woman who looked to be in her late forties stepped out to meet him. Omar noticed her green eyes right away. So that's where his new friend had gotten her looks! "Excuse me, Señora, I would like to talk to a girl who lives here. Is she your daughter? I danced with her at Los Lidos last night."

"I guess you mean Gema."[15] The lady smiled. "She's still sleeping, but I can wake her."

She went back into the house, and Omar stood at the door savoring the name of the green-eyed girl. *Gema! What a beautiful name for a beautiful girl! Indeed, she is a gem. A very precious gem!*

---

15   Gema: gem.

"Who are you?" The mother's voice rang from inside the house.

"My name is Omar Montenegro. I'm the man who danced with your daughter last night at Los Lidos," Omar answered.

Minutes later the voice rang out again. "Come on in."

Omar stepped into the dilapidated living room. Gema was waiting for him, her hair still tousled. She gave him a sleepy smile. "How did you find me?" she asked.

Omar smiled back. "That doesn't matter, Gema. You can't escape from me easily, can you? What's important is that I found you again. I was afraid I had lost you forever."

"I told you I'd call you about going to that Christmas party," Gema rebuked him gently.

"But that's still weeks away," Omar answered. "I just couldn't wait that long!"

They both laughed, and Omar could tell that Gema liked his persistence in pursuing her.

Gema's mother, Doña Juana, disappeared into the kitchen, giving Omar and Gema some privacy. Again, Omar tried his best to get information from his new girlfriend, but she was evasive. "I don't really live here," she admitted. "I only stayed with my mother last night because she wants me to help her today. I live with my brother."

"Well, where *do* you live?" Omar asked, unable to hide his mounting desperation.

"I have a boyfriend," Gema answered quickly, watching Omar's face.

Omar's heart dropped. Now he understood why Gema had been so slow in giving him information. It all made too much sense. Speechless, Omar could only look at her tenderly, pleading with his eyes, *I don't care. Can't you love me too?*

"The truth is," Gema continued slowly, measuring her words, "I'm quitting the fellow. We aren't hitting it off. And actually, my friendship with you might help me break loose from him. But you have to be patient. This will all take time."

Suddenly the sun was shining again in Omar's heart, and his hopes soared. This was going to work after all. As soon as she was rid of the boyfriend, she would be Omar's.

"What's your job?" Omar asked, wanting to know more about the girl he was wooing.

Again, Gema was evasive. Omar finally tore away with only two new bits of useful information—her name and where her mother lived. That was better than nothing. But would she actually call him, and would she go with him to the Christmas party?

The next several weeks seemed too long for Omar. He suddenly discovered that he wasn't interested in any other girls, and even his partying slowed down. Several times Omar stopped by Doña Juana's place, but she was even more evasive than her daughter.

One day Omar was walking toward one of the more distant Tacos Mexicos where Javier had scheduled him. He was early, so he was in no hurry. As he ambled by a photo studio, he paused to glance over the many portraits in the window, idly wondering which of the girls was prettiest. Then his heart leaped into his throat. Right out in broad daylight was a four-by-six photo of Gema.

Omar entered the studio and asked about the photos. "Oh," the attendant explained, "those pictures are extras that the customers don't want. If they're good, we hang them up to advertise what we can do."

"Could you sell me that one?" Omar asked, pointing at Gema's photo. "I've met her, and I'd really like to have a photo of her."

The attendant chuckled. "You're obviously in love with her. You can have it!"

Euphoric, Omar stuck the photo in his shirt pocket and left for work, his steps energized. Now he had a treasure to remind him of Gema.

That day Toño, one of Omar's drug sellers, stopped by for more snow. After making the delivery in the restroom, Omar and Toño chatted out in the restaurant. Soon Omar was telling his buddy about his new flame.

"What about this girl is making you so nuts, Omar?" Toño asked.

Omar whipped the photo out of his shirt pocket and held it up. "This," he said. "Just look at this lovely chica!"

Toño stared at the photo and then exclaimed, "I know her! They call her La Gata."[16]

"Do you know where she lives?" Omar demanded.

---

16   La Gata: "the cat," because of her green eyes.

"No, but I know the dancing club where she works." Toño named the place.

"Are you sure?" Omar asked, eyeing Toño suspiciously.

"I sure am!" Toño assured Omar. "If you don't believe me, I'll prove it. I'll take you to surprise her tonight."

The rest of the day, Omar could hardly contain his happiness. *Tonight I'll not only meet Gema again, but I'll learn to know about her job and her life. Tonight is the night!*

One small cloud dampened Omar's joy. A dancing club wasn't like a nightclub where anyone could go to have a good time. A dancing club was where lonely well-to-do men stopped by to hire time with supposedly high-class women.

At a dancing club, the client chose from a lineup of beautiful girls the one he wanted to spend time with. Paying by the hour, he was entitled to choose how to spend time with his companion from the variety of entertainment the place offered. It might be a quiet hour in a lounge filled with sofas and televisions, eating in the dining room, or dancing in the dance hall. There was also a casino and a room full of electronic games. Gema made her living entertaining many men, Omar realized. Why would she choose him above them?

But as Omar mulled it over in his head, he was encouraged by two conclusions. First, the men Gema spent time with were likely nothing more to her than lonely clients who wanted a lady friend to help soothe their troubles. And second, the clients at the dancing club were not riffraff, but high-class people. Dancing clubs did not offer the immoral services that many other night places did.

Omar could easily see why Gema had been hired to work at a place like that. She understood and loved music, and she danced naturally and well. *Regardless of what I discover tonight,* Omar decided firmly, *I want that girl. I will accept her for exactly who she is.*

But the question that burned all day long in the young man's yearning heart was, *Will she accept me?*

25

GREEN-EYED DANCER

THE NEXT EVENING, Omar dressed in his best clothes and dabbed on cologne. He and Toño headed for the dancing club.

"We're going to really surprise Gema!" Omar exclaimed. "She has no idea that I finally found out where she works."

At the dancing club, they entered a spacious room where the clients chose from the lineup which girl they wanted to spend time with. Gema was not there, but Toño knew the ropes. He strode to the counter. "Is La Gata in tonight?"

"Yes," the lady at the counter answered. "She's with a client for the next hour. But after that, she's available."

"I'll wait," Omar answered quickly. "Reserve her for me next."

When Gema returned to the main hall and saw Omar, she blushed and looked troubled. Omar went to meet her and took both of her hands.

"Omar." Gema sighed, stopping in her tracks. "How did you find out that I work here?"

"It doesn't matter, Gema. I found you, and I'm going to pay for all the time we need."

"Not here, Omar, please," Gema pleaded quietly, standing her ground. "I don't want you to have to pay to spend time with me. For you, I am free!"

"I said it doesn't matter, Gema. Here or anywhere. I have the money. I pay, and we talk."

"But I'm ashamed, Omar! I didn't want you to know that I work in a place like this."

"Gema, listen." Omar looked deeply into her eyes. "I don't care where you work. I love you enough to accept you for exactly who you are. You don't have to feel ashamed. Ever."

Gema finally accepted Omar's plan. He paid for three hours of Gema's time, and she led him to a large television room filled with expensive lounging furniture. They chose a secluded corner, and Omar ordered drinks.

After they were comfortable on a splendid couch, Gema persisted, "Omar, how did you find me?"

"Like I told you before, it doesn't matter." Omar smiled. "But since you're curious, this is how I found you." He pulled her photo from his pocket and flashed it before her eyes.

"Where did you find *that?*" she cried.

Omar told Gema how he had paid to track her after they had danced together at Los Lidos, how he had found the photo, and how Toño had recognized her and led him to the dancing club. Omar's story ripened the evening for both of them to bare their hearts. Gema told Omar all about her sad life and why she was working in the dancing club.

"I grew up in a poor family in a city in Jalisco, Mexico. My father died when I was young, and for a while my mother made money as a prostitute. When I was still a little girl, she shacked up with my stepfather. When I was fifteen years old, my stepfather tried to rape me. Mama was away, but my oldest brother defended me.

"After that, life at home became unbearable, so I ran off with a man and had two daughters with him. They are nine and seven years old, and my mother usually takes care of them. I soon discovered that my man was a drug addict, an alcoholic, and physically abusive. Eventually he left with another woman.

"Mama also left my stepfather and came to the United States, and my brothers soon joined her. After my mother found a place to live and my brothers found jobs, she sent for me and my daughters. I have lived here in the United States for only two years.

"As you well know, life here is tough. The only work I could find was this horrible job, dancing for my living. Because of my looks and my capability with music, I excel in the dance halls. But I'm ashamed of this kind of job."

Omar smiled at Gema, wanting her to know that he understood and loved her anyway. "What are your girls' names?" Omar asked kindly, with genuine interest.

"Daiana is nine years old and Noemi is seven. As you can imagine, I have to work hard to make a living for me and the girls. Well, actually, I provide for Mama as well, since my brothers aren't very faithful in helping her. That's why I accepted this dancing job. It seems to be the only way that we can make it."

"I understand," Omar answered slowly. "Actually, it's amazing how alike our lives have been. I also grew up in a poor area in Chiapas, down close to the Guatemalan border. My childhood was also a sad one, because my father abandoned us for a younger woman. He started selling everything we had so he could live it up with his mistress.

"The worst thing that happened in my youth was when my father sold my horse that I had trained and loved. All the security in my life went down the drain. I felt as if I was lost in a bad world. Because of my father's influence, I became a violent person. When I was fourteen he bought me a pistol, and by the time I was seventeen I had already tried three times to kill somebody.

"I came to the United States three years ago, and it's been a lonely road for me. I also want you to know that *my* job isn't the nicest either." Omar watched Gema's face closely as he told her, "I'm a drug dealer."

Gema took this news calmly. Omar wondered if maybe her brothers were in the same business as he was, because she didn't seem to be bothered by the idea.

By the time three hours were up, what Omar had hoped for had happened. He and Gema found it easy to open their hearts to each other, and now they were definitely bonded. They were both ready to accept each other just as they were. By the time they left the dancing club, they were naturally talking about their future together.

After their time at the dancing club, Omar took Gema to his apartment so she could see where he lived. Then in the wee hours of the morning, he took her to the house where she lived with her brother Ramón. They parted happily, knowing that very soon they would have their first night out at Tacos Mexico's Christmas party, which was only a week away.

That morning when Omar got home, he surveyed his apartment with new eyes. Things would have to change. He was glad Bato had moved out, and he would tell his two roommates that they could keep this old apartment and pay the rent.

I'll rent a nice apartment somewhere for Gema and me. I'll accept Daiana and Noemi like my own daughters and be a real daddy to them. I'll make Gema feel like a queen.

Omar couldn't wait for his dream to come true—the happy family he had always longed for.

Several times a year Tony Moreno financed a party for his Tacos Mexico employees. The hall owned by the company was not large enough to accommodate all the workers at one time. But because Tacos Mexico was open around the clock, more than half of the workers had to be at their jobs.

The Christmas Eve party was the biggest of the year, and Tony and Javier were preparing for over a hundred people. At six o'clock, Omar picked up Gema and her daughters, and the four of them headed for the party.

Gema had asked if her two brothers and their families could join the party. "Sure!" Omar agreed. "Tony always says, the more the merrier!"

Now that Omar and Gema were seeing each other every day, they felt comfortable together. Though they both hated the dancing club and what it represented, Gema still worked there. Often Omar drove her to work in the evening and then home again the next morning.

How soon could Gema quit her dancing job and move into an apartment with Omar? It was something they often discussed. Omar longed to have a family—to take Gema and her two girls under his wing. He was happy to observe that Gema's daughters were friendly and well-behaved.

"Mama's the real problem," Gema admitted as they drove to the party. "My dancing job provides for her and the girls, so she's afraid that if I move in with you, she'll lose her source of income."

"But I could support Doña Juana as well," Omar assured her.

"I understand that," Gema agreed, smiling at him sweetly. "But you don't know Mama. She'll never believe that you're better than the men she abhors."

As Omar and his new little family entered the hall, a clown carrying a loudspeaker was strutting around on the platform, welcoming the people in and asking them to take seats. At one end of the room, a group of folk musicians was waiting to perform. A side door opened to a courtyard where food was being prepared, and delicious smells of grilled meat and spicy Mexican foods wafted in.

Tony himself went up and took the mic, thanking his employees for their good work. Then he called the workers forward by name and gave them each a new Tacos Mexico jacket and a new red cap. Next, he raffled off the gifts piled on a table near the front. Omar and Gema were delighted when Matías, Gema's oldest brother, won an immense stereo set. After the raffle, the musicians took the stage. The hall vibrated with Mexican rancheras as the food was served.

Omar's fun began after the meal. Taking Gema by the hand, he led her to meet Tony and Javier. "This is my girlfriend," he announced proudly.

"Congratulations!" Javier cheered, and even Tony looked impressed. Then Omar led her from table to table, greeting the Tacos Mexico workers that he knew well.

Close to midnight, Omar and Gema drove slowly back to Ramón's place, savoring their time together. They had all enjoyed the evening immensely. Omar spoke of his desire for them all to live together as a family. Daiana and Noemi were all ears, but didn't say anything. Gema was slow about making a decision. Was she willing to give herself totally to a man she knew so little about?

With just a little more time, Omar was sure his dream would come true. Giving Gema a good-night hug when he dropped her and her daughters off at her mother's place, he told her what he was feeling. Her shimmering green eyes told him that she agreed.

But what would Doña Juana say? Neither Omar nor Gema could answer that.

"And who do you think you are?" the gnarled old man demanded. Gema and Omar had been sitting in her room, discussing their plans for the evening.

Omar jumped up. "And what do you want with me," he sneered, "that you address me so kindly?"

Pancho was renting a room in Juana's house. Though he meant nothing to Gema, the old man had a strange crush on her.

Omar had arrived early that evening, wanting to take Gema out to eat. As usual, he walked right on in to Gema's room, ignoring old Pancho in the living room. Irritated, the jealous man followed Omar and stationed himself in the doorway, his eyes aflame.

"You act like you own this place," he snarled. "You just walk in and don't even say hello to the rest of us. Do you want me to kick you out, or what?"

"If you can, help yourself," Omar challenged. "Kick me out if you can."

The old man lunged at Omar. Furious, Omar knocked him down and pounded him till Gema and Doña Juana grabbed his arms. But the damage was done. Omar shook himself loose and turned to Gema. "I'm leaving," he said. It was up to Doña Juana and Gema to clean up Pancho and tend to his injuries.

The next time Omar came to see Gema, he brought along Pepe, his favorite bodyguard. Omar stationed him by the public phone on the street where he knew old Pancho might try to call the police. "Don't let him touch that phone," Omar demanded. Then he went inside and once again made himself at home.

After the incident with Pancho, it was clear to the whole family that Omar could be violent at times. One of Gema's aunts warned her, "Gema, don't shack up with that violent man. You can see he has a terrible temper."

But Gema argued that Omar was considerate of her and especially kind to her little girls. And Omar kept on wooing the little threesome, taking them to parks, to the beach, and out to eat. When he took them shopping, he bought whatever they wanted.

His business was prospering more than he had ever expected. He could afford to lavish money on Gema and her girls, and he also stashed savings in the back of the old sofa in his apartment.

After three months, Gema agreed to quit her job and move in with Omar. They went together to put in her notice at the dancing club. They took the girls along downtown and rented a small apartment. Omar moved his things in, and they bought more furnishings. Finally, they went to Doña Juana's to help Gema move her things.

When Gema announced the move, Doña Juana protested, "Why do you have to take the little girls? He isn't their father! They're better off here with me." She didn't care that Omar was right there, hearing it all.

"Omar is very kind to my daughters," Gema insisted, gathering her things. "We'll be okay."

"It won't last," Doña Juana predicted, stalking her daughter around like a tiger. "You'll be back in no time. How can you dare trust a man again?"

Omar took Gema to work for one last night, and then went to pick her up the next morning. As they drove away from the dancing club, Gema looked back and sighed. "Omar, I hate that place! Don't ever let me go back to that horrible job. Promise? If I ever want to go back, put a bullet in my head!"

"You'll never need to go back," Omar assured her. "My job will provide easily for all of your needs. It's a deal!"

"Let's go pick up the girls, and then we'll be a family." Gema beamed at Omar. "I can't wait any longer."

"The family I have always dreamed about," Omar agreed, parking the car in front of Doña Juana's place. "Let's go make it happen!"

26

DREAM COME TRUE

LOS ANGELES WAS lit up as usual, and attractions glittered on every block. But Omar hurried down the street, oblivious to it all. He had just finished his shift at Tacos Mexico, and now his legs could hardly go fast enough. He was going home!

As Omar burst into the little apartment, his heart warmed to see Gema in the kitchen, preparing the evening meal. Daiana and Noemi were watching television in the little living room.

"What's on for supper?" Omar asked, giving Gema a quick hug.

"I'm making your special—Omar's tacos," Gema replied, chuckling. "I went to the supermarket today and picked up everything we need to fix them."

"Isn't it funny how we invented our own special tacos?" Omar laughed. "Here, let me help you." While Gema fried eggs and plantains, Omar set out four plates and placed a large tortilla on each one. He diced a pile of avocado onto each tortilla, followed by a thick smear of sour cream. Next he plopped on slices of squeaky white cheese. Gema placed two fried eggs on top of each pile. Last of all, she crowned each serving with slices of fried plantain.

"Girls, come. Let's eat our supper," Gema announced, pulling a bottle of pop out of the refrigerator. "Let's enjoy our special Omar's tacos."

"Oh, they're so good!" Omar exclaimed. "Can't wait to sink my teeth into mine!"

After the meal Omar helped Daiana and Noemi with their homework. "Do you enjoy school?" Omar asked. Daiana nodded vigorously, smiling at him. But Noemi didn't answer. She kept her head down and plugged on with her homework.

Omar grinned. He was making headway with the outgoing Daiana. But Noemi, who had her mama's looks, was more quiet and harder to get close to.

When the homework was done, Omar joined Gema in the kitchen. It had been a chilly day, and Gema was wearing a sweater with a mystifying painting on the back. Omar had often tried to figure out the picture. It showed the torso of a man surrounded by dark clouds. The man's face was contorted in fear of the poisonous snake wrapped around his shoulder, and the snake was staring at the man with an electrifying glare.

"What does that painting on the back of your sweater mean?" Omar asked.

Gema shrugged. "I don't know. I never really tried to figure it out."

"I don't like it," Omar said. "It's too creepy. That poor man is forever pestered by that snake."

"It's just a sweater," Gema countered.

"But I'm sure it has a meaning," Omar insisted. "I wish I knew what it was. Why don't you stop wearing the thing?"

Gema didn't answer, and the subject was dropped.

By the time Omar and Gema had lived together for three months, they had begun to discover each other's flaws. Omar realized that Gema was far from perfect. She was temperamental and often scolded the girls angrily, even when Omar couldn't see that they deserved it. When Omar tried to correct Gema, she didn't accept it well.

Gema discovered that Omar wasn't always a gentleman either. His selfish streak emerged, especially when he was tired. Usually she served him gladly, but when he was demanding, she hated his whims. She kept quiet and did what she had to do, but it irritated her.

Gema did not miss her dancing job, but she often felt bored at home while Omar was gone and the girls were at school. So she started accompanying

Omar on his narcotics business at times. Soon Omar was bragging to his cronies that Gema was the best business associate he had ever had. On the surface, Omar and Gema seemed happy together. Omar, who had yearned so long for a home and family, was pleased, and he delighted in family outings.

One bright summer day they took the girls to the fair. The horses in the merry-go-round seemed extra frisky as Daiana and Noemi rode. Every so often the girls looked over and smiled at Omar and their mother as they clung to their mounts. "Those girls love that, don't they!" Omar chuckled.

"It's a good break from school," Gema agreed, beaming. "Omar, let's take a photo of us today so we can always remember this happy day for our family."

"Sure," Omar agreed. "We came past a place where we can get a photo printed on a cloth wall hanging. Would you like that?"

"Yes! Let's do that next."

That afternoon, Omar and his family carried home not only happy memories in their hearts, but also a wall hanging with their family photo on it. As soon as they got home, Gema hung it on their apartment wall.

Omar's dream for a family had come true. But would it last?

Omar stopped abruptly on the street corner and held his phone close to his ear.

"Who is it you want to talk to?" Omar asked again, frowning.

"Gema," a man's voice answered. "Doña Juana's pretty daughter, the dancer."

"Who are you? And why do you want to talk to her?" Omar's voice was icy.

"She and I are great friends. I just wanted to chat with her. Isn't she at home?"

Omar abruptly cut off the call and hurried home. This was the third call he had received for Gema that day, and all three had been from men. Was Gema playing tricks on him? What in the world was going on?

Omar found Gema in the living room watching television. He gave her a hug, sat down beside her, and asked quietly, "Gema, are you having contact with men these days?"

"No," Gema answered, turning from the television and looking at him innocently. "I have you. Why would I be contacting other men?"

"I got three calls from men today, asking for you," Omar answered, watching Gema's face carefully. "I want to know what's going on."

Gema gave Omar her full attention. "I have no idea why men would be calling me. Since I moved in with you, I've had nothing to do with other men. I haven't called anybody. My old boyfriend totally gave up on me. Are you sure it wasn't one of my brothers?"

"I know your brother's voices," Omar retorted. "This is someone else. I sure hope you're not up to some trick with me, Gema—because if you are, you'll be sorry." But Gema's innocent eyes and easy answers helped calm Omar's doubts. He decided to believe her.

It was probably just some of the men who used to dance with her a long time ago, he consoled himself. *Probably nothing to take seriously. I'll watch her, but if she plays any tricks on me, I don't know what I'll do!*

One day Omar rushed into the apartment waving a paper. "Look what a Nicaraguan friend of mine gave me today at Tacos Mexico!" he exclaimed, waving the paper in Gema's face. "It's called the new NACARA Law.[17] Any Nicaraguan who came to the United States before 1995 and has lived here for five years or more can automatically get his residency!"

"Well, what does that have to do with you?" Gema asked, giving Omar a blank look. "You're Mexican."

Omar grinned sheepishly. "Actually, I'm not. I never told you or anybody else, but I'm a Nicaraguan. I bought my Mexican citizenship on my way here."

"What in the world?" Gema exclaimed. "Here I've been living with a Nica all this time and didn't know it." Then she threw her head back and laughed.

"Aren't you glad now that I'm a Nica?" Omar hooted. "Look, the paper says that if I have a wife and children, they'll automatically get their residency as well."

"Does that mean we'll have to get married?" Gema asked.

Omar nodded, watching her face.

---

17   NACARA: Nicaraguan Adjustment and Central American Relief Act.

"Let's get married then!" Gema bounced over to hug Omar. "I would sure be happy if we didn't have to worry all the time about being here illegally."

"One requirement is that I have a job," Omar explained further. "Javier says he's sure that Tony will get me a work certificate from Tacos Mexico. We're set to go!"

The very next day, Omar and Gema and the two girls visited the closest immigration office and signed up under the NACARA law. Everything went well. Omar and Gema weren't married yet, but they had three months to take care of that. On the way home, they stopped at Ramón's place, where they found the whole family together, including Doña Juana.

"Look, we have some good news!" Gema announced. "Because of a new law, Omar is able to get U.S. residency for himself—and for me and the girls. We just signed the papers at the immigration office."

"How can that be?" Ramón asked, perplexed. "Why can't we get ours too?"

Gema grinned. "Because you're Mexican. You see, this rascal has been playing a trick on us all this time. He isn't a Mexican after all. He's a Nica. And the new NACARA law applies only to Cubans and Central Americans."

Everybody was quiet, digesting this news. Most Hispanics dreamed of obtaining their legal papers, so the family couldn't help but be happy for the couple—everybody except Doña Juana. She was scowling.

"The best part is—I'll have to marry a Nica!" Gema snickered. Everybody except Doña Juana laughed along with her.

"This President we have is sure a good one!" Matías declared.

But Ramón wondered, "When will Bill Clinton make a NACARA law for us Mexicans?"

That night Omar took Gema and the girls to a family restaurant, cherishing the family moments that he had been deprived of in his growing years. During the meal, Daiana called Omar *Daddy* for the first time. Omar thanked her with tears in his eyes. Noemi was watching closely.

The next day while Omar was out on a drug run, he got a call from the school, asking him to pick up his sick little girl. He raced back to the apartment to pick up Gema, and they drove to the school together. Daiana was the one who was feeling ill, but Omar suggested that both girls come home with them. As they walked across the parking lot, several of the girls' friends left the playground and crowded around.

"Why are you leaving?" one girl asked.

"Daiana's sick," Noemi answered. "Can't you see?"

"Is that your daddy?" another one asked, eyeing Omar.

"Yes." Noemi nodded proudly. "Can't you see?"

As he led the way to the car, Omar could hardly see the tarmac. His eyes were too filled with tears.

Omar was still too busy to be at home as much as he would have liked. He needed the Tacos Mexico job so that it wouldn't be too obvious that he was selling narcotics. Even though he didn't sell during his work hours, the restaurant was a good place to make contacts. Javier let Omar work as he could, which amounted to three or four days a week.

After Omar shacked up with Gema, his life changed dramatically. He and Gema kept in touch by phone almost every hour of the day, and Omar enjoyed this frequent contact with the woman he loved. But he understood that her frequent calls were partly due to her worry. Gema knew he had been a womanizer, and she was suspicious of any attention he might give to other women. To alleviate her fears, Omar went to the night hangouts only if Gema went along. They would leave the girls with a friend and go to a dance or a party—never to the dancing clubs Gema hated. But Omar's night business suffered.

More and more, Omar conducted his drug business on the phone. Even at home, he was often interrupted by calls when a client wanted some snow or when a pickup or delivery was ready. Omar began selling more cocaine wholesale. He didn't make as much per gram that way, but it still profited because he was selling greater quantities. Omar was pleased to be able to fit his business in with his family life.

Then Omar started getting calls from strange men again. One day he got a call almost every hour. At first the callers sweetly asked for Gema, but eventually they swore at Omar. Did someone want to get rid of him so they could have Gema?

By evening Omar was in a terrible stew. He had stopped calling Gema or receiving calls from her all afternoon. When he got home, he started asking Gema pointed questions, trying to hide his stress. To his surprise, Gema again seemed innocent and free. Either she was a good actress, or someone was playing tricks on him. He had to know what was going on.

After the girls were in bed, Omar approached Gema directly, his voice icy. "Gema, I'm getting phone calls from men again."

Gema's large green eyes filled with tears. "Omar, I don't know anything about it. I have no friendship with any man besides you. I've been faithful to you."

Omar was at his wit's end. "One guy is even threatening me," he spat out. "Oh, I wish I could get my hands on his throat. Gema, if I ever find out you're lying about this, I will never forgive you. Do you hear?"

Gema crumpled on the couch, crying softly. "Please believe me, Omar. Something is wrong. Somebody is playing tricks on us. I am innocent."

Omar finally dropped the subject, went to bed, and fell into a troubled sleep. But even in his sleep, questions zipped through his dreams, and he woke up as tired as he had been when he went to bed. As he left for work, his mind was still screaming, *I must have an answer!*

On Omar's next day off, the mystery was finally unraveled. A lady who rented an apartment in the same building was a friend of both Doña Juana and Gema, and she came over to talk.

"Doña Juana came to your apartment yesterday when you were both gone," the woman told them. "Since she didn't find you, she came over to my apartment to release some steam. She's really upset, Omar, because you took Gema and the girls from her. But the thing that makes her the maddest is that you don't give her enough money. She says you're starving her."

"But I give her plenty for her groceries every week," Gema countered, shaking her head. "She is not starving!"

"And where are her two sons?" Omar growled. "That's what I want to know!"

"Anyway," the lady said, "Doña Juana admitted that she's determined to get you two separated by getting men to call Omar all the time."

Omar leaped out of his chair. "There you go, Gema! There's our answer. That crazy woman! And those stupid men! I wish I could get my hands on their throats!"

Gema jumped up too, her eyes gleaming. Throwing her arms around Omar, she cried, "I told you I'm innocent!"

Omar felt like a ton of bricks had been lifted from his back.

After the woman had left, Gema said, "Omar, I'm calling my mother tomorrow to let her know we're coming over to talk. This is ridiculous, and it has to stop."

The next evening Omar and Gema left the girls with a friend and headed toward Matías's place. They had barely settled in the living room when Doña Juana came roaring in, ready for war, but claiming she had nothing to do with the phone calls.

"Gema, ever since you shacked up with Omar, you've abandoned me," she accused. "You hate me now that you love that stinking Nicaraguan. Your mother doesn't exist anymore!"

"But can't you see that Gema and the girls are happy with me?" Omar asked, forcing himself to stay seated in his armchair. "All I'm trying to do is make them happy."

"Mama, I'll tell you what your problem is!" Gema cried. "You're selfish. All you're worried about is yourself, and now all you want is Omar's money. Ever since I was small, I have never mattered to you. Now that I've found happiness, you can't stand it. You're doing your best to take my happiness away."

"Doña Juana," Omar stated firmly, "Gema is mine and will not be going back to you ever. Just accept that."

Doña Juana threw herself at Omar, ready to beat him with her tiny fists. But Omar was out of the chair in a flash, and he warded her off easily. Just when Omar was about to burst out laughing, someone came flying from the kitchen.

It was Gema with a broom, determined to give her mother the pounding she deserved. But Omar jumped between Gema and Doña Juana and grabbed Gema's hands. "No, honey. Just let her go. She'll get over it."

"Stop it!" Matías said, forcing himself between the couple and his mother. "That's enough. Calm down."

Doña Juana fled from the house, swearing as she went. Omar and Gema followed her to the door. Again, Omar had difficulty holding back his laughter. And yet, he pitied the poor woman and her uncontrollable anger.

He sighed to himself. *And I pity poor Gema, who was raised by that woman.*

27

BEGINNING OF THE END

TACOS MEXICO WAS buzzing with activity during the noon hour. Omar was working the cash register, and he had just made himself a super taco when his phone rang. He placed his plate on the counter and pulled out his phone. It was Matías's wife.

"Yes?" Omar answered, reaching for a bite of his spicy taco.

Then he froze. "Gema what?" His whole body went cold.

"You say Gema's going to an abortion clinic? What do you mean?"

Omar hung up slowly and placed his phone back into his pocket. He forgot his taco. He forgot everything except the terrible news he had just received.

I don't believe Gema will do that! Omar's heart screamed. *She knows how much I love that baby. Even she is excited about having it.*

But Omar suddenly remembered some things Doña Juana had once spewed out about her daughter. "Gema is crazy," she had ranted. "You just don't know her. She gets depressed and does the craziest things. She's tried to commit suicide several times and ended up in the hospital. She went to a psychiatrist and was on meds for depression for a long time. She aborts her babies. You wait and see..."

But I never knew Gema like that, Omar reasoned, though his heart was full of dread. *I've been good for her. With me, she's become a happy woman. So why this—and why now?*

From Omar's perspective, his little family was enjoying the happiest time of their lives. The girls were doing well in their studies, and they seemed well-adjusted. Best of all, they always called him Daddy now.

They were also excited about their residency papers. All Omar and Gema needed to do yet was get married and turn their papers in. In a matter of months, they would be residents of the great United States of America.

Gema had told Omar she was unable to have any more babies. So when Gema had discovered that she was pregnant, they were both surprised. Omar was elated, but he had detected fear in Gema.

At her first doctor appointment, Gema had asked if they did abortions. Telling Omar about it later, Gema admitted that the clinic staff had scolded her. "We're here to give life," they had retorted, "not to kill."

"Why don't you want this baby?" Omar had asked, shocked and mystified. "It's the best thing that could happen to us!"

"I'm scared," Gema had confessed. "If only you knew how much I suffered having my babies. I was only fourteen when Daiana was born and sixteen with Noemi. In Jalisco, Mexico, hospital conditions were horrible. Omar, I almost died. Plus, my man was a beast."

"That was different," Omar had reminded her. "This baby will have a real daddy. Back then you didn't have me. This time I'll be with you through thick and thin, and everything will be fine. Don't you dare kill my baby!"

Gema had snapped out of her depression and seemed to have forgotten her qualms. She became as excited as Omar about the pregnancy. They had planned that if the baby was a boy, they would call him Omarcito, and if it was a girl, she would be named after her mama. These past three months had been special for the whole family, even the girls. Omar loved Daiana and Noemi as if they were his own, and they were excited about the addition to the family. He and Gema were planning to get married. Now this.

I don't really think Gema will do it, Omar reasoned, working mechanically all afternoon. *She can't. She knows how excited I am over this baby. She's just in one of her moods.*

Omar had called his mother in Regadío and told her how happy he was. Gema herself had taken the phone and told his mother in her sweet musical voice how happy she was and how much she thought of Omar.

Just three days earlier, Omar and Gema had gone to the clinic for another checkup. The pregnancy was three months along, and everything was fine. The clinic had given Gema a tiny disposable diaper that became the symbol of their joy. That evening Omar and Gema had celebrated by eating out. When they returned home, Omar showed Daiana and Noemi the little diaper and cheered, "Our little baby will wear this the first day of its life!"

That afternoon was one of the longest in Omar's life. He had been hoping that this baby would solidify his relationship with Gema and bond them together forever—that it would make all of his dreams come true. Now the dream was crashing . . . if it was really true that Gema had gone to an abortion clinic and killed his baby.

Wave after wave of strong emotions washed over him as he went about his work—anger most of all, but also disappointment, terrible sadness, and confusion. By evening he was worried sick.

Right after work Omar hurried home, but the apartment was dark and the doors were locked. Fearing the worst, Omar jumped into his car and headed to Doña Juana's place. Gema was not there, but Juana blurted out the truth. "Yeah, I already know what Gema did. Like I told you, it's not her first time. She aborted her last boyfriend's baby as well."

Omar hung his head, turned, and walked out to his car in a daze. He called Gema's cell phone. She had not been answering all day, but now she answered him from their apartment.

At least she had come home.

He found her sitting in the living room, her head hanging low. She was pale, and Omar could see she had been through terrible trauma. Controlling his emotions, Omar tipped her chin up. "Gema, look at me."

Gema refused to talk. She refused to face him. She was emotionally locked up and in obvious physical pain. "Gema," Omar insisted, "talk to me! Why did you do it?"

Gema fled to the bathroom. Omar expected her to come out soon, but when she didn't, his anger grew into rage. Knocking on the bathroom door, he hollered, "Open up, Gema! We need to talk."

But she wouldn't.

What was she feeling? What was happening in that quiet cubicle? *Why doesn't Gema open up and face me?* he fumed. Several times he knocked on the door and commanded Gema to at least answer. Nothing emerged but thick silence.

Finally Omar's rage mushroomed into fury. With one kick, he forced the door open. Gema was sitting on the commode, her head down and her thick black hair hanging over her face. In one leap Omar was standing in front of her. "Gema, look me in the eyes!"

But Gema refused.

Suddenly it was not a man but a maniac who stood before the broken woman. He grabbed her by the throat with both hands and slammed her against the bathroom wall. "You killed my baby!" he screamed.

"I'm so sorry," Gema croaked.

Fortunately, Omar heard the desperate confession, and his anger melted. He dropped her, and she crumpled onto the floor, crying. Omar helped her to her feet and led her to the couch in the living room where they sat side by side.

Omar's anger was cooling slowly. "Why, Gema? Why did you kill my baby?" he asked again.

"I don't know, Omar. I really don't know. I just did it. I'm so sorry. I'll never do it again! From now on I swear that I'll give you all the babies you want."

Slowly Omar drew the crushed woman to him. "I don't understand myself," she sniffled. "I knew how much you loved the baby. I was a coward. But I'm sorry. I'll never do it again."

Now it was Omar's turn. Tears welled up in his eyes as he held her. "I'm sorry I got so mad. I almost strangled you. Yes, we'll start all over again. We'll still have a baby sometime."

In time Gema healed physically, and things slowly limped back to normal. The girls still went to school. Omar still went to Tacos Mexico to work and did his usual drug runs. Gema still made the meals, and life's activities resumed. But the joy had disappeared. Something had died between Omar and the woman of his dreams.

Omar called his mother in Nicaragua and told her that Gema had lost the baby, but he didn't tell her how.

A week after the dreadful fight, Gema went to visit one of her aunts. The aunt noticed a purple mark on her throat. She pulled Gema's collar back. Raising her eyebrows, she asked, "What happened here?"

"Oh, I hurt myself," Gema answered lamely.

"No, you didn't!" the aunt snapped. "Those are finger marks. Omar tried to strangle you!"

Gema was quiet.

"Gema," the aunt whispered. "I'm going to give you some advice. Get rid of that man. He's dangerous. Someday he'll give you big trouble."

But Gema defended Omar, telling her aunt the good things he had done for them and how kind and gentle he was with the girls. She didn't mention the abortion that had stirred Omar's wrath.

Sometime later Omar met the aunt at Ramón's place. Wagging a finger at Omar, the aunt scolded, "Omar, you'd better be glad that I'm not a bad person, or I'd make sure you get ten years in jail. I saw purple finger marks on Gema's throat!"

The aunt's words made Omar think deeply about his life and his terrible anger. *Why am I such a beast?* he asked himself. *I so nearly killed the girl I love. What is going to happen to me? And what is going to happen to Gema and her two precious girls?*

28

A MAN CRAZED

STEPPING INTO THE apartment one morning after a drug run, Omar stopped abruptly in the doorway, frowning. Gema had company again. *She knows I don't like when she invites people into our apartment—especially strangers.*

Gema smiled at him nervously. The visitor looked nervous too. Omar looked the girl up and down, noticing something different about her. She didn't wear makeup, her hair was pinned up in a simple bun, and she wore a modest skirt and blouse. Though light-skinned, she was obviously Latina, for she spoke impeccable Spanish. Omar slipped into the kitchen to pour himself a drink. His frown relaxed. The girl's modesty told him she was probably not up to any mischief.

But soon the visiting girl excused herself, said goodbye, and fled.

"What did she want?"

"She just wanted to visit with me," Gema answered. "You don't have to worry about her being a bad influence. Rebecca is a really nice girl."

"You told her I don't like when strangers visit, didn't you?" Omar ventured. "I could see she was scared to death of me."

"Of course I told her. You chased off the last two ladies who started coming by to visit me, so I warned her that you don't like if just anybody stops by."

"You know good and well why I chased off those other two," Omar growled. "They were up to no good and were a bad influence on you. What did this one want?"

Gema sighed. "She's a Christian. She talked to me about God and how good life could be if we served Him. But since you chase all my friends away, she probably won't ever be back."

"Look," Omar answered, pouring Gema a drink, "I'm glad if that girl comes to see you. Invite her back if you see her again. I can see she's a good girl."

"She invited me to her church," Gema added, relaxing slowly. "It's not far—just three blocks from here. Would you let me go?"

Omar smiled. "Not only would I let you go—I'd go along and we'd take the girls."

Omar and Gema were trying hard to make a go of their relationship. But since the abortion, everything was different. In Omar's Nicaraguan culture, women were subject to their husbands, even asking for permission to leave the house. But Gema was used to doing her own thing. Omar was still infatuated with Gema, but the more they fought, the more Omar panicked. He did not want to lose the girl of his dreams.

When Gema found she was pregnant again, Omar was afraid to let his expectations soar. But Gema seemed happy to talk about their future with a baby. Just maybe Omar's dream would still come true. Maybe this baby would do the trick.

Omar did his best to encourage Gema's excitement. At the same time, he watched her every step. He couldn't trust her. Did she really want this child? *I think she wants to keep her shape in case she needs to go back to her dancing,* Omar surmised. *She's afraid she's losing me, and I'm afraid of losing her.*

The more Omar breathed down Gema's neck, the more she resented it. In a fit of anger one evening, she screamed, "Why can't you let me go? Why can't you just let me live my life? You act as if I were your property, and you don't trust me one bit!"

"That baby you're carrying is not just yours," Omar retorted, controlling his anger. "It's also mine. The last time you betrayed me and killed my child. But this time you won't—I'm not going to let you."

Gema had been telling Omar all week long that she was bleeding off and on. It looked as though she might be losing this baby too.

"I believe you're taking something to get rid of that baby," Omar accused. "I just know that the baby would be all right if it wasn't that you want it to die."

Omar's allegation made Gema furious. The angrier she became, the more Omar doubted her. *Gema is aborting my baby again!*

The fight lasted long into the night. In his rage, Omar jerked the canvas family photo off the wall, threw it on the ground, and stomped on it. This was the picture they had taken after one of their happiest times together, their wonderful day at the fair. Next, Omar grabbed a bottle of ink and poured it all over the happy faces in the picture.

At that, Gema packed her bags, took the girls, and moved in with her brother Matías.

Two days later Gema called Omar and begged him to come pick her up. Omar forgave her and brought her home, saying to himself, *This lady is a lunatic. I just have to accept her angry moods and depression. She'll be okay.*

Again, they tried to make things work. Omar did his best to please Gema, buying her gifts and taking her out to eat. But nothing seemed to help. What could he do to keep Gema? If she lost this baby, he feared it might be over for them.

Several weeks later, Gema did lose the baby, and she and Omar fought again. She declared it was a natural loss, but Omar was sure she had aborted it. Once again, Gema left Omar and moved in with Matías. And once again, Gema called Omar after several days and begged him to forgive her and take her back.

During their bouts of peace alternating with lonely separations, Omar discovered how much Gema meant to him. *I cannot live without Gema!* he told himself. *Life just wouldn't be worth it. I must figure out a way to keep her forever.*

Rebecca came back to see Gema one day when Omar was away. Once more she invited Gema to her church. "Come to our worship service next Sunday at ten o'clock," Rebecca urged. "It would be great if Omar could come with you, and your little girls would love Sunday school." Gema was glad to report that Omar had consented to attend with her sometime. She would remind him about it.

Sunday morning dawned bright and clear, and by nine o'clock everybody was up and in a good mood—a blessed lull in the storm. "Gema, let's take the girls to the park today," Omar suggested, joy bursting from his heart. "We haven't gone for a long time."

As the family walked along the street soon after ten, Gema stopped in her tracks. "Listen, Omar! I think that singing comes from Rebecca's church. I forgot—I practically promised her that we'd stop by today."

Sure enough, just up the street, beautiful singing floated through the open door of a large stone building. All four stood still and listened to the lovely music. Nostalgia stirred in Omar's heart. Gema, the music lover, stood in rapt attention. Though Omar also loved music, he had seldom listened to the soothing chords of the old hymns. But now "Amazing Grace" was doing its job in his heart.

"Shall we go to the service?" Gema asked almost reverently. "I kind of promised."

Omar hesitated. Would God have anything to offer them? He loved this music, and he knew God existed. But it was hard to believe God would want them to get too close to Him right now. Omar felt much too wicked; church didn't seem like the right place for them.

"Not today," he answered finally. "We dressed for the park, not for church. Maybe we can go next Sunday."

Gema didn't argue, so they resumed their walk to the park and forgot about Rebecca and her church with the beautiful singing.

Years later, Omar often wondered if things would have been different for Gema and him, had they given God that chance.

One night Omar's family was invited to a birthday party of a friend. Before they left the house, Omar ordered, "Gema, I don't want you to drink tonight. You know it doesn't go well with you when you drink. You won't be worth a hoot tomorrow to take care of the children."

"So you won't drink either?" Gema snapped. "If you don't drink, I won't drink. It's that simple."

"Look, I can drink and still go on with life perfectly well," Omar retorted. "I'll do what I want tonight, but you are not to drink, do you hear?"

Gema did hear, and she shut up, but she was angry.

They found the music turned high and the party going strong. A big ice chest, brimming with beer cans, sat on the table, and the guests mingled, laughing and visiting. Omar helped himself to a beer as soon as they arrived. Soon after he took a third one, Gema popped open a can for herself. Just as she raised it to her lips, Omar hissed, "Gema, no!"

Gema flashed Omar an angry, defiant look and raised the can again. As quickly and quietly as a cat, Omar pounced. He grabbed her hands. "I said you're not going to drink tonight!" he hissed. "Get a Coca-Cola." He snatched Gema's can and returned to his seat.

Gema was more upset than she had been in a long time. Ten minutes later she did it again, right in front of Omar as if daring him, "Do that again."

Omar grabbed the hand that carried the beer, but Gema was ready for him this time. She slapped Omar in the face, hard. Omar's face burned like fire, and he was so angry he wanted to knock her flat. But because of the people all around, he just grabbed both of her arms. The two lovers, who now hated each other, stood grappling and fuming at each other.

Gema hissed, "I'm out of here!"

Omar spat back in her face, "Good riddance!" Then he flung her hands down and returned to his buddies. Gema called her two girls, and they disappeared into the night.

When Omar arrived home that night, he discovered that Gema had stopped by the apartment and taken everything she owned. That worried him, but as he got ready for bed, he sneered, *She'll be back! In a few days she'll be begging me to let her come back.*

But this time she didn't. When a week had gone by, Omar felt desperate. He stopped by her brothers' places, but they refused to say where she was. They both said, "She doesn't live with us anymore," but Omar knew that they had helped her disappear. She wasn't with Doña Juana either. Obviously, Gema had rented an apartment of her own and was back to dancing for her living, and that made Omar's heart burn. Hadn't she made him promise to shoot her if she did that?

The next month found Omar back in the night clubs, bars, and dancing clubs searching for Gema. His drug business surged, but he could not find Gema. He missed her and the family life they had enjoyed more than he ever imagined he would. The longer he searched, the more futile it seemed. His desperation escalated. *Gema, where are you?* was the cry of his lonely heart.

Finally one night, Omar found Gema in a dancing club much like the one where he had found her the first time. She was elegantly dressed and perfumed.

Gema was surprised to see Omar. "I'll talk with you if you wait till I get off work at 3 a.m.," she promised.

That morning Omar and Gema talked for several hours. Then Omar took Gema to Matías's place. Gema was willing to date Omar, but she was not willing to move back into Omar's apartment. "Not yet." She sighed. "Give me time, Omar. I'm just not ready."

Life settled into a new routine. Gema let her apartment go and moved in with Matías. The girls moved back to Grandma Juana's place. Omar took Gema to the dancing club in the evenings and then went to pick her up in the wee hours every morning.

Omar played the game carefully. He was determined to get Gema to move back into his apartment again, but he knew he had to win her love back if he wanted the family life he craved.

But it was not to be. Their fighting escalated, and Omar sensed that every day Gema's heart was growing colder toward him. They were fast becoming strangers, not lovers.

As things progressed from bad to worse, Omar's world started closing in. He felt as if he were living in a dark hole, miles deep. Yes, he had all the money he wanted, but he wasn't happy. All his physical needs were supplied, but his heart was empty. What Omar mostly wanted was love—and that was slipping away. The less Gema loved him, the more his passion for her grew. As one day slipped into another, Omar felt like he was going crazy.

One day Omar parked his vehicle on a street where parking was prohibited. When he came back, a wrecker had hauled it away. Omar had long before put all of his belongings in Gema's name, so he needed Gema to come free the vehicle after he paid the fine.

Matías drove over with Gema, and they got the vehicle released. After the paperwork was done, Omar joked, "Those guys never found the place in my car where I hide my cocaine and revolver. I'm too smart for them."

As a gesture of appreciation, Omar continued, "Hey, let me take you out to eat."

During the meal, Omar tried to make eye contact with Gema and get her to smile. But she totally ignored him, confirming what he feared: Gema was done with him.

A chant began in his mind, "She'll never be yours. She'll never be yours! She'll never be yours!"

When they left the restaurant, Gema jumped into Matías's vehicle. "Wait!" Omar screamed, leaping out into the parking lot and grabbing at the open window as Matías started his car. "Wait! Gema, you're coming with me!"

But his command was lost in the darkness. Matías stepped on the gas, jerking away from Omar, and they were gone.

Omar drove back to Matías's place, fuming. The plan that had been formulating slowly, almost unconsciously, in his mind for weeks, suddenly voiced itself. *If I can't have her, no one else will either! But I must not show my anger. I must be cool and collected. I must bide my time. If not, she'll catch on, and I might never get my chance.*

Several hours later, when Omar went to take Gema to work, he was as cool as ice. He didn't even mention the fact that Gema had refused to travel home with him. "I'll be by at 3 a.m.," Omar said as he dropped Gema off at the dancing club.

Gema had a rough night. She had never liked dancing with men she didn't love. Her mind was so full of questions about her future that it was hard to be nice to her customers.

Chabela, Gema's close friend, was also working that night, and Gema confided in her. "I used to love Omar," she said. "My love for him is all gone now, but I'm afraid to drop him. He's a violent man." Then Gema told Chabela how Omar had bragged about hiding his revolver and cocaine in his car.

Chabela shook her head. She knew Omar well and was afraid of him. "Look, Gema, you have to get rid of that man. If he's in the narco business, he's too dangerous! This morning when he comes to pick you up, show him you're done. Travel home with me and the others who carpool." Together, Chabela and Gema agreed on a plan to let Omar know once and for all that Gema was done with him.

Punctual as always, Omar was waiting for Gema with a big smile on his face. But Gema jumped into the car with her friends and was gone, leaving Omar standing on the sidewalk, gripped with fury. He jumped into his car and followed them closely till they reached Matías's apartment. Before Omar could stop her, Gema raced into the house and locked the door. The car left, and Omar stood alone on the street, his rage boiling.

He drove back to his apartment and parked his vehicle. Then he headed for Matías's place again on foot. He carried along only one thing—his tiny revolver.

Omar knew which was Gema's room. He tried to convince Gema to come to the window to talk to him. She tried to convince him to go home and leave her alone. Omar got louder and more insistent. "I'm not leaving till you open up!" he yelled to the empty window.

Gema was afraid Matías would wake up and become angry. So she finally agreed to come around to the front and open up for Omar if he promised not to argue.

Omar followed Gema to her room. What he saw there totally melted his heart. Daiana and Noemi were sprawled out sleeping on their mother's bed. Suddenly Omar's plan was done for the night. He would not have his last argument with Gema in the presence of these little girls.

Omar did ask Gema one question. "Why did you refuse to ride with me this evening?"

Gema whispered back, "Because I told my best friend what you said about the police not finding where you hid your cocaine and your gun. Then she begged me, 'Don't you dare get close to that man again. He's too dangerous.'"

Omar bade Gema good night and left, promising to come pick her up the next evening to take her to work. When he arrived at Matías's place early the next evening, Gema was getting ready for her job. Matías and Ramón and their families were just leaving for a concert. The girls were with their grandmother.

Just like that, Omar and Gema were alone.

Gema seemed loving and friendly, almost like old times. She said she was hungry, so Omar ran to a fast-food store and picked up a meal he knew Gema liked, and they ate the meal together, sitting on Gema's bed. The music in the living room was playing a gentle song, and as they ate, Omar shared with Gema his lifelong dream—how she and her girls were the fulfillment of his dream, and how happy he had been while they were together in peace.

"Gema, I'm inviting you to come back and live with me. I'll give you one more chance. You're not going to dance tonight. You're going to stay here with me tonight to make your decision. Will you come back to me so that this dream can become true, or won't you?"

"Who said I'm not going to go dance tonight?" Gema jeered, her green eyes contemptuous. "And who are you to tell me what to do? Tonight I'll tell you the truth. You're absolutely crazy if you think I'm moving back in with you."

Omar stepped out into the living room and turned up the volume of the stereo. As he strode back into the bedroom, he continued talking to Gema in quiet, controlled tones. The argument went on and on, but neither would give in. No one witnessed the two ex-lovers spewing their frustration at each other.

When Omar pulled his little revolver, Gema mocked him. "You would never hurt a flea!" She snatched up her high-heeled shoe and hit the angry man.

The dark evening exploded.

Suddenly Gema was in Omar's arms as they sat on the bedroom floor, and she was telling Omar exactly what he wanted to hear. "Oh, Omar," she sobbed, "I'm so sorry! Forgive me, please! I mocked you too many times. You're the only good thing that ever came into my life, and I never valued the gift you gave me. You always wanted the best for me and my girls, but I never accepted your love. I'm so sorry. I'll be yours forever."

"I'm sorry too, Gema!" Omar cried, tears streaming down his face. "But now it's too late. You're leaving. But I promise—I'll follow you right away."

Yes, it was too late. Gema's lifeblood was draining out of the bullet hole in her heart. Omar held her tightly as she left him forever. It was 7:30 p.m. on the 28th of November 1998.

Omar fumbled for the revolver. He had used only two bullets and had four left. That was plenty to take him to where Gema was. *We were together in life*, Omar thought. *We'll be together in death.*

He pulled back the hammer of the revolver and smiled grimly as he held it to his temple. *Here I come, Gema,* he whispered. Then he tried to pull the trigger.

But Omar Montenegro couldn't make himself do it. He had seen this scene in his dreams a thousand times. It had always seemed so easy—so romantic. He was the tough man who feared nothing. But now it was as if someone had grasped his wrist and squeezed it tightly.

No, you don't, something whispered as quietly as the night breeze wafting in through the open window. *No, you don't. I'm not done with you yet!*

In extreme frustration, Omar hurled the pistol against the wall and jumped to his feet. It was not all over with after all.

What can I do now? his mind screamed. If he couldn't shoot himself, he would have to turn himself in.

29

ON THE RUN

OMAR SLUMPED LOW in the seat of the international bus, holding a small backpack on his lap. His head was bowed, and although it was close to midnight and his body was bone-tired, he couldn't sleep. Too many mind-devils were waiting to pounce on him as soon as he dozed.

The bus was full of people, but he felt totally alone and overcome with depression. Was life worth living anymore? The question haunted him every inch of the way. His memories were so painful! He wished a thousand times that he could erase everything that flared up in his brain, but he couldn't.

The memory that was slowly killing him was those last minutes with the love of his life. Knowing that Gema had slipped away forever was almost unendurable. The loving words of acceptance that she had uttered, too late, ran through his mind like a recording. *If only she had said those words before I shot her,* he thought numbly, *we still might both be alive. But as it is, we're both dead.*

Gema had begged him to call the ambulance. He had refused, because he was still planning to die with her. Then something had prevented him from pulling the trigger.

What if they could have saved her?

After Omar knew Gema was dead, he had flown into action. He had quickly taken a shower, but no amount of water could ever wash off the horrible, haunting memories. He always kept a change of clothes at Matías's place, so he had dressed, picked up his revolver where it had fallen, and run out into the night.

At that moment, Omar longed for family. Not Uncle Bato—he was the last person Omar wanted to see. Bato was as violent as Omar, and besides, he was in Nicaragua right then. *I'll run to my aunt Yolanda,* he decided. *She lives close by, and she's a sensible woman. She'll have good advice for me.*

Feeling lost and crazed, he stumbled into his aunt's living room. His aunt and cousin were surprised to see Omar come running in so early in the evening. Omar blurted out the truth, ending with, "I'm going to turn myself in."

Yolanda was horrified to hear what Omar had done. "What will happen to our family now?" she cried.

"Omar, what time do you expect Matías and Ramón to be back from the concert?" his cousin asked.

"Not before midnight."

"Look," the cousin advised, "the border is only two and a half hours away. Run for it."

Omar stared at his cousin. Slowly the suggestion registered.

"If you turn yourself in, you'll go to jail for life, man. If you run and they catch you, it won't make much difference. But if you make it across the border before the authorities are alerted, you might be able to get back to Nicaragua."

Omar snapped into action. He ran out onto the street, got back into his car, and drove to a friend's place. Before jumping out of his car, he stripped off his gold necklace and gold bracelet and dropped them into the console. Then pulling the keys, he went to the door and spoke briefly to the lady of the house.

"I need to leave the country. My mother is dying," he lied, controlling his emotions and trying to act normal. "I'm leaving you the car to use as your own till I get back."

Omar was so distressed that he didn't even think of returning to his apartment to get his things. He left behind all his treasures for someone else to find—money, clothes, jewelry, cocaine. He had about a thousand dollars in his pocket, plus something else he could not afford to lose: the tiny notebook that he carried in his billfold. It contained all of the phone numbers of his drug friends and contacts. That little book had the potential of a tiny sliver of dynamite.

Next, Omar stopped at the closest Tacos Mexico. Old Juan was at the cash register. Omar slipped the revolver to him, saying hurriedly, "Hold this for me. I'll be back to pick it up later."

Omar's last stop was at a place called Viajes La Nortena.[18] An old gentleman who drove for the agency was Omar's good friend. Omar told his friend that his mother had called from her deathbed. "I need to get across the border tonight," he explained urgently. "I have to get to Chiapas as soon as possible."

The gentleman agreed to take Omar, and soon they were flying south as fast as traffic allowed. As they drove, Omar's friend gave him some good, though unnecessary, advice. "Be brave, Omar. Losing a mother isn't easy. My mother died seven years ago, and I still miss her."

Omar nodded numbly, feeling awkward about deceiving his friend.

The travel agency was used to taking their clients across the border into Mexico. As they drove up to the border just before midnight, the driver flashed his card, and the official waved them through.

Zipping down the Tijuana streets toward the bus stop, Omar's thoughts crystalized. A plan formulated in his mind, and it became a prayer. "Lord," his heart screamed silently, "I ask just one thing of You tonight. Help me make it home so I can give my mother a hug and tell my family goodbye. That's all I ask."

Omar's prayer didn't include the rest of his desperate plan. *After I get back to see my family, I'll shoot myself. I'm a scoundrel, and I don't deserve to be alive. I have no reason left to live anyway. My whole world has collapsed. I'm still walking, but I'm already dead.*

Omar's friend dropped him off at the bus stop where he could catch an international bus to Mexico City and then on to Guatemala City. Omar found a seat on a bus that was scheduled for Mexico City and hunched down, trying to get some sleep. But it was impossible to doze off.

In Mexico City Omar took the time to take care of some important business. First, he found a barber and asked for a very short haircut. He asked the barber to leave a little tuft of hair in the front and had it dyed copper-red. He also asked the barber to whack off his thick black mustache.

---

18   Viajes La Nortena: The Northern Travel Agency.

Then he bought different clothes to kill the cowboy look he had worn in LA. He chose the casual dress of a college student going home for vacation. However, he did keep his gold watch, his gold ring set with a diamond, and his cream-colored ostrich skin cowboy boots that had cost him a thousand dollars.

After crossing the Guatemalan border, Omar felt freer. Mexican officials would be searching for him and would turn him in, especially since Gema was Mexican. But maybe Guatemala wouldn't care.

At the border, Omar risked calling his uncle Bato in Nicaragua. As Omar had expected, the news of the crime had spread like wildfire—and not just in LA. Omar's relatives in Nicaragua already knew what had happened and were worried about his well-being. "Be careful!" Bato advised. "They already have photos of you pasted all over the Huntington Park area, and they're searching for you. If they manage to get you, you're sunk for a long time, man!"

"Tell my family I'm on the way home," Omar requested.

It was evening when the bus left the border, weaving its way through crowded streets. Several hours later, before they got to Guatemala City, Omar was resting his head against the seat in front of him, trying to kill his thoughts so he could sleep. But all he could do was remember and remember and then remember some more.

Suddenly the bus slammed to a stop, and the night was shattered by the sound of sirens. Eight armed men, dressed in black and carrying automatic rifles, invaded the bus from both ends.

Omar was sitting near the middle of the bus, and his heart froze. He was sure they had caught him. They had probably bugged Bato's phone and heard when he had told Bato he was at the Guatemalan border. Special police forces had been sent to stop the buses.

The men carried strong flashlights and shone them into everyone's faces as they walked the aisles. Omar sat as straight and tense as a fiddle string, trying to look innocent as the light flashed into his face.

To Omar's amazement, the officer looked at him for only a few seconds and then flipped the light to the bewildered face of his seatmate. Another couple of seconds, and he continued on down the aisle, checking other faces.

They didn't recognize me! Omar realized, slumping back into his seat in relief. His disguise was working well. He was free!

The police left, and the bus resumed its trip down the mountain toward Guatemala City. As Omar relaxed a little, he realized he was trembling so badly that his knees were practically knocking together.

Surely the bus had been stopped to search for Omar, but they had overlooked him. Why? Maybe, Omar concluded soberly, he wasn't supposed to go to jail for the rest of his life after all.

The bus roared into Estelí in the early afternoon, about a week after Omar had committed his horrible crime. Wearing sunglasses and a bill cap, Omar walked down the busy streets toward Bato's house. He didn't think Nicaragua would turn him over to the United States, but he knew he'd better still be careful. Even with a non-extradition law, Nicaraguan officials might turn him in if bribed with enough money.

Bato and his woman seemed glad to see Omar and invited him in, but Omar could see they were afraid. Bato didn't waste any time. "Omar, you can't stay here. If they're looking for you, they'll come here first because of my connections with you and with the United States. Please find another place to stay."

Omar's aunt Piedad had recently moved to the States, and several of Omar's cousins were living in her house on the outskirts of Estelí. Would they have a room for him? "I'm very tired," he told his cousin. "I've hardly slept this past week."

The cousin showed Omar to a room, where he fell asleep midafternoon and slept soundly till evening. When Omar woke up, he was pleased to see his mother sitting by his bedside, weeping softly. Omar got up slowly and they embraced, his mother's tears falling on his shoulder. "Son, I'm so glad you made it back! At least you're with us now. I prayed every day to at least see your face again, and God answered my prayer."

Omar sagged onto the edge of his bed and buried his face in his hands. He had longed for this moment, as if it were the only thing that really mattered anymore, but now he felt strangely numb. Though his heart was torn to shreds, he couldn't shed a tear. And though his mother spoke comforting words, his heart was not soothed.

While Omar had slept, Miriam had gone through his things. She was glad to see that, for once, Omar wasn't armed. When she found his tiny notebook with all his telephone numbers, she put it into her purse.

Miriam's heart ached for her son. What could she do to help Omar? He had been infatuated with Gema. Now life had stopped for him, and he had nothing to live for. She worried that he might commit suicide. She would watch him closely to make sure that didn't happen. Could she find a way to encourage him to live again?

After a little time with her son, Miriam whispered, "Omar, we need to go somewhere else. These people are scared, just like Bato was. Fermín's side of the family isn't ready to help you, but my sister Janet, who lives in a distant suburb of Estelí, will help."

Omar nodded. "I don't even *want* to see my father!"

Arriving at Janet's place, Omar requested, "Mama, tell my brothers to come see me. You know it's too dangerous for me to go to Regadío, but I want to see them one more time."

The next day Omar's three brothers appeared at the door. There was Milo, who had long ago been Omar's shadow. Next in line was Melvin, a quiet little fellow. Alvaro, the youngest, was a live wire, much like Omar had been at his age.

As the brothers took turns hugging Omar, he finally shed some tears. His younger brothers seemed so innocent, having no idea what a dark, wicked world was out there waiting for them. Omar's fierce love for his brothers welled up within him. They were his flesh and blood, and he hadn't seen them for six long years. How they had grown!

As he stared at them, memories flooded him. Memories of Naranjita, especially—those happy years when they had all been together as a family. Now that family was gone forever. Oh, if he could only call those years back so he could start his life over again!

But Omar knew it was not to be.

He had forgotten how poorly his family dressed. His brothers wore secondhand American clothes that Miriam had picked up at thrift stores and simple army boots, the only footwear poor Nicaraguans could afford. Meanwhile Omar was wearing expensive, brand-new clothes. What would his family think if they knew how much his ostrich skin boots had cost? At least the boys were clean. Miriam saw to that.

Wanting to preserve this memorable time with his brothers, Omar had an inspiration. He asked his aunt to take a photo of the four of them. *Then when I'm gone,* Omar reasoned, *they'll at least have this to remember me by.*

Omar's brothers went home the next day, but Omar, not knowing what else to do, stayed at his aunt Janet's place for a week. Miriam stayed too, unwilling to leave her son's side, afraid of what he might do to himself. Omar watched everyone around him enjoying life, laughing, playing, and going to work. But his own heart was dead, and he became bored.

Left to right:
Milo, Alvaro, Omar, Melvin.

When he wasn't remembering the last couple of traumatic weeks of his life, he was scheming to kill himself. *But unless I can get away from my mother,* Omar realized, *I won't be able to do what I need to do.* She knew him too well, and Omar was sure she suspected his plan to take his own life.

Miriam reassured Omar daily, "Son, everything will be fine in the end. Let the past be past. Forget Gema and get excited about the future."

But her words didn't penetrate Omar's cold heart, and they couldn't bear fruit out of stone.

Frustrated after one of Miriam's sermonettes, Omar protested, "Mama, you don't understand. Everything I lived for is gone. The love of my life is dead. I'm a dead man! For me, life is over. Things will never be the same."

Miriam prayed and wept for her son, but Heaven seemed silent.

But God was listening to their piteous heart cries. Though long in coming, help was on its way.

Omar, depressed and suicidal.

30

TO LIVE AGAIN

THE TALL EVERGREEN pierced the evening sky high above the steeples of the Catholic cathedral. The sky was the color of a ripening papaya, with several silver-lined clouds poking along ahead of the gentle evening breeze. Doves cooed in the well-trimmed trees adorning the spacious park in front of the cathedral.

Miriam stepped out of the church where she had just prayed for her son Omar and attended the evening Mass. As she walked across the park, she noticed the little doves marching along the pavement under the trees. Oh, if only Omar could be as happy as those carefree birds. If only he could muster up enough courage to live again!

Neither the sky nor the trees nor the birds had the answer. But God did.

An idea flashed into Miriam's mind. It just might work! Miriam's feet carried her home as fast as they could. She could hardly wait to hear Omar's response.

By the time she reached Janet's simple residence, darkness had fallen. Little evening bats fluttered around the yard light as Miriam approached Omar, who was sitting on the porch. "Omar, I've been thinking a lot about your future," she started hesitantly. "We all know you can't stay here much longer. So why don't you go to Costa Rica and spend some time with your sister Cándida?"

Omar listened carefully. His mother was right. He couldn't stay with Aunt Janet forever. If he had to leave anyway, he might as well go to Costa Rica. In doing that, he would leave his mother behind, and maybe he could finally carry out his desperate plan to take his own life.

Omar nodded his agreement.

Relief washed over Miriam. "I'll call Cándida right away. I can send Jáqueling with you so you don't have to travel alone."

Omar shrugged.

Two days later, Jáqueling and Omar were heading for Costa Rica on the bus. Eventually they arrived at Jaco Beach, a small coastal town nestled in a bay in northwestern Costa Rica.

Omar's sister Cándida lived in a small rented apartment in the center of town, close to the restaurants, nightclubs, bars, and discos that clung to the beach around the bay. She had shacked up with another Nicaraguan named Juan.

Cándida received her brother and sister joyously. Starved for fellowship with other Nicaraguans, and especially for family, she took them in like celebrities. "Omar, you're going to love it here in Jaco Beach!" she said. "I'm going to find you a job, and you're going to forget all about LA."

Omar frowned, suspicious that their mother had alerted her to his suicidal depression. It sounded like Cándida was trying some kind of positive psychology on him.

Cándida and Juan shared their tiny one-bedroom rental house with Juan's cousin Mitchel, who slept in the living room. When Omar arrived, Mitchel had to move out. Cándida had a job lined up for Jáqueling in a restaurant that provided room and board. So Omar took Mitchel's place, sleeping on the floor in the tiny living room.

In spite of Cándida's cheerful attempt at therapy, Omar's emotional condition grew worse. The first evening after their arrival, Cándida suggested, "Omar and Jáqueling, let's go down to the beach for a stroll. That way you can begin learning to know the place and its people. You'll love it, Omar!"

Unfortunately, the beach only reminded Omar of Long Beach where he had spent so many happy hours with Gema and the girls. He came home that evening feeling more despondent than ever.

Nights were bad for Omar, because he usually couldn't sleep much at all. When he did doze off, he had nightmares. Somebody, or something terrible, was after him. Sometimes it was the police. Sometimes it was armed men. Sometimes it was monsters. But they were always after Omar to kill him.

In his dreams, Omar would run desperately, trying to get away. Sometimes he scaled walls or frantically climbed mountains. Sometimes he killed some of the enemies. Then, just before the enemy grabbed him, he'd wake up with a start, his body drenched in sweat. He felt worn-out all the time, bone-tired even before the day began. A fugitive in the daytime, Omar felt doubly so at night.

What Omar suspected was true: Miriam had warned Cándida that Omar was suicidal, and she had taken it upon herself to salvage the discouraged man. "You'll get over this, Omar," she pleaded. "You're an intelligent man. You've always been the courageous kind. You can get back on your feet."

The next several days seemed futile. Omar couldn't find the craziness in himself to actually end his own life. His mind was constantly filled with bizarre plans, but he didn't have the strength to make them happen. Something held him back.

Cándida invited Omar and Jáqueling to parties to meet her many friends. She even introduced Omar to some pretty girls, but Omar ignored them. Jáqueling fitted in easily, but Omar seemed like a walking corpse.

After a few days, Cándida lost her patience. "Omar, you're still crazy over Gema—I can tell it. But she's dead. Get a grip, man! She's not coming back. You have to get hold of yourself and pull your life together so you can live again. You aren't getting anywhere like this."

"You don't understand," Omar sighed, staring at his sister. "You'll never understand what I lost when Gema died."

"Let me find you a good job at some restaurant," Cándida suggested next.

Omar shook his head, but after a week of Cándida's insistence, he finally answered, "Okay, find me a job—a tough job with hard physical labor." He would test his strength and see if he could be a man again.

"Just what kind of work?" Cándida questioned, unsure of what he meant.

"Construction. Get me the hardest job you can find."

"Okay. I have a friend who's a building contractor. We'll see if he has any work for you."

The next afternoon Omar and Cándida met with the contractor, El Macho. Omar's hair was slicked back with gel, and he wore his fancy LA clothes, including his ostrich skin cowboy boots and Mexican belt. His smooth hands looked as if they had never done manual labor.

El Macho stared at Omar and shook his head. "I don't really think this man is cut out for the job. He seems too fine."

"You'll be surprised," Cándida countered. "Just give him a try. He won't let you down."

"Okay, meet me at the junction in the road just out of town at five o'clock tomorrow morning," El Macho told Omar. "We'll see what you can do."

The contractor's positive answer, Omar knew, was only because of his friendship with his pretty sister. Omar knew the man didn't expect him to last long. But Omar grinned to himself. *I'll prove to that man that I'm worth my wages.*

Cándida was delighted when Omar woke her in the wee hours of the morning to fix him food. She filled a thermos of drinking water and packed a lunch while Omar sipped a cup of coffee. Omar wasn't smiling, but at least he was finally ready to work.

El Macho was surprised to find Omar waiting at the junction and pleased to see that this time he wore work clothes and a pair of rubber boots. Omar jumped on the back of El Macho's pickup, joining a half dozen other workers and a pile of tools.

El Macho had taken a contract to build a hotel on a beach a half hour away. A large flat area was staked off with a maze of lines strung up. "Digging footers is what we start out with," El Macho said, waving his hand over the building site with a flourish. He handed Omar a shovel, pickax, and measuring tape.

"I want these footers to be exactly the width between the two lines. I want the edges nice and straight and five feet deep. You can take one hour off at noon. I'll be back at four o'clock to see how things have gone for you and take you home. Okay, get to work."

The other workers knew exactly what to do. They divided into groups and took up various jobs, but most of them dug footers. Picking up his tools, Omar chose a section of footer off to the side and set to work.

Omar had been used to manual labor as a teenager back on the farm in Naranjita, and he had always worked hard and fast. But this felt different. Back then, Omar had been innocent and free. Now he was a man who had tasted the worst life had to offer. He was down, but it was time to see if he could get himself back up. Could he be a man again and prove to himself that there was hope for him?

Omar began working like a man possessed, tackling the huge three-foot-wide footers as if he were tackling the devil himself. The dirt was hard and rocky, and as Omar whacked away at the horrible mass with the pickax, he got angrier and angrier. Fury overcame him, and the pent-up feelings of the last several months poured out in compact energy and sweat. Anger... disappointment... loneliness... longing for what couldn't be—and depression. It all had to go if Omar was to live again.

The climate in Regadío and Estelí was cool. LA, though warm during the summer, was also cool most of the year. Omar wasn't used to the heat here at Playa Jaco. At sea level, it was hotter than Omar had ever experienced. By eight o'clock in the morning, he was dripping with sweat and had pitched his shirt. By ten o'clock he felt as if he couldn't go anymore. *Am I having a heatstroke?* Omar wondered, wishing he could die.

But the worst thing was not the heat. It was his hands. By the first hour Omar knew that he was getting blisters, but he refused to look. Angry that his hands were so tender, he continued to wallop at the dirt harder than ever. By nine o'clock the blisters had burst, and his hands burned like fire. But he just kept working.

At nine o'clock, the men stopped for a fifteen-minute break, but Omar didn't quit. "Hey," the crew called out to him, "come on, guy, here we just work at a steady pace. No use to kill yourself, man. Come on over for a break."

But Omar acted as if he hadn't heard. He didn't want them to see his bleeding hands, and he didn't want their pity, nor their advice.

Just before noon the crew stopped again and gathered under a shade tree to eat their lunch. Omar meandered off to another tree, where he ate his lunch alone. Omar knew the men thought he was weird, but he didn't care. Let them think he was crazy. They were probably right.

After an hour's break, Omar was back in the ditch before his buddies were. Again, the dirt flew, and by evening, when the pickup came to take them home, the crew realized that they had a madman with them in the ditch.

Cándida was shocked when Omar came stumbling into the house that evening. His clothes were stiff from dried sweat and stained with dirt. His face was streaked and dirty. The skin on his hands was shredded and bleeding. But was that a little glint of life in his eyes?

Omar took a shower, ate a quick meal, and then he lay on his mat in the living room and slept more soundly than he had for months. No nightmares now. At three-thirty the next morning, Omar was pounding on Cándida's door. "Aren't you going to fix my food again?"

When Cándida saw the condition of Omar's hands, she begged him to stay at home to let them heal. But Omar responded, "I told you I wanted work. Now I have work, and I'm going to work until we finish all of those footers, okay?" As Omar sprinted out the door, he saw that his sister was crying.

For a week Omar's body operated like a machine. The rest of the crew was upset with him, because the boss was catching on that they didn't get nearly as much done as Omar did, and he was beginning to complain. They begged Omar to slow down, but if anything, he just sped up.

Slowly Omar's hands healed. His muscles responded and became stronger. He got used to the heat. In two weeks' time, Omar was feeling good. His machine was tuned and working better than it had in a long time. He felt almost as agile as he had been in Naranjita as a teenager, or during that first year in LA when he had practiced martial arts. It was then Omar realized that he just might be able to live again.

Two weeks after Omar started the job, Cándida convinced him to take a stroll with her down to the beach one evening. After slipping past the biggest disco on Playa Jaco, they reached the beach and walked toward the waves smashing onto the sandy shore.

Would the beauty of the sea be healing for Omar? Cándida hoped so.

A soft breeze, laced with a salty edge, played with Omar's butch haircut. A sad, wailing love song floated out of the disco and seemed to follow the breezes. The message of broken love gripped Omar's heart, and soon tears were streaming down his cheeks.

After leaving the buildings and the song far behind, Cándida ventured, "You can't forget Gema, can you, Omar?"

Omar was silent, except for the slap, slap, slap of his sandals on the beach.

"You'll eventually forget her, Omar," Cándida tried again. "You have to. You see, she's gone, but life must continue. You have to resign yourself to the facts, brother."

Omar didn't answer, but his heart was filled with gratitude. If he ever got out of this dark hole of depression, he would owe his life to Cándida and to his mother who had sent him here to Playa Jaco.

On the way back from their stroll, Cándida convinced Omar to stop at a restaurant for a drink. There they met Mitchel, Juan's outgoing cousin, and Cándida called him over to share a drink with them. She hoped that Omar and Mitchel would become friends.

Though Omar didn't say a word to Cándida that evening, she sensed that healing was on the way for her brother. She relaxed and stopped watching Omar's every step. He wasn't going to kill himself after all.

From then on, after working on the ditches every day, Omar would shower and take a stroll on the beach—usually alone. Sometimes Cándida and Jáqueling went with him, but often he ended up spending the evening with Mitchel. It didn't take long for Omar to discover that Mitchel was as knowledgeable as any on the subject that Omar knew so well—cocaine. Then and there, their friendship was sealed.

They worked on the ditches for seventeen days. When Omar got his paycheck, he thanked El Macho for the chance he had given him. But he also told him the truth. "I needed this job to get a start. But I won't be back."

"That's too bad," El Macho said. "You're a great worker. I hoped you'd stay. I was going to promote you next week."

"Sorry," Omar replied, "but I plan to start a business of my own."

"Well, thanks a lot!" El Macho shook Omar's hand firmly. "If you ever need a job again, count on me."

31

EL MEXICANO

OMAR USED HIS first wages from digging footers to have a tattoo etched into his upper arm. The tattoo, like the weird picture on Gema's sweater, was the image of a man with a snake around his shoulders. *To remind me of Gema,* Omar told himself. *I'm the man, and Gema is the snake who charmed me ever since I first met her. She totally wrapped herself around me, body, soul, and spirit.*

Then he went with Mitchel to meet a contact and buy a wedge of cocaine. As naturally as a magnet attracts steel, Omar was pulled back into his drug business. He and Mitchel became a team. They also hired a big tough man called Cebolla.[19]

Not only was competition stiff in Jaco, but Costa Rica's FBI kept intense vigilance over the area. Omar never carried cocaine on his person; he let the vendors run that risk. He did the wholesale buying and prepared and packaged the drug in private. Then he sent it out onto the streets with his agents. If he were ever caught, he would appear clean.

When Omar took his business to the streets of Jaco, his depression disappeared. Suddenly he felt alive again—passionate about making money,

---

19 Cebolla: onion.

drinking, and attracting girlfriends. Because Omar dressed, acted, and talked like a Mexican, he quickly acquired the nickname *El Mexicano* as he gained renown on the streets of Jaco.

Within months, El Mexicano's business was thriving. Vendors, clients, discos, restaurants, and nightclubs flocked to do business with him. Omar was soon a threat to other drug dealers, and though they hated him, they couldn't prevent his success.

The most powerful man in the Jaco drug world was El Marquense, leader of the largest and strongest gang in the area. The next most powerful gang was run by a man called El Coyote. Soon El Mexicano was running neck and neck with El Coyote. They sometimes worked together, but neither trusted the other.

Since Omar had plenty of money again, he stashed part of it in a special hiding place in his apartment. He bought new clothes and other luxuries he had enjoyed in LA, and he and Cándida rented a fancy apartment. Omar paid for everything, including their groceries. Cándida no longer needed Juan for financial support, so she told him to leave. She was tired of him anyway.

Juan left, but he wasn't happy. Meeting Jáqueling and Cándida on the street one day, Juan scolded angrily, "You think I'm going to let you get away with treating me like a nobody, Cándida? You're badly mistaken. I'm going to tell the police that you're hiding a criminal in your apartment."

When Jáqueling and Cándida came home in tears, Omar asked what happened, and the girls told him about Juan's threats.

"Don't worry," Omar assured them. "I'll take care of him."

The next day Juan came to the apartment to argue with Cándida; he did not expect El Mexicano to be at home, and he had barely entered the door when a tiger accosted him.

Grabbing the silk string Juan wore around his throat, Omar twisted it tightly, choking Juan. Then he jerked him forward and sat him down on the floor. "What are you going around saying about El Mexicano?" Omar snarled, jerking the tourniquet.

Juan's face was as pale as a sheet. His eyes bulged, and he whimpered, "Mexicano, I'm sorry. I won't do it again."

Omar didn't hit him—actually, he pitied the man groveling at his feet. "Okay," Omar snapped. "You don't know anything about my past! Do you hear?"

Juan nodded.

"You will completely avoid my two sisters. You will not touch them or even talk to them anymore. Understand?"

Again, Juan nodded as best he could with the iron grip on his throat. He was having a hard time breathing, so Omar turned him loose. As Juan got up off the floor, Omar yelled, "Now get out of here and don't you dare come back."

Juan fled.

At first, Cebolla did well working for El Mexicano and Mitchel. Every few days he would bring the exact amount of money Omar expected, and settle accounts with him. But gradually Cebolla became careless.

One day Cebolla didn't bring in the right amount, and Omar suspected he had blown the money with his cocaine-consuming friends. Omar reprimanded him. "Look, Cebolla, you don't play games with me. I need my money right away."

"Come on," Cebolla whined, lowering his eyes. "I'll get it for you in time. Just have patience with me."

"What's patience?" Omar barked, staring his buddy down. "I'll give you until tomorrow at midnight to bring me the money. If it's not in by midnight, I will hunt you down." El Mexicano turned on his heel and walked away.

On his way to the beach that evening to meet a drug contact, Omar noticed a gang of hoodlums lounging by the wall of a disco. Right in the center of the group was Cebolla, laughing and clowning with the rest.

Just before he reached the wall, Omar met a friend and paused to chat. The friend pointed to the cluster of men and whispered, "Cebolla is saying he owes you money, but he's not one bit scared of you."

"Really?" Omar chuckled, shaking his head. "I'll see if that's true." He swaggered up to the wall and pushed through the gang until he was standing face-to-face with Cebolla. "What are you saying about El Mexicano?" Omar snarled.

"What do I care—?" Cebolla began. But the words were barely out of his mouth when El Mexicano knocked him to the ground. Then Omar turned and marched off toward the beach. Cebolla paid him early the next morning.

But Omar was worried that Cebolla would tattle to the police, and he did. The police already knew that El Mexicano was deep into the narco business. However, they didn't want to arrest him for a fistfight. They would rather catch him with evidence of drug dealing, so they were biding their time. They promised Cebolla they would watch Omar closely.

After Omar's encounter with Cebolla, the police in Jaco watched his every move. "Let's go to Nicaragua for a break," Omar suggested to Cándida and Jáqueling. "I have some money saved up, and I want to get my legal papers straightened out."

Omar's sisters, homesick for their family, were more than ready to accompany him north. They also hoped that once they got to Nicaragua, Omar would share some of his wealth. He had promised, among other things, to help fix up their mother's house. Omar paid the fare for all three of them, but when they got to Nicaragua, Omar selfishly refused to give the girls anything more.

Back in Estelí, Omar lived a double life. During the day, if he wasn't lying low, he took to the streets in disguise. One day he'd dress like a vagabond. The next day he would wear military clothes and pretend to be a soldier. The next day he would dress like a businessman.

At night, Omar partied with his friends, spending money faster than he had made it in Jaco. He bought a Mitsubishi pickup truck, making it easier for him to get around in disguise. Soon the five thousand dollars he had brought from Costa Rica was almost gone.

When Cándida and Jáqueling saw that Omar wasn't going to share his money with them, they asked for bus fare to go back to Jaco, and Omar paid their way.

One day Daisy, Omar's old flame from La Naranjita, came to Estelí looking for him. As far as Omar knew, Daisy had been happily married to Walter since the time Omar had left for the United States. But now she hunted him up with a sad story to tell. They met in Estelí's central park.

"I was never happy with Walter," Daisy confessed bashfully. "I made such a mistake to go with him instead of you. He never made me happy, and I could never forget you."

"Did you marry him?" Omar asked, looking her over closely. She had matured and was prettier than ever.

"No..." Daisy hesitated. "We never married. But I did have a little girl with him."

"Where is the girl now?" Omar asked suspiciously.

"Walter has her at his mom's place in Costa Rica."

"Why isn't she with you?"

"Cándida told me I'd have a better chance that you'd take me if I were alone."

"Look, Daisy," Omar started out slowly. "Yes, our memories of Naranjita are sweet. But things have changed a lot. Realistically, I can't take you. I'm not that carefree boy from Naranjita anymore. I'm a delinquent."

"I realize that! But I don't care. Please take me with you!" Daisy cried, wringing her hands.

"I'm heading for Costa Rica as soon as my papers are ready. I have nothing to offer you, Daisy. I'm a fugitive, hiding from the law. If I took you to Costa Rica, I'd be inviting you to suffer."

Omar finally convinced Daisy that he couldn't take her. But he did let the truth slip out that he still liked her, and though Daisy didn't go with Omar, the hour they spent together at the park convinced Daisy that Omar was still the dream man she wanted. She was not about to let her dream die.

Omar decided to take along his brother Milo, whose full name was Pablo Emilio, and their cousin Erlin to Costa Rica. Having serious problems with his own papers and having learned some tricks to the trade, Omar helped Milo get a passport under a false name. Then Omar got a passport for himself in Milo's name, using Milo's birth certificate. Since Milo and Omar resembled each other, there should be no problem with being detected. So when the threesome headed south, Omar was Pablo Emilio and Milo was Omar.

Omar was out of money, but happy to be back in Jaco Beach. In a matter of a week, Omar had made enough money to party with his brother and cousin and to live it up like he had before.

Omar was surprised to find that while he had been gone, Cándida had found herself a husband. Douglas Marshal, a rich real estate dealer from New York City, had lost his heart to the little Nicaraguan lady he had met during his vacation in Jaco Beach. Never mind that Doug didn't know her language. He seemed to be a millionaire, and suddenly Cándida had access to all the money she could spend. All she had to do was ask for it.

Doug was generous to his new wife's relatives also, and Omar discovered that being Doug's friend was nearly as profitable as dealing in cocaine. Very soon Omar, Cándida, Milo, and their friends were involved in a daily fling of riotous living, and Doug paid all the bills.

When he returned to the United States to take care of his businesses, Doug told Cándida to go back to Nicaragua and wait for him there. He promised to spend some time with her family, and then he planned to take her to the United States to live. In the meantime, if Cándida or Omar needed money, Omar could call Doug, and Doug would deposit the money in Western Union. So Omar would call Doug and say, "Cándida needs a thousand dollars." Then he would add, "And I need a thousand as well." Doug never flinched.

Cándida returned to Nicaragua to wait for her husband, and Omar decided it was in his best interests to follow her and keep his connections with the millionaire. So Erlin, Milo, and Omar returned to Nicaragua with Cándida.

But the bigger the bubble, the bigger the explosion when it bursts. How long would the million-dollar bubble last?

32

FOUND BY A DAISY

WHEN DOUG RETURNED from the United States, his arrival made a big splash in Regadío—and the whole town watched. Although Cándida and Doug spent most of their time in Estelí, they came to Regadío off and on. The Estelí relatives often came with Doug, and the back of his rented pickup truck was stuffed with liquor, food, and gifts.

Omar had learned some English in LA, and he served as Doug's translator. Doug's promises to the Montenegro family were outrageous, but they believed him. He was going to build Miriam a brand-new house. He was going to buy Omar the best farm in Regadío. He actually did buy a nice pickup for Fermín, and a fancy horse that Cándida spotted one day.

While Doug was in Nicaragua, he paid all the expenses for the Montenegro family, including their groceries. The whole family thought their financial troubles were over.

Then Doug went back to the United States again to catch up on his work and get Cándida's papers ready for her move to the United States.

For the next six months, Omar didn't even consider going back to Costa Rica. Life was easy in Nicaragua with a brother-in-law who paid for everything. Omar stopped hiding and instead lived a normal life, almost forgetting that he was a fugitive. *I guess they won't come all the way from the United States to look for me after all,* he decided.

Omar visited his friend Harvin, Daisy's cousin, in Naranjita several times. Harvin told him that Daisy had gone to Costa Rica with her man. Walter had relatives in Costa Rica. Was she looking for Omar? Harvin thought so. Omar had been in Costa Rica when Daisy left.

While Doug continued to send money for the Montenegros, Omar discovered a horrible secret. Cándida was seeing another man. What would happen when Doug returned for his wife?

When Doug came, he swore that he wouldn't return to the United States without Cándida and Omar. Omar had no intentions of returning to the United States, but maybe Doug would buy him the farm he had promised. Then Omar could easily drop out of the plan to travel north.

And then one evening during a wild party in Regadío, Doug became so drunk that Cándida risked spending the rest of the evening with her new flame. But either Doug caught on, or someone who knew enough English enlightened him. Doug went back to the States a brokenhearted man, because he had really loved Cándida in his own worldly way.

The bubble had burst.

Because no one in the Montenegro family had invested any of Doug's money in anything that would generate income, they slipped back into their poverty. Cándida returned to Jaco, and Omar and Milo followed, taking Harvin along from Naranjita. Fermín sold his pickup, and Omar loaned his own pickup to his cousin.

Once back in Jaco, Omar and his buddies regrouped, and their cocaine business soared. Harvin tried his best to fit in. But he was a countryman at heart—he didn't have the stomach to be a drug vendor, especially when he saw how the police tracked Omar.

So Omar used Harvin as his spy. Mingling among the tourists, Harvin would pick up tidbits of information from the other drug gangs. Omar also needed to know what the police were saying—and it wasn't good.

"They're determined to get you!" Harvin warned. "They know you're in it big, but they just don't have enough proof yet."

"And they'll set trap after trap for me, determined that I fall. But I'm too smart," Omar bragged. "I can sense their traps a mile away. They can't touch me."

"I'm getting out of here!" Harvin would say almost every day. But something happened before he actually took flight.

Omar was on the street one morning as usual, mingling with even the police who patrolled the beach and the other haunts of Jaco. Omar carried no evidence of his trade except the little revolver hidden in his boot or at his belt. The gun wasn't registered; if he were caught with it, it could get him into trouble—but not nearly as much trouble as he would be if they caught him with cocaine. So Omar was wary, but not really worried. He felt his power.

Then one of his friends approached him. "Look, down at the Rancho de Pancho some people are asking for you. They must be your relatives."

Omar headed to the Rancho right away. *Who would be looking for me at this time of the morning? Could this be a trick?* he wondered, making sure his pistol was well-concealed.

He saw some familiar faces as soon as he entered the restaurant, and his heart skipped a beat. "Daisy!" he exclaimed under his breath.

Daisy wasn't alone. Her brother, whom everybody called El Chele,[20] was with her, and a big satchel was plopped at her feet. *That woman is coming to stay,* Omar realized. The two men greeted each other, and Omar asked El Chele, "What brings you here, my friend?"

El Chele grinned. "Well," he drawled, "I brought you the goods. I did my job in delivering. That's the best I could do."

"Good job!" Omar flashed. "Sit up and let's take drinks."

After the drinks were served, Chele joked, "Yeah, Omar, I delivered the merchandise—now I want my pay."

Omar laughed. "Now wait a minute, the deal hasn't been made yet." Then turning to Daisy, Omar asked, "And what are you doing here?"

Daisy blushed a deep red. "You know."

Omar looked at her, his mind racing. It would be awfully nice to have a woman around to do the cooking and laundry. Omar's memories of Daisy

---

20   El Chele: paleface.

were sweet, but could she handle his kind of life? If her cousin Harvin couldn't, how could Daisy?

"Look, Daisy," Omar started slowly, watching her face. "I've told you before. I don't think you know what you're doing. I have nothing to offer you except a hard life. I've done some terrible things, and I'm a wanted man. Besides," Omar whispered, glancing around, "the way I make my living now is dangerous. I'm afraid you couldn't make it here."

"Try me," Daisy insisted, her eyes meeting Omar's boldly. "I know what you mean. But I've made up my mind. I came to stay."

Omar was weakening fast. Even as he argued against it, his memories of Naranjita and their times together since then slowly won his heart.

The deal was clinched, and Omar took his Daisy home. *If things get bad,* Omar consoled himself, *at least I warned her properly.*

For a short time, things went well. Though Daisy didn't help Omar with the drug business like Gema had, she did cook and take care of the apartment. She couldn't take Gema's place, but she provided companionship.

Daisy had been working in a factory in San Rafael. "When I quit," she told Omar, "they paid my wages and promised to pay my worker's compensation. I can pick up my check next week. I really don't want to lose that money. May I go pick it up?"

"Sure," Omar agreed. "Not only will I let you go, I'll go with you. Let's take Harvin along and make a pleasure trip out of it. And if I'm with you, Walter should leave you alone."

But Omar didn't know that Daisy's family was on Walter's side. Daisy had barely set foot in the factory when Joni, one of Walter's brothers who worked there, saw her and called Walter. Walter called Daisy's sisters, and they all agreed to come to the factory to try to convince Daisy to come back home.

After Daisy got her check, she joined Omar and Harvin in the parking lot. About the same time, Joni came out of the factory and met Walter and three of Daisy's sisters who had just arrived on a bus. Joni came toward Omar and shook his hand. What was he after?

"Hey, we came to tell you to let my sister go," Joni snapped, staring at Daisy.

Omar's voice was cool. "Can't you see that I don't have her tied? I didn't come to San Rafael to hunt for her. She came to Jaco and found me. I'm not keeping her there by force. If she wants to stay with Walter, that's perfectly all right with me. But if she wants to go back to Jaco with me, that's fine too."

"If you tell her to come home where she belongs, she'll do what you say," Joni insisted.

"Look," Omar said. "Walter and Daisy aren't married. It's a free country. Daisy decides what she will do."

While Joni argued with Omar, the sisters were working Daisy over. "Look, girl, you're crazy to be living with that man. Omar's a criminal. You have a little girl who needs you—and Walter loves you and misses you. And Harvin," they scolded. "You're a traitor."

Daisy listened to her sisters with one ear. But she also heard what Omar was telling Joni.

Daisy's sisters formed a circle around her and started pulling her away. As Walter slowly edged closer, Omar shot him a glance. "Look, Walter," he barked, "you and I have always been friends. Please don't meddle in this! Get back."

The argument headed into another round. Daisy would have to decide.

When Omar turned to leave, Harvin followed him. Daisy screamed and clung to the mesh fence of the parking lot, hanging on as her sisters pulled at her arms.

"You think you're smart, don't you?" Joni taunted. "Today you meet your match!"

Omar turned and planted himself in front of Joni. "If you want to hit me, Joni, help yourself!" he yelled. "Just get it over with."

Joni lunged at Omar like an angry bull. Enraged, Omar swung his fist and knocked Joni to the ground. Then he turned on his heel, yelling over his shoulder, "Go get the police on my trail next! Do it quickly so they can still catch me before I leave this horrible place."

Daisy broke loose and ran after Omar. Her sisters and even Walter were weeping. It was over. They had lost the battle.

Omar hailed a taxi, and he and Daisy and Harvin sped toward the bus station where they got the first bus toward Jaco. Harvin returned to Nicaragua the next week, more than ready to get away from Omar's wild lifestyle.

For Omar and Daisy, life returned to normal—at least as normal as such a wicked life can be. Omar didn't tell Daisy about his daily business activities as he had done with Gema. He just bought her the things she needed for the apartment and the fancy things that made her happy. For the first time in her life, she could splurge and buy jewelry and better clothes.

Daisy never complained. She never said that she missed her daughter Wendy, who was being raised by her in-laws. She knew better than to ask for permission to even go see her. But she appeared to be happy because Omar was her hero—he provided for her and apparently loved her and was faithful to her.

The lull did not last long. Omar soon noticed that Mitchel was lagging. Mitchel had been Omar's main vendor for a year and had been as loyal as a farm dog, but he no longer seemed happy with the setup. Was Mitchel starting to buddy up with the competition? Omar braced himself for a showdown.

One weekend Omar traveled by bus to San Jose to pick up cocaine. While Omar was gone, Mitchel threw a party at his home on Saturday evening. By the time the party was over, Mitchel's stash of cocaine was gone, along with the money he had collected in the past few days.

On Monday morning Omar called Mitchel out onto the beach. Suffering from a hangover, Mitchel looked unkempt and depressed. A stiff wind churned up the bay as the two men talked, and they nearly had to shout to be heard. Mitchel sheepishly handed over only a small wad of cash, refusing to meet Omar's eyes.

Omar counted it, his anger mounting. "This isn't nearly enough money, Mitchel!" he yelled. "What happened to it?"

Mitchel came up with a lame story about customers who didn't want to pay. "Give me time to pay up!" he whined.

"You're lying to me, Mitchel." Omar spat out his words. "Don't you know that you can't do this to El Mexicano? Ever!"

Mitchel covered his fear, acting as if Omar's threats meant nothing to him. Omar grew even more furious. "I want every last penny back by tomorrow night at midnight," Omar snarled. "If you don't come up with the money, I will hunt you down. There's nothing more to discuss."

Omar turned and left Mitchel whining to himself on the wind-whipped beach.

33

NO NEGOTIATION

THE WEATHER WAS beautiful the next afternoon. The wind had died down and the sun shone brightly. Omar sat at a table inside El Rancho de Pancho drinking coffee with Cándida and two of her friends. In the midst of this enjoyable socializing, a dark troubling cloud loomed on Omar's horizon—Mitchel.

I'm not scared of that critter, Omar argued with himself. *He knows better than to mess with me. And yet, if he gangs up with El Marquense or the police, I'll have to be very careful.*

"Tourism will really pick up with this nice weather," Omar said, sipping his coffee. "And as Christmas gets closer, business will grow." He winked at Cándida. "Times are good." Cándida nodded.

Omar looked around and noticed Mitchel standing just outside one of the wide-open windows of the restaurant. His heart did a little flip-flop when he also spotted Mitchel's companion, his cousin Roberto.

"What do those men want?" Cándida asked, fear flickering in her face.

Roberto was a large man, well-known as a tough character. Omar understood why Mitchel, the coward, would sidle up to a man like Roberto. *Those two are up to no good,* Omar realized. He had better be alert.

Mitchel beckoned for Omar to come to the window. Taking his coffee with him, Omar sauntered over. The men wanted to talk, so Omar nodded and listened.

"I-I came to negotiate with you," Mitchel stammered, eyes full of fear. "You know that things went bad with me. But I'm going to pay you. I just need more time. There's no way I can pay you back by midnight."

Omar answered Mitchel, but his eyes were on Roberto. "There's no negotiation. Mitchel owes me money, and he'll have it all to me by midnight tonight. I'll see you both at midnight, with or without the money." Omar returned to his table, sat down, and coolly resumed sipping his coffee. But his heart was pumping madly. Those fellows wouldn't give up with that little encounter. He had to be on his guard.

The three ladies were nervous. "What do those men want? They look mean."

"Oh, they want more time to pay me what they owe. But I didn't give them more time."

"Won't this make trouble for you?"

"Probably. But I'm ready anytime."

Anytime was right then.

Roberto and Mitchel strode into the restaurant as if they owned it and approached Omar's table from behind. Omar watched them out of the corner of his eye. Roberto marched ahead boldly, but Mitchel tagged along nervously. *This is going to be interesting,* Omar thought.

Roberto circled around and confronted him. "Omar, who do you think you are?" Roberto demanded angrily. "And why do you answer my cousin so roughly? You know he's not alone in this. He needs more time, and you're going to give it."

Omar sat still, letting Roberto talk. The frightened women held their breaths.

"I don't have anything to discuss with you, Roberto," Omar answered, calculating each word. "I have no dealings with you. I settle my accounts with Mitchel whenever and however I want. He knows very well what he's up against with me."

Roberto blurted again, "Who do you think you are, you—"

The offensive word was only halfway out of Roberto's mouth when Omar leaped to his feet. He lit into Roberto with pounding fists, knocking him senseless. Still enraged, Omar turned on Mitchel and gave him the same treatment.

As Omar turned from the scene and headed for the beach, he was satisfied that Mitchel didn't owe him anything anymore. The account was settled. Instead of paying Omar the money, Mitchel had paid for his negligence in pain. Before Omar reached the beach, sirens wailed as an ambulance came to pick up the two battered men and haul them off to the hospital.

Omar lost himself in the rocky coves on the far side of the beach, totally unscathed, his head whirling. *How can I be so quick and strong in a situation like that?* he wondered. *It must be that the devil himself gets into me and gives me extra power when I fight. Now I have to be more careful than ever before.* Trouble was cooking for Omar. He surmised that next he might have to deal with the police.

The next few days, Omar was constantly on edge, watching his every step, prepared for trouble. But he relaxed when one of the police officers, his buddy and a cocaine consumer, told him what had happened when the two men were released from the hospital. They had gone straight to the police office and accused Omar.

The head police had shrugged. "You guys walked into a restaurant and accosted a customer. He beat you up. Serves you right!"

"Yeah, but he sells drugs all the time," Roberto complained, "and you know it."

"That's right," the head police admitted. "But don't you worry, he's going to fall into our hands. It's only a matter of time, and we'll get him. But we have to get him with his hands in the dough, or we won't gain a thing."

The next day Omar met Roberto and Mitchel on the street. Roberto's head was all bandaged up. Mitchel shuffled like an old man, bending over slightly in pain because of his broken ribs. Omar crossed the street and confronted them. As they met, Roberto muttered, "Man, you almost killed us."

Omar nodded without smiling. "Look guys, I have some advice for you. Please don't ever cross my path again. I don't want to have any more problems with you two, okay?"

Mitchel avoided Omar the next few weeks, but Omar knew that he had made an enemy. He suspected that Mitchel was cooperating with either the police or with El Marquense—maybe both. But Omar was extra careful, and things seemed to slowly settle back to normal.

With Mitchel gone, Omar was short of help. Needing another vendor, Omar began to notice a new fellow—a mean-looking man who was built like an ox, with an enormous scar on his throat. The strange newcomer roamed the streets and beaches. He didn't seem to be working for any of the gangs. *Maybe he could work for me.*

"Who is that man?" Omar asked one of his local vendors.

"His name is Tony," the vendor answered.

"Who's he working for?" Omar pressed.

"He isn't working for anybody," the vendor said. "He used to be the biggest cocaine vendor in Jaco, but the police caught him and he went to jail for several years. He just completed his sentence, and now he's back on the streets."

Here's my chance! Omar rejoiced. *He's the perfect man for me.*

While Omar had been checking out Tony, Tony had been checking out Omar and his setup. One day Omar and Tony met on the beach, and Tony told his story. "I'm just out of jail," he confided, "and I really need work. I've been watching you, and I like the way you do your deals. Neat. Quick. Thorough. You're fast climbing to the top here in Jaco. Could I work for you?"

Omar didn't hesitate to trust the man he barely knew. "Sure. When do you want to start?"

Omar gave Tony a limited amount of cocaine to sell for the first round. Three days later, Tony was back with a perfect account and all the money. So Omar tried him again with the same amount. Perfect again. By the third time, Omar was gaining confidence in Tony's efficiency. So he doubled the amount of product.

But things quickly turned sour when Tony came back claiming he wasn't able to get the clients to pay. "I need more time," Tony begged, his eyes darting around Omar.

Omar knew the man was lying. He had watched Tony during his test runs and had seen that he was able to not only sell quickly, but also get paid quickly. Tony was more than able to continue doing quick, efficient sales for Omar. What was the problem?

Omar's eyes narrowed into slits, and he didn't mince any words. "I don't want any excuses. I want either the money or the snow back by midnight tomorrow night."

"That's too quick," Tony countered, refusing to meet Omar's gaze. "You have to give me more time than that."

"That's my last word!" Omar barked. He turned and left Tony standing alone.

Later that night Omar was sitting at a table in the disco with his buddies. By all appearances they were having fun, but Omar was on edge. He suspected Tony would come by asking for trouble. He wasn't mistaken.

About ten o'clock, Tony came slinking into the disco, and Omar realized the man wasn't working alone. Others were behind the whole thing. *It's Mitchel,* Omar guessed, swearing under his breath. *Mitchel with El Marquense, or Mitchel and the police. I know it. This is it—the time has come for the showdown. It's either Tony or El Mexicano.*

Tony slipped up to Omar's table and asked quietly, "So what are we going to do about our deal? Is there going to be more time or not?"

"I'm a man of my word," Omar hissed through clenched teeth. "I said what I meant, and I meant what I said."

"So you're threatening me?" Tony asked icily, looking out the back door toward the beach.

Omar watched Tony closely—especially his right hand. If Tony had reached toward his belt for a knife or a gun, Omar would have exploded, though he looked totally calm sitting in his chair. But Tony wasn't ready yet.

Omar hissed, "Follow me. We'll settle this outside."

Tony followed, but before he disappeared into the dark, his friends accosted him. "Don't you dare follow that guy!" they said. "He'll kill you at the drop of a hat."

Omar kept right on walking toward the beach with slow measured steps. "Yes, I'll kill him," he muttered to himself. "Then I'll haul him around the point and throw him into the sea. Nobody will ever know what happened or who killed him."

When Tony didn't follow him, Omar stood on the beach alone, thinking hard. He now clearly understood that this whole deal with Tony had been rigged. Tony would not have the money at midnight. Somebody knew how smart and powerful Tony was, and they knew that if anybody in Jaco could take care of Omar, it was Tony. So all that remained was a showdown between the two of them.

Although Omar trusted his own abilities, he also knew that Tony was not a Mitchel or a Cebolla or one of the many others whom Omar had conquered easily. This would be a matter of life or death.

Omar decided to not trouble Daisy with his worries. Expecting that Tony was stashed away safely somewhere, he went home and tried to act normal. He caught several hours of sleep and prepared for the crisis.

The next morning when Omar met with his vendors in a lonely cove on the beach, they told him what they had heard. "Tony is plotting to either turn you in to the police or kill you."

"I already know it," Omar acknowledged. "So be careful today. Tony knows it's his last day to play around with me. If he doesn't have my money back by midnight, he's a dead man."

Carefully, Omar revealed his scheme to his vendors. "Look boys, today we're going to work differently. I'm not afraid of the police—except for this gun. I'll hide it so the police can check me at any time. If the police trick doesn't work, Tony might try to kill me. So unless you hear or see something new, stay clear of me all day. Sell carefully and keep your eyes peeled."

Then, turning to his toughest seller he called Chaparro, Omar added, "You'll spend the day with me as my bodyguard. I'll need you since I won't be carrying my gun."

Chaparro was ready.

Omar found an excuse to go back to his apartment, and there he hid the pistol in one of Daisy's flowerpots. He and Chaparro spent a half hour in the apartment, chitchatting with Daisy before they headed back out to the beach.

The day went by without incident. Was the whole thing just a scare tactic? Omar wondered. But he didn't let down his guard. It was dark, finally, when Omar and Chaparro were drinking beer in El Rancho de

Pancho. Was Tony watching him, lying in wait all evening? Tony knew he had till midnight to do his dirty work.

Omar emptied his beer. "I'm going to the restroom," he told Chaparro. "Keep your eyes peeled."

The restroom was at the end of a little hallway in one corner of the restaurant. Chaparro was looking the other way when Tony slipped through the restaurant and into the hallway. When Omar came out of the restroom, the first thing he saw was a man standing in the middle of the hallway, his hands buried in his jacket pockets as if it were a chilly day. Omar's heart went cold.

"Here you are!" Tony hissed, blocking Omar's way. "I'm here to settle with you. Yesterday you humbled me in public, you beast."

Out of the corner of his eye, Omar saw Chaparro sidle into the hallway. Suddenly Tony lunged at Omar, and Omar caught sight of a knife blade coming straight for his throat. He instinctively darted backward.

Chaparro yelled, "They're killing Omar!"

But Omar's reflexive move had saved his life. The knife blade caught only the tip of his chin. But for once Omar went all the way to the floor, at the mercy of his assailant. Before Chaparro could react, Tony kicked Omar with his heavy boot.

Chaparro pulled Tony away from Omar, who was picking himself up off the floor, ready to fight back. But the bartender grabbed Omar and whispered, "Just let that guy go, Omar. He's a bad one."

Seconds later, Tony wrenched himself free from the men who held him, jumped through a low window opening, and ran out into the dark. *He'd better run!* Omar told himself. *But I'll find him.*

As the bartender turned Omar loose, he said, "Let that man go. You don't want to get yourself into more trouble. Just be glad he didn't kill you!"

But if ever Omar felt like doing the opposite of what he was advised, it was now. He turned and whipped out onto the dark street. Dabbing his handkerchief at the cut on his chin, he flagged down a taxi. In a matter of minutes, Omar ran into his apartment and grabbed his gun. Then he disappeared into the night.

Omar figured Tony would head to the police station, fearing for his life and seeking safety. After finding the beach empty, Omar returned to the street where vendors still had their stands open, and dozens of tourists and locals were strolling leisurely from stand to stand.

Standing in the shadow of a tall straight palm tree, Omar waited. As he waited, his fury escalated. Tony had tried to kill him!

Tony would come. Very soon.

Sure enough, Tony strolled in from the beach, stepped warily onto the street, and started walking toward the police station. Just as Omar had suspected, Mitchel was with him. The two were working together.

Omar waited until the two were very close. Then he stepped out of the shadows. "Just a minute, my friends!"

Tony turned pale. "Calm down, calm down," he blubbered. But it was too late to calm Omar down. Three shots rang out.

The street erupted with screams. Panicked tourists ran, having no idea what was going on. The locals, who well understood the settling of a drug account, ran too. In minutes, police sirens joined the chaos.

The chaos worked in Omar's favor as he sprinted toward his apartment. His heart thumped madly in his chest, and his mind condemned him, "You killed again! You killed again! You killed again!"

34

A FUGITIVE AGAIN

OMAR BURST INTO the apartment, bleeding and distressed. Daisy ran to him, exclaiming, "What happened, Omar?"

"I killed someone," Omar panted, throwing some things into a backpack. "I have to run."

"But what about me?" Daisy cried, wringing her hands.

"I don't know, but I have to run," Omar answered gruffly. "Remember what I told you? I warned you this might happen."

He reached into his pocket and gave Daisy a stash of money. "I'm heading for Nicaragua. If you want to follow me later, that's up to you."

Retrieving his savings from his hiding place, Omar slipped into the darkness. His shirt wore a streak of blood from his cut chin. He had slipped a jacket over it and left, swabbing blood from the chin wound that was still bleeding slightly.

Out on the street, Omar hailed a taxi. "Take me to Liberia," Omar told the elderly driver, "and I'll give you twenty bucks." As they traveled, Omar struck up a friendly conversation, pretending to be traveling to Liberia on business. The taxi driver warmed up to Omar just as he hoped. Maybe he'd be able to return to Nicaragua without getting caught.

A half hour later, as they neared Liberia, Omar announced, "If you take me to the border, I'll give you another thirty dollars."

That was a hefty sum for the distance, and the driver willingly accepted. But as they drove past Liberia on the Pan-American Highway, they ran into a police check. Two officers stepped out onto the road and stopped the taxi. Peering into the window and shining his flashlight, one of the officers announced, "We're looking for a taxi that's been hijacked by a criminal. The man is wounded, and they say the taxi is heading this way."

"Well . . . it's not us," the taxi driver stammered, perplexed. "I'm voluntarily taking this nice young man to the Nicaraguan border."

Omar, sitting on the passenger's side, smiled at the officer, hoping he wouldn't notice his bleeding chin. The darkness helped, and soon the officer waved them on.

The taxi driver turned on his radio. Immediately, they heard the news about the shooting at Jaco Beach an hour before. The driver listened intently and then exclaimed, "I'm sure that was somebody settling a drug account. It's happened before. Those drug traffickers are crazy!"

Omar played along, agreeing that the drug world was becoming terribly dangerous. "It's a wonder that not more of those guys get killed," he said.

As the taxi cruised into the outskirts of La Cruz, the next town between Liberia and the border, Omar's heart fell when he spotted another checkpoint and more police cars ahead. Again, they stopped the taxi and went through the same rigmarole. More confused than ever, the taxi driver claimed innocence and assured the police that Omar was a most honest citizen.

"Up ahead is the main police check," the officer said. "Stop there, and they'll verify what you're saying."

Shaken, Omar had a quick decision to make. He couldn't afford to get checked one more time. They were going to catch on that he was their man, and the innocent taxi driver would be in deep trouble. Turning to the driver, Omar said, "Look, I need to make a stop here in town briefly. Take me down this side street into the middle of La Cruz."

Now it was the taxi driver's turn to be shaken, but he complied, steering his vehicle into a side street just blocks from the next police check. It was time for Omar to tell the truth.

"Look," he blurted as the taxi driver slowed down. "I need to talk to you straight. I'm the man the police are looking for. I just settled a drug account in Jaco a couple hours ago."

The taxi driver stared at Omar, his mouth hanging open. Even in the shadows, Omar could see that his eyes were wild with fear. "I-I would never have guessed," the driver stammered, stopping the car altogether.

"Don't be frightened," Omar soothed, smiling the best he could. "I'm going to pay you the fifty dollars. You've cooperated well with me, and I'm not going to hurt you. I did *not* hijack your taxi, did I? Just take me to the end of this street, and I'll run."

"But what will *I* do?" the man wailed, clutching the steering wheel. "The police will get me, and I'll be in big trouble!"

"No, they won't," Omar assured him. "You should be fine on the way back, because they're expecting me to be coming from the other direction. But if they do stop you, just tell them the truth. You didn't know who I was. Or if you want to, tell them that I held you up and took you at gunpoint. You shouldn't have any trouble."

The driver pulled away from the curb and drove to a dark alley at the end of the street. Before Omar jumped out, he begged, "Do me one favor, sir. I don't think they'll stop you, but if they do, tell them I ran east from La Cruz. Okay?"

The taxi driver nodded vigorously.

Then Omar handed him a hundred-dollar bill and shook his hand firmly. "Thanks a lot, man! You were a great help. Take care."

"Hey, thank you!" the taxi driver answered, sticking the money into his pocket. "I hope everything goes well for you too."

Omar sprinted through the alleyway and across the fields beyond the little town. It was ten o'clock in the evening. He ran due west until he knew he was a safe distance from town. Then he set his course due north, keeping the Pan Am within hearing distance. The rumble of trucks and buses oriented him as he walked toward the border. He needed to cross it before daylight, and it was nineteen miles away.

The next five hours were a nightmare. Clouds kept covering the thin sliver of moon, making it hard for the fugitive to find his way. Some of the fields he crossed were clean and easy to walk through. But more often than not, Omar found himself pushing through thick brush, crossing rocky gullies, fording creeks, and slipping through barbed wire fences.

But the worst thing wasn't the rough terrain—even worse was the turmoil seething in Omar's breast, threatening to choke him. *I did it again! What's wrong with me? Now I'm a wanted man to the north of Nicaragua and a wanted man to the south.*

Would he ever be able to live an ordinary life like other citizens? Was there room for him anywhere in the world?

As he fought his way through yet another stand of brush in the dark, Omar's thoughts turned even more sinister. *If life is over for me again, will I be able to kill myself this time? If I have nothing left to live for, why can't I just die?* He made up his mind to go home to see his family one more time. Then he'd decide what to do.

By early dawn Omar was exhausted. His clothes were torn from brambles. His pant legs were muddy from slopping through creeks. Every muscle screamed for rest, and he could hardly put one foot in front of the other.

He slipped into a stand of woods on the Costa Rican side of the border and sat at the foot of a tree, resting until the sun came up. Then he mingled with the crowds lined up to enter the main building to be stamped out of the country. While no one was watching, Omar slipped into the woods that covered most of the no-man's-land between the two borders. If only he could get to the other side without being caught, he would be safe in his own country. He wasn't guilty of any crimes in Nicaragua—at least not yet.

But Omar was stopped on the Nicaraguan side by an unfriendly official who wanted to see his papers. Omar decided that it was too dangerous to show them, so he pretended he didn't have any. "You're not a Nicaraguan," the official said, looking him over. "I can easily see that you're Mexican or something like that."

Omar started naming towns and cities in Nicaragua to prove that he was at home in the country. "I'm from Estelí, and as soon as you let me go, I want to get my bus and go home."

"What were you doing in Costa Rica?" the officer snapped, pointing south. "And why are you so dirty and wounded? You look like a criminal running from the law."

Omar shrugged off the officer's comments. "Look," he said, smiling broadly, "I was partying with friends just across the border. The reason I'm so buggered up is because I'm having a dreadful hangover. While I was at the party, someone beat me up. Please let me go. I need to go home and rest."

The official was hard to convince, but finally Omar bribed him with a twenty-dollar bill. Shaking hands as if they were great friends, the official waved him on. Soon Omar was on a bus again. But again, it was hard to fall asleep. His mind was in a tumult, and he couldn't turn off his anxious thoughts.

What now? Omar wondered. He had escaped arrest again, but what purpose was there in living?

While Omar slept fitfully on a bus, a brokenhearted Daisy was doing the same thing. She had boarded a bus heading north out of Costa Rica. Her eyes were closed and her head was against the window. But Daisy was not sleeping. She was crying and worrying about Omar, who had disappeared into the night without telling her his plans. What had happened to him? Maybe he was in jail—or dead. Or had he escaped and was on his way home? Whatever the case, Daisy wanted to find him.

As soon as the news media had confirmed that a man had been killed on the streets of Jaco, Cándida and Jáqueling had rushed to Omar's apartment. Daisy told them what little she knew, and they called to Regadío and told Omar's mother. "We think Omar is headed your way, Mama. Of course, we can't be sure. What if the police caught him? Or what if he couldn't get across the border? But you know how sly he is."

The police arrived to ransack the apartment, and they questioned the three ladies for what seemed like hours. Fortunately, the women knew little of Omar's doings, and they had no idea what might have happened to Tony.

Very soon Omar's whole family in Estelí and Regadío knew the awful truth—Omar had killed another person and was a fugitive again. What would happen to the man they all loved and feared?

Miriam asked herself that question again and again as the long night and the next day ticked by. Would Omar return? If so, when? What could she do for her son now?

Omar stopped short in the doorway of Uncle Bato's living room in Estelí and stared. He hadn't dreamed that so many relatives would be here to welcome him back. Quiet as a whisper, they stared back at Omar, their expressions somber.

Doña Miriam was the first to break the silence. Jumping to her feet, she rushed over and hugged Omar, weeping as she whispered, "My son, my son! I am so glad you're back safely! I was afraid I'd never see you again."

Then it was Grandma Ester's turn. Embracing Omar, she looked into his face kindly. "Omar, Omar, I came to see you. They told me that you were wounded, and I wanted to make sure you're okay. I also want to give you some advice." As only Ester could, she told Omar what he should and should not do with his life.

Omar took a chair in the living room, his emotions numb. Yes, he was glad to be back with his family, and anything was better than running from the law. But what was his future now?

Quiet and stern, Fermín had not moved from his chair since Omar had entered the room and nodded at him. But when Omar left to use the bathroom in the back of the house, Fermín followed. He met his son in the dark by an old cement sink. As Omar washed his hands, his father cleared his throat awkwardly. "Son, you can't go on like this," he said.

Omar turned slowly and faced his father. His hate for Fermín was still very much alive. But his heart mellowed just a little when he detected tears in Fermín's eyes. His father seemed embarrassed.

Fermín continued, "Son, you can't solve life's problems by using violence. You won't get anywhere that way."

Omar bristled. *As if you have any advice for me when you're just as violent as I am,* he fumed inwardly, staring at the ground. *Anyway, who taught me to be this way?*

As if reading Omar's mind, Fermín plunged on. "I know I'm partly to blame for the way you turned out. Forgive me. But it's time you stop and think about where you're headed."

Omar looked sadly into his father's eyes and sighed. "It's too late, Dad. Your advice comes way too late. What's done is done."

More relatives showed up for the evening meal. Bato turned up the music, food was served, and then the drink appeared. But Omar's heart wasn't in the party. The homecooked food was delicious, and it felt good to be back with the family. But Omar had no inkling of what he was going to do next. Nothing made any sense at all.

Ever since Omar had conquered his depression by digging footers in Jaco Beach, he knew he could get on with life and win. He had never been as suicidal after that. But once again, Omar was running away from the law because he had killed someone. And even though he didn't expect Costa Rican law enforcement to cross the border to look for him, he was still a fugitive all over again—a criminal who had murdered twice. The burden was a crushing weight on Omar's heart.

I don't fit in anywhere. Omar sighed to himself, taking another sip of his beer. *What does life have for me now? I've become a dangerous man. Who will I kill next?*

A voice from across the room jerked him out of his reverie. "Omar, why don't you go to Waslala?" His cousin Luis was grinning at him.

Waslala? Omar didn't answer, but he pondered the idea. He had never been to Waslala, but he had heard a lot about that remote place. Some said it was where the devil lost his suit coat.

In a short while, Bato's dining room was a hubbub of ideas. "Omar, you could go stay with your uncle Chema or with your uncle Juan. You have plenty of cousins living back in there," Fermín said.

"No authorities would ever find you there," Bato said, smiling. "Waslala is over one hundred fifty miles from Managua, and the roads into it are horrible. I think it's a great idea."

"You could work cattle with your uncles," Miriam suggested. "You'd like that, wouldn't you?"

"And you'd be safe there. You could start a new life," Fermín added.

A ray of light began to pierce the darkness of Omar's future. Maybe in Waslala he could be different. He wouldn't sell drugs there. He could work like a man and stay out of trouble. He'd stop drinking. Maybe he could change and become a normal person after all.

Two days later Daisy showed up in Estelí and begged Omar to take her back again. When she heard about the plans in the making, she was eager to be part of them.

Yes, Waslala was a remote frontier town, but none of the family seemed to remember that it was also famous for its lawlessness and violence. Generally when Waslala was mentioned, someone would be sure to shudder and say, "Oh, I've heard a lot about that scary place."

35

IN SEARCH OF A HOME

WASLALA, 2001

Puffy white clouds hustled across the blue sky ahead of the huge IFA passenger truck as it topped yet another hill and then barreled down the other side, ejecting clouds of black smoke.

Omar, perched on the truck's iron pipes that held up the heavy canvas tarp, gazed with keen interest down into the lush valley tucked into the bowl of green jungle ahead of them. Surrounded by towering mountains, a few houses huddled in the center, with the Waslala River meandering between them.

That must be Waslala! It better be. Omar sighed, hanging on for dear life as the truck careened around yet another curve and slammed into a mudhole. He had been riding this beast for six hours since they had left Matagalpa, and his tailbone felt as if it were breaking in two.

Omar glanced down into the bed of the truck, which was full of people and merchandise. Because the weather was nice, the canvas tarp had been rolled toward the front of the pipe frames he rode on. Large boxes and big red sacks were stacked high at the front of the truck bed, and rolls of barbed wire and a saddle lay on the floor. Milling among the people sitting on board seats running along both sides of the truck bed were chickens, dogs, and even a pig.

Omar's teenage brother Milo sat on a sack in front of Grandma Montenegro, Fermín's mother, who sat on one of the board seats hanging on for dear life. Milo smiled up at Omar when he saw him looking his way. Omar thought warmly about how willing his grandmother was to take him to see her Waslala sons. He was also grateful for Milo, who was always willing to accompany him on any adventure.

When the IFA finally bounced along Waslala's rocky streets, Omar noticed how different Waslala was from Estelí. Whereas Estelí's cobblestone streets were usually dry, the Waslala streets were littered with potholes, brimming full of water from the last rain. Most Estelí houses were built of concrete and painted in bright colors, but here the wooden houses knew very little paint. The people of Estelí dressed up and wore shoes to go out in public. But the people walking along the streets of Waslala wore rubber boots and peasant's clothes.

This sure is a frontier town! Omar observed as the truck roared up to the bus station and heaved to a stop. *This must be the right place for me.*

As they climbed off the truck, Grandma Montenegro announced, "Now we need to get another truck that travels toward Siuna. We'll get off on Papayo Hill."

Soon they were on another truck meandering up the steep Papayo Hill. As they plowed on down the other side, Omar was again impressed by the scenery. The Kusulí valley looked like a quilt laid out in blocks of different colors of crops—plantations of corn, cocoa, bananas, and beans. To one side of the road a piece of the virgin jungle was still holding its ground against the encroaching deforestation. Omar stared at a stand of massive jungle trees, thinking how they dwarfed the short gnarled trees that adorned the hillsides in Regadío and Estelí.

Omar was suddenly startled by a sound reverberating from the belly of the jungle—a sound that made his hair stand on end. What on earth was the source of those deep bellows and grunts?

Omar's keen eyes soon spotted the culprits in the treetops. A troop of black howler monkeys were scrambling through the jungle canopy, putting as much distance between them and the noisy truck as they could.

Grandma Montenegro knew where to get off at the foot of the Papayo Hill where her son Don Chema lived, his rickety wooden house perched on a knoll close to the road. The trio climbed off the truck and headed toward the house, splendidly surprising the family.

Introductions were made between family members who had not seen each other for years. Then Quintín, Don Chema's son-in-law, invited Omar to hike to a waterfall at the back of Chema's farm. Tired of riding on the truck, both Milo and Omar willingly followed the young man into the outback.

While the trio swam in the deep pool underneath the spectacular waterfall, Quintín and Omar appraised each other. "So what brings you to Waslala?" Quintín wondered. He crawled out of the pool and plopped down on the big flat rock where Omar was lounging.

"I want to buy some land and move back into this neck of the woods," Omar stated, eyeing his new friend warily.

"Why come way back in here to buy land?" Quintín asked, grinning slyly.

Suddenly Omar didn't care if Quintín knew the truth—he lived so far away from anybody who knew Omar. So Omar shared his story, starting with his crimes in the United States. Then he told Quintín about his drug dealing and the murder in Costa Rica.

Quintín shook his mane of drying hair. "Omar, I know of the perfect farm for you—a place where the law would never find you." Pointing at the rugged range towering over the Waslala valley to the west, Quintín rattled on, "My mother is selling fifty acres of good land behind that mountain range in a place called San Pablo, Las Vallas. It's the perfect place for you to hide."

Omar's eyes were glued to Quintín's face. "What does the land have on it?" he quizzed.

"Coffee. And lots of other things as well," Quintín answered. "Tomorrow we'll go see that farm."

Bright and early the next morning Quintín, Omar, and Milo were on an IFA on their way to Waslala. After they got off the bus, they took one of the byways heading out of town. They hiked into the mountains for several hours to the place where Quintín's clan lived in a crowded, ramshackle hut. After meeting Quintín's mother Doña Paya and her descendants, Omar understood Quintín better. But Omar didn't really care that they appeared to be a crude bunch.

After walking the boundaries with Quintín, Omar promised to buy the farm—and started planning to move to Waslala. He didn't have the money that day, but he told Doña Paya that he would go back to Estelí to sell his pickup and then come back to San Pablo in two weeks.

"Once you come to buy," Doña Paya said, "we still have some crops to harvest. So we'll need a month to actually turn everything over to you."

"That's all right," Omar said, eyeing the tiny house. "I think we can manage to live together for one month."

The crop that wasn't ready to harvest yet, Omar discovered, was several patches of marijuana concealed in the coffee groves and in the jungle. "No problem," Omar assured Doña Paya and Quintín. "As long as I don't have to mess with the weed myself."

Omar looked over the crowd gathered in Bato's Estelí house and grinned. If he had been surprised at how many relatives had gathered to welcome him back from Costa Rica, he was even more surprised at the number who came to bid him farewell. He could almost feel their relief that finally a solution had been found for their violent young relative. *It's not that they actually want to get rid of me,* Omar reassured himself. *It's just that they know, as well as I do, that Waslala is where I belong.*

As the evening progressed, and Bato and his woman again laid out a meal, Omar felt overwhelmed by his family's support. Miriam gave him several cooking kettles; Fermín, a saddle. Bato gave a tarp and chain saw. Omar now owned a Dalmatian from his cousin Erlin, and a blanket and foam mat from Grandma Ester. Dozens of relatives showed up, and most of them brought something for Omar to use in his new home.

Daisy attended the farewell party, and everyone knew she planned to go along with Omar and Milo the next morning. Miriam had warned Omar about the folly of taking Daisy back into the mountains. "Omar, you don't know Daisy's mother. She believes that you keep Daisy under some satanic spell that drives her to always want to be with you."

"But Daisy wants to go with me, Mama. What can I do?" Omar grumbled. "I'm not asking her to go—she begs me to take her along. And you know good and well that I need a woman to keep house back in there."

"You're right about that part," Miriam agreed. "But if you take her, you'll face no end of problems with that woman."

Omar had tried once again to persuade Daisy to forget about him. "Look, Daisy, all I have to offer is more trouble. As you can see, misfortune stalks me wherever I go. Waslala is remote, and I don't think you'll make it back in that wild place. I'm not even sure I can stand up to such a difficult life myself."

Daisy had just smiled and answered, "If you can make it, I can too. I'm going with you."

"Daisy," Omar tried one more time, "ever since you've lived with me, I've always had plenty of money, and you know how I made it. All of that ends in Waslala. The money I have on me will eventually run out, and we'll be poor. We might even go hungry. It will be a tough life. You'd better just stay here with your parents. Or you could go back to Walter and be with your little Wendy."

But Daisy stood her ground, and once it was clear that she wouldn't be dissuaded, Omar was actually glad. The tough life in Waslala would be easier with Daisy by his side.

Omar had sold his pickup to Uncle Bato, who seemed glad to help out. With the money from the pickup and what he had saved, Omar would have enough to buy Doña Paya's land. But there sure wasn't going to be much left over.

Though it was sad to say farewell, everyone at the farewell party knew that Omar's decision to head for Waslala was wise. It took Omar a long time to fall asleep that night as he sorted through his thoughts, trying to make some sense out of his life and the future. Finally, only hours before the sun came up, he slept a little. But even his dreams seemed haunted as he ran to escape from sinister foes.

It was a crazy-looking packtrain that left Waslala's main street the next day, taking a trail leading north toward the highest mountain peaks surrounding the town. Quintín, dressed in the poor clothes of a Nicaraguan peasant, took the lead. He led a horse that Don Chema had loaned for the move. The horse's wooden pack frames were stacked high with paraphernalia, making him look like a dromedary with a hump almost too big to carry.

After the packhorse came Omar, Daisy, and Milo. They were dressed like the city people they were, from a more modern world and a drier climate. Their clothes and footwear were not really suited for the vine-choked fencerows and the long stretches of knee-deep mud. But Omar wasn't worried about it.

Omar waded through the mud with his shiny leather cowboy boots as if it were normal. He wore a brand-new bill cap turned backward and toted an immense stereo set in one hand. In his other hand, he carried a sack of groceries he had just bought. He also held the rope that kept the Dalmatian dog in tow. Milo was also loaded to the gills, and in one hand he carried a bag of cassette tapes of the style of music that Omar liked. At first, Daisy tried to tiptoe around the deep mudholes to keep her fancy shoes clean and dry. But that wasn't possible for long.

The packtrain had barely left Waslala when Omar decided to make the trip a festive one. Fishing out one of his wildest music tapes, he soon had the stereo bouncing along with Mexican ranchera music to the rhythm of their feet. Omar sang along at the top of his voice. During the beginning of the trek, every so often, Omar and Milo exchanged wild *yipi-yipis* of the rebels. Then they burst out laughing at their own ridiculousness. Daisy just grinned as she gave up trying to stay clean and waded through the mud like the rest. Quintín laughed, wondering what the people they met on the way thought of the amusing packtrain.

But the tune changed once they hit the long steep hill that led to the top of the mountain. The party was in no rush, but even so, they were soon bone-tired, and the sun beat down mercilessly. All the fun had escaped the party, and a spirit of melancholy enveloped them.

Though this was the second time Omar had confronted Waslala's trails in rainy season, it seemed twice as bad with the packtrain. He pitied Daisy wading barefoot through the mud. The trail had a few drier sections where the horse's hooves did not create a muddy slop. But in the mudflats, the horse hooves created what the natives of the area called "staircases."

Horses are beasts of habit, and they copy each other. So when a horse comes to a slough that other horses have waded through, it will always place its hooves at the same place, creating a trough. The troughs become deeper as they are constantly replenished by the rains, and as the troughs grow deeper, the steps become higher.

As the packhorse encountered one staircase after another, Omar stared at the packs lurching back and forth. Some of the steps were so high that they scraped the horse's belly as he gingerly picked up one leg and then another to step from trough to trough. Not only was that a tedious exercise, but his hooves often stuck in the clay, causing the horse to stumble as he jerked his hoof loose before he could move forward. This painstaking process slowed the packtrain to a snail's pace.

Omar fumed and swore under his breath. Why did it rain so much in this place? How could horses survive such a beating? He knew how long it had taken them to get there the last time when they had had nothing to carry. He groaned. At this rate, they'd never get to their destination!

When they finally reached the top of the mountain at a place called Lone Tree, the packtrain stopped. The stout green mountain peak they were perched on stood higher than most of the peaks around them, making it feel as if they were on top of the world. They were, in fact, standing high on the rim of Waslala's basin.

In spite of their exhaustion, they turned to gaze at the lush green patchwork of the Waslala valley. The tropical grasslands were a light, rich green, sprinkled with thousands of trees like a speckled garden paradise. The scattering of houses far below added the silver of new tin roofs and the rusty red of the older roofs.

Smiling, Omar looked over at Daisy to see what she thought of the view. "It's beautiful!" Daisy whispered, absorbing the joy of the moment. "But why is it so far?" she asked, turning to Omar. "Do we still have a long way to go?"

"We're about halfway." Omar gazed down over the valley again. "The advantage is that now we hike along the mountaintops, and we won't have to climb such high mountains anymore."

About an hour after resuming their trek, the packtrain got into trouble. The horse, already almost too tired to move, hit another mudflat. As he plowed across yet another staircase, he floundered and promptly gave up, lying down on the steps, exhausted.

Omar placed his sack of groceries and the stereo, now silent, on the road bank. He didn't even have to tie the Dalmatian—the dog had plopped down, too tired to take another step. The normally black-speckled white dog was now mostly mud-red. Omar tried to coax the horse to his feet, but he wouldn't budge.

With Quintín's help, Omar unstrapped the load from the poor horse's back. Then they hauled the paraphernalia to a drier spot on the road and removed the wooden saddle pack. Even then the horse didn't want to get up—he seemed to think it was easier to remain prostrate in the mud forever. But a bite from Quintín's quirt brought him to his senses, and he lurched to his feet and followed Omar to the drier spot.

By now, both men were caked with mud to the waist. With the sun beating down upon them, they resaddled the horse and reloaded the sacks. While Omar and Quintín sweated in the tropical heat, the horse, Daisy, and Milo caught some much-needed rest.

As the packtrain pressed on, Omar began to have mixed feelings. The reality of the life they were to live back in this wild place hit him. Still, he knew he must accept that this was the best place for him to live—the farther back in the jungle, the better. *No policemen will ever come find me here,* Omar consoled himself.

But something even more important than avoiding the police drove Omar to keep placing one foot in front of the other. Just maybe, in this remote place called San Pablo, Las Vallas, he could change. Here he would have nothing to do with drugs or the filthy money he made by selling cocaine. Here he would have no reason to fling money around like a rich man and use women like he had done in Los Angeles and Costa Rica. Maybe he could stop being the wicked man he had become. *Maybe I can even stop drinking,* Omar thought.

Sweat dripped from Omar's brow. His mind kept on pumping, just like his legs. The main thing he wanted to leave behind was the violence that had gripped him all his life. *I get so angry at every little thing and lose my cool,* he told himself. *Maybe back in here I can get hold of myself and get rid of violence. Maybe, just maybe, I can become a normal person.*

Looking over at Daisy, Omar wondered some more. *Will this woman make it here in this wild, harsh climate? And if she can't make it, can I?*

Five hours after leaving the main street, Omar and his group finally reached an area where the winds were cool and the gnarled, wind-whipped trees were covered with moss. This was the highlands of the mountain range north of Waslala. Taking a narrow path off the main trail, Quintín led the group back into the hills. After climbing a knoll and following the path through a stand of fruit trees, they spotted their destination.

Nestled among the trees, a small house stood surrounded by a dirt yard, swept clean of leaves and trash. Standing around the house were a group of children, their bellies extended from malnutrition, their fingers in their mouths, staring. Several men, long-haired and shirtless, were scattered throughout the yard.

As they approached the house, Omar watched Daisy's face closely. *What does she think of this shack that we will now call home? And how will she react to this uncouth family with whom we'll have to share quarters for a month?*

The packtrain stopped in front of the house. Doña Paya came out with a big smile, her hands on her hips. "Welcome!" she bellowed. Then seeing Daisy, she gushed, "I'm so glad to see you, my darling. I know you will love this place! Come right on in!"

While Omar, Milo, and Quintín unloaded the horse, Doña Paya took Daisy into the shack for her first grand tour, boasting all the while about this wonderful land they were to live on if Omar bought the farm.

Two things happened simultaneously. Daisy's heart dropped all way down to her mud-caked knees. And it started to rain.

This was Daisy's initiation to the place called San Pablo, Las Vallas.

36

WASLALA JAIL

THE SUNNY MORNING that had ushered Omar and his tribe in from the Waslala valley disappeared as the afternoon sneaked up on them. A stiff wind and black clouds blew in, dumping torrents of rain upon the poor Nica house perched among the trees on that lonely mountaintop.

On a flimsy bamboo bench on one side of the living room, Omar and Daisy sat staring at each other and their surroundings. Omar wondered whether Daisy was questioning his sanity in bringing her here.

The roof of the shack was covered with warped, half-rotten wooden shingles. As the rain pounded down, it leaked like a sieve. Little puddles formed slowly at a dozen places on the scarred dirt floor. The walls were not weatherproof either. Wind and mist rolled in through the cracks between the upright pieces of split logs. The Dalmatian whined softly under Omar's bench, causing him to grin. Even the dog was spooked by this rickety place!

Doña Paya sat on the opposite side of the room, surrounded by a half dozen grandchildren. Quintín's brothers, the four men of the house, were crowded into the lean-to kitchen with their sisters, dodging raindrops, drinking coffee, and soaking in the warmth from the cookstove. After discussing the farm deal with Omar and his mother, Quintín had headed back to Waslala.

From where Omar sat, he could see through the doorway into the only bedroom in the house. It was separated from the other two rooms by a flimsy bamboo wall. As Omar eyed the bedroom, which was also leaking, his mind raced. He needed to come up with a plan for surviving the month with these people.

When the rain let up a little, Omar announced, "Daisy, you and I have work to do. You cook some rice for supper, and I'll fix that bedroom so we can sleep dry tonight."

Daisy found the rice they had bought in Waslala and headed for the kitchen. Omar rummaged through their belongings until he found the tarp that Bato had given him. On this rainy mountaintop, the need for it was quite obvious!

Simple beds were attached to the bedroom walls, and another bed sat in the middle. Each bed was made of four two-by-fours slammed into the ground, with bamboo slats stretched across a pole frame. The beds were covered with gunny sacks, cardboard, and whatever the poor family could scrounge up.

Omar claimed the biggest bed in the middle of the room. First he cleared it of all its paraphernalia, and then he threw on the foam mattress they had brought along. Next he fastened a string to the rafters and flung the tarp over it, creating a little tepee tent. He chuckled, giving the bed a pat. *Let it rain!*

Omar collected the bags of clothes and bedding belonging to him and Daisy and plopped them on the bed. At least he and Daisy would remain dry during the night. The rest of these rough people could make do. They were used to it.

Omar realized that Doña Paya and her family had very little to eat. He could see no groceries in the kitchen except for a filthy bag of sugar, a crusty can of salt, and some lard in a battered bowl. Hangers of bananas dangled from the outer eaves, some ripe and some green. An assortment of malanga and yuca tubers that grew in this area lay on the makeshift shelves. Several black pots on the stove were bubbling with food grown on the little farm. The big sack of coffee beans in the corner supplied them with the beverage they drank in immense quantities.

Easing over to Daisy, Omar whispered, "Cook enough rice for everybody. These people have only malanga and green bananas to eat. Tonight, at least, we'll all have rice to eat."

After the meal, darkness pounced, the mists thickened, and a chill embraced the homestead on the hill. Like Doña Paya's flock of chickens already roosting in the trees in the yard, the family members started thinking about beds and blankets. Several kerosene lamps flickered bravely, creating little swirls of black smoke that shivered their way up into the rafters.

But before everybody dispersed, Omar announced, "Tonight Daisy and I will be sleeping on the bed in the middle of that room." He pointed. "I will allow only women and children in that room with us. All of you men sleep out here in the living room. That includes you, Milo. String up your hammock and sleep with the men."

No one had made Omar the leader of the clan, but nobody dared argue—they were all afraid of Omar. Quintín had thoroughly warned his brothers: "Don't make that man mad. We want him to buy this place, remember? He's already killed a couple of people and won't hesitate to kill *you* if you cross his path. Do what he says if you want all to be well."

After everybody had bedded down, Omar found out what it was like to overnight on top of the world. Regadío often had cold nights and stiff winds, but this place was not only cold and windy; it was also wet—much wetter than Regadío. As the dank mist curled in through the cracks, Omar balled up under the covers and sighed, *Man, this is like sleeping in a refrigerator. If I stay in this damp place long enough, I might sprout!*

Like some ghostly galleon, a sliver of moon sailed across the wild night sky. Snatches of moonlight flickered through the cracks, giving the room an eerie atmosphere. Dozens of fruit bats zipped in under the eaves to snitch bites of ripe bananas, and they whistled in the trees that hung their soggy branches over the weather-beaten shingles.

Soon everyone else was fast asleep, even Daisy, who had just survived the longest, hardest day of her life. Omar was just as tired as the rest, but he couldn't sleep. How would he, Daisy, and Milo survive in these harsh, primitive conditions? How would he handle Quintín's brothers, whom he didn't trust one bit?

Finally he forced his thoughts aside and yawned. Tomorrow was another day. He had chosen to come here, so he would be brave, and together he and Milo and Daisy would conquer this wild place.

Doña Paya's big red rooster had crowed only twice at the crack of dawn before Omar jumped to his feet. "Come on, Daisy," he whispered, shaking her lightly. "Milo and I need our breakfast early. We have a lot of work to do."

While Daisy heated the rice left over from the evening and fried some eggs that Doña Paya's chickens had laid the day before, Omar woke Milo, and together they sharpened their machetes. The rest of the household was still fast asleep when the two men disappeared into the morning fog, heading toward the overgrown coffee grove.

"This place is abandoned and all grown-up," Omar explained as they trotted down the trail. "These lazy people haven't even started cleaning out the weeds since they harvested the coffee crop several months ago. Now the coffee's already blooming again. If we want to have any crop at all this year, we have to get the weeds out of that coffee."

Milo trotted along silently. He was used to obeying Omar's commands. Omar said, "We'll show that lazy quartet that we're here to work. Even if they don't lift a finger to help, we'll clean up those coffee patches. We'll show them what life is all about, won't we?"

Milo just grinned.

"The only crop these fellows are interested in is their marijuana. I saw their three plots on my first trip here. They're well-cultivated, and they'll make money on it if they actually get to harvest it. But I can hardly bear the thought of us working our heads off this month while those lazy fellows sit around smoking pot and eating our food."

Omar took his wrath out on the weeds in the coffee grove. The hard work soon paid off. As the weeds fell away, the beauty of the coffee bushes began to appear. Their tan trunks grew straight as arrows, with dozens of branches sprouting from them. The ends of each little branch were dressed in round, shiny green leaves. In this month of February, the whole length of each branch was adorned with clusters of snow-white flowers. They emitted a strong, sweet fragrance that delighted the nose.

At noon Daisy brought them lunch. No sooner had Omar plopped down on a stump to eat his rice and beans when he asked, "What are those four lazy fellows doing?"

"Nothing," Daisy answered. "I've never seen such a lazy bunch. They spend all day sitting on those little benches along the kitchen wall, watching us women cook while they smoke pot and tell vulgar jokes."

"Don't worry!" Omar hissed as he wolfed down his food. "I'll take care of that once I get back. Please be careful though. I don't trust those men."

Before he left the coffee patch that afternoon, Omar sharpened his machete more carefully than he had all day. When he was done, the keen edge glistened in the afternoon sun. "Let's head home," Omar growled, setting his face toward the hilltop.

As they approached the house, Omar saw that all four men were still in the kitchen where Daisy and Doña Paya were patting out tortillas for the evening meal. Asking Milo to stay back, Omar paused at the edge of the trees and watched.

Because of the thick shade, the yard was bare and smooth. Doña Paya's chickens scratched around looking for any corn kernels leftover from the morning's feeding. The afternoon shadows drew odd dappled pictures on the moss growing under the trees as the sun peeped through the leafy canopy.

Soon Omar heard what he was waiting for. From the little kitchen, only a few steps away, the four fellows cackled at yet another obscene joke. Omar marched to the kitchen door, machete in hand. "Today I'm setting up a new rule," he barked as he stepped inside. "I don't want any men in this kitchen anymore. Out, every one of you lazybones!"

The quartet zipped out of the kitchen as if a rattlesnake had struck at them. Before they had gotten far, Omar had kicked every little bench to pieces. Then he grabbed the pieces and threw them into the yard, bellowing, "Daisy, this will make good firewood!"

The evening was tense as Omar watched the whole tribe eating his food again. Daisy had made a cabbage salad and cooked beans to serve with the rice. Omar was sure these people had never eaten such treats.

After the meal, Omar and Daisy sat out in the yard and talked. "I don't know how much longer I can take this," Omar complained. "Look at my hands. They're already torn up with blisters from working in the coffee patch. And you should see Milo's hands. But these lazy fellows don't do a thing besides check on their three marijuana plots once a day."

"Be patient," Daisy suggested. "A month will go by fast, and then they'll be gone. You don't want to do anything drastic."

"But they're eating me out of house and home! I can't afford to feed this lazy crowd."

The tense days ticked by slowly until a week was up, and Omar found an opportunity to give the quartet another lesson. While Omar and Milo slaved away in the coffee patch, they found a sloth. Sloths were rare in Regadío, so Omar and Milo had never seen one before. Omar managed to coax the sloth down from the low tree, and they toted the animal back to the house on a long pole to show Daisy. She had never seen a sloth either.

In the middle of the yard sat an old stump that the men used to sharpen their machetes. When Omar rested one end of the pole on the stump, the sloth crawled up onto the stump, hissing and swiping at anybody who got close. Doña Paya's scrawny dogs were barking their hearts out at the hairy creature.

Everybody grouped around to see the sloth, including the lazy quartet. Then came Omar's chance. In one quick slash, his razor-sharp machete flashed through the air. The sloth's head went rolling, and the onlookers jumped back as the sloth slumped, spewing blood. Omar laughed at the four ashen-faced men standing as rigid as statues. "It was time for that critter to die!" he asserted, as if he did that kind of thing daily. Then he turned and headed for the house in search of a cup of coffee.

The next morning before Omar awoke, the lazy quartet left. When Omar got up, Doña Paya approached him nervously. "Omar, my four boys left early this morning because they had a job offer in Jinotega," she lied. "That's where we lived before we moved here."

"That's wonderful!" Omar exclaimed, knowing the real reason the men had fled. "If they have a job offer, they sure shouldn't turn that chance down."

"All they asked me to tell you is that within a month they'll come to harvest... eh... you know what." She glanced around fearfully.

Omar nodded vigorously. "That's perfectly all right."

Two weeks before the date they had agreed upon, Doña Paya left with the rest of her tribe. Omar felt much more at home, now that he and Daisy and Milo had the place to themselves. Suddenly the little shack felt much bigger, and the thought of living on the top of the world was not so bad after all.

After cleaning the three acres of blooming coffee bushes, Omar and Milo began to rescue an acre and a half of old bushes that looked useless. Omar rose to the challenge of stepping into what looked like a miniature jungle and whacking away the tall brush. There they found the old, straggly coffee bushes and trimmed them down to mere stumps. Within another year and a half, Omar knew, the old stumps would produce brand-new shoots that would bear coffee berries again.

One afternoon after they were done in the coffee patch, Omar was lounging in a hammock under the avocado tree in the yard, sipping coffee. Milo was leaning against the old sloth stump with a cup of his own, when they spotted someone running through the trees toward them.

Omar was on his feet immediately. One of Doña Paya's daughters rushed into the yard, her hair askew and her face contorted with worry. "Omar, I came to warn you that the police are coming tomorrow to confiscate the marijuana," she gasped, wringing her hands.

"Calm down," Omar said coolly. "How do you know this?"

"My sister is living with a policeman in Waslala... and he told her," the girl stammered, trying to hide her legs that were muddy to the knees. "My brothers have an enemy who apparently went to the police station and tattled on them."

"But since your brothers are gone and I'm the owner of this place, I'm the one who'll go to jail, right?"

"Exactly," the girl agreed. "You have to do something today, because they're going to hit early in the morning, according to what the policeman told my sister."

"Well, what can we do with the stuff?" Omar asked, thinking hard. "I never expected I'd be in trouble for your brothers' crimes. I should've known better. I moved up here to get away from crime and the drug world—not to fear the police again. Now this."

Omar knew the police were always looking for marijuana because they could sell it after they confiscated it. The growers often tipped them well to conceal their corruption.

Daisy stepped closer to Omar and whispered, "I'm sure glad you were warned. Imagine what would have happened tomorrow if we hadn't known about it!"

Omar nodded and turned back to the girl. "Will your brothers come to help get rid of the evidence?"

"No!" the girl wailed. "They left for Pantazma immediately. But they said I should let you know. They said the best way to get rid of it in a hurry is to burn it."

"Does it burn even if it's green?" Omar asked.

"Yes, if you have a hot fire, it burns like crazy."

"Well, then, no time to lose!" Omar growled, jumping up. He was glad they had a good collection of dry firewood stored under the eaves. "Daisy," he ordered, "you start a hot fire right here in the yard." He pointed at the girl and barked, "And you and Milo and I are going to haul marijuana."

Omar was surprised at how easy it was to pull out the tall, green plants by their roots. In no time flat, he and his two helpers were hauling bunch after bunch of the six-foot-high plants to the top of the hill and throwing them onto the roaring fire.

Daisy faithfully stoked the fire, and the whole yard took on a sweet, pungent odor. Soon all four of them felt drugged from breathing the smoke.

It took several hours to uproot and lug the hundreds of stalks from the three hidden plantations. By the time Omar announced that all of the plants had been burned, it was completely dark. Then Doña Paya's daughter, experienced in these things, suggested, "Omar, we should go over each plantation, picking up all the fallen leaves. If not, the police will see that there was a plantation there, and you'll still be in trouble."

So they returned to the three plantations, scooping up all the loose marijuana leaves by the light of a lamp. An hour later, Omar poured water on the fire and strewed the coals in the orchard beyond the yard. Daisy swept the yard free of all evidence of the fire.

Omar thanked the sister profusely for the timely warning, and she returned to Waslala yet that night, wanting nothing to do with the morning activities. Omar, Daisy, and Milo went to bed exhausted and on edge.

At five in the morning, Omar roused them like usual and stoked the fire for the early morning coffee. The mountaintop seemed extra still. Even the rooster that Daisy had bought from Doña Paya wasn't crowing to his harem. Omar turned on the little radio that they used to hear the news. Soon the shack was filled with lively rancheras.

It was time to open the door and see what the morning offered. No sooner had Omar done so than he realized the little house was surrounded by policemen and soldiers. *That girl was right!* Omar gulped, stepping out to confront the law.

The head policeman started the conversation. "What's going on up here?"

"Nothing," Omar answered quickly. "Everything's fine."

"We've received a complaint that you have marijuana growing up here. Someone also claims you have an assault rifle. We're here to check things out."

"Well, it's not true," Omar answered, keeping calm. "Search my house and the farm as much as you want. You'll find nothing."

"My men are already searching the farm. When they get back, we'll know if you speak the truth." The head police then directed a soldier to search Omar's house.

Both searches came up empty, of course.

As the visitors milled around the house, snooping for anything they could find, one of the policeman sidled up to Omar and whispered, "I'm the one who sent that girl to warn you yesterday. You did a good job of cleaning out all the evidence. Everything will be okay."

Omar suspected that the man wanted a tip, so he mumbled back, "Hey, thanks a lot for letting me know. I'd give you a little cash for your help, but I don't have a cent. Maybe someday I'll give you a gift."

The man accepted Omar's story, and soon the whole group left. Omar, Daisy, and Milo met in the little kitchen where the fire had gone cold and the coffee was still unmade. "Wow, that was close!" Omar sighed. "If we hadn't got the warning, they'd be locking me up about now for a crime I didn't commit!"

"Boy, you're right!" Milo said. "I was sure they'd discover what we did."

"Everything's okay!" Daisy smiled at Omar. "Now, let me make coffee and get some breakfast."

Later, as Omar sipped his coffee, he thought, *Here I voluntarily put myself into this jail called Waslala, in order to stay out of trouble... but trouble still finds me.*

37

MOUNTAIN LIFE

A STIFF WIND whipped at the avocado tree, rustling its leaves. Though the early morning sky was clear, and the east was a rich pink, the chilly air seemed to penetrate all the way to the bones. Omar stood facing Milo with his hands on his hips. Milo leaned against the stump in the yard and stared back.

"You can do this, Milo!" Omar insisted. "You know I'm completely out of money, and we need groceries."

"But I don't know where to sell that old stereo set," Milo whined, looking at his feet. "I just know I'll get to town and not be able to do what you want."

Omar was too ashamed to go to Waslala himself to try to sell the old stereo. But they were so pitifully out of food that they had to do something. Besides groceries, he needed bags to fill with dirt for planting new coffee bushes. He also needed batteries for the radio, a new machete, a file . . . so many things!

Conditions had become difficult for the trio on the mountain. First, Omar had to sell the chain saw Bato had given him for much-needed cash that was soon spent. Slowly, one by one, they were eating the chickens Daisy had bought from Doña Paya. They were sick and tired of the diet of tubers that Doña Paya's tribe had lived on. All three were hungry for some real food.

Then Omar had remembered the old stereo set. They had quit using it because it consumed too many batteries. For several months it had just sat on a makeshift shelf in the bedroom. "It's time we sell that thing. We don't need it," Omar told Milo.

But when Omar suggested that Milo go to Waslala to sell it, Milo strenuously resisted.

Annoyed, Omar yelled, "Really, Milo, you know good and well who's boss around here! I'm not *suggesting* that you go to Waslala—I'm *commanding* you. You'll take that stereo set and walk all over Waslala until you sell it. Then you'll buy what I listed on this paper and get your hide back here. Do you understand?"

Knowing what would happen if he continued to oppose his brother, Milo finally swung the stereo up onto his shoulder and stomped out of the yard, still angry.

Omar stepped back into the little kitchen where Daisy was trying hard to get the fire going. "Omar," she wailed, "the coals died again during the night! We've been out of matches for a week. I hate to ask, but you'll have to go to the neighbors again to borrow some coals."

Omar was angry. "Why didn't you bank the fire better last evening?"

"I did!" Daisy retorted, blowing at the dead coals in an attempt to revive even a feeble spark. "I was sure it would last. But this firewood isn't good quality. It burns up too fast. If you don't go get coals, I'll have to."

Omar wheeled around and headed out the door. Don Jesús, his closest neighbor, was a friendly, toothless fellow who cheerfully gave Omar red-hot coals whenever he needed them. *This is ridiculous!* Omar fumed to himself. *My woman can't even keep a fire going. Who knows what time breakfast will be? I wanted to get to work early today, even if Milo isn't here to help me. This just blows my day!*

Later, sitting on a bench in the tiny kitchen, Omar struggled to hide his displeasure at how the morning was going. He stared balefully at the pile of cooked green bananas steaming on his plate. How in the world was he going to choke down this sorry excuse for food? If it wasn't for the cup of black, sugarless coffee to help wash it down, he felt like he could throw up.

Omar's anger subsided as he worked in the coffee field by himself, whacking down weeds in the area where he wanted to plant new coffee shoots. As soon as Milo brought him the little bags he needed, Omar planned to pull up the shoots that sprouted under the big bushes from the coffee beans that had fallen during the last harvest. He hoped to fill a thousand bags with new little bushlings that he could transplant later.

By early afternoon, Omar was back at the house in a better mood, looking for his lunch. But his irritation rose again when he found that a pot of malanga was the only thing they had to eat. *Malanga.* The very word made Omar shudder. If there was anything he was tired of eating, it was malanga! Down a slope about fifty yards from the house, the elephant-eared plants with edible tubers grew in a little flat area where a tiny spring kept it swampy year-round. It was the perfect habitat for malanga.

That morning, tired of the steady diet of green bananas and yuca, Omar had jogged down to the swamp, jerked out an elephant-eared plant, and *voilà*—there was their lunch. The immense tuber, washed and cooked, produced a soft, purple-colored potato-like meal with a peculiar taste. Sure, malanga was edible, but who wanted to eat it more than once a week? Omar and his tribe were forced to eat it a lot oftener than that.

"I wonder when Milo will be back," Omar muttered, walking to the door and looking through the trees toward the trail that led to Waslala. "Surely he'll be here soon, and we can have some decent food for a change."

Eventually Milo did come back, but all he was carrying was a small bag of what Omar hoped were groceries. "How did it go?" Omar asked as the mud-splattered boy strode across the yard.

"Terrible," Milo answered, walking past Omar into the kitchen, where he plopped the bag on the wooden slab that served as a counter.

Daisy poured a cup of coffee for Milo, and Omar found a seat while Milo told his story. "When I got to Waslala, I did like you said. I began stopping at the houses along the street, trying to sell the stereo. At the very first house, the man asked, 'Where did you steal that machine?' "

Omar's eyes widened. "Nobody knows you in Waslala," he said, shaking his head. "So they thought you had stolen the stereo?"

"That's right," Milo muttered darkly. "They thought I was a robber, trying to sell my loot in broad daylight. I soon got tired of being questioned, so I asked where I could find a stereo repair shop.

"I found the shop, but Omar—we were sure stupid. That thing had been sitting up on that shelf for over a month, and we should have tried it out before thinking we could sell it."

"What happened?" Omar asked, his heart sinking.

"When the radio technician plugged the stereo in and pushed the button, nothing happened. So he offered to take it apart and check it while I waited. When he removed the cover, he found hundreds of those little tan roaches that this shack is infested with.

"He quickly took the stereo out into his yard and fed the pests to his chickens as he cleaned it out. He laughed and said it was no wonder the thing didn't work. He figured it was probably good for nothing now."

"What did you do then?" Omar asked hoarsely, eyeing the little bag of groceries.

"The shyster gave me only two hundred córdobas, saying, 'I'll pay you a little so you don't lose the machine altogether.' He said he'd try to fix it. If it's an easy job, I can stop by and he'll give me more. But if it's ruined, at least he won't lose his shirt. So I took the money and got out of there fast. All I bought were some matches, a little sugar, some rice, and some beans—that's all I have from my day's hike."

"Well," Omar said, chuckling, "things could be worse. A mess of roaches in exchange for a little bit of food . . . not too bad a deal. It's disgusting that you got only two hundred córdobas out of it, but you did what you could."

Turning to Daisy, Omar ordered, "Get a pot of rice cooking, and make a batch of fresh coffee that we can drink with sugar. Milo and I are starved for some real food!"

The next day, Omar and Daisy had a fight over some insignificant little thing. Omar lost his temper, and before he realized what he was doing, he whacked Daisy over the back with the flat side of his machete. His cruelty turned the day sour for all of them. Daisy, wearing a huge bruise, cried for a long time. Milo was afraid that Omar would do something worse. Most of all, Omar was angry at himself.

That evening before the chilly mist rolled in to hug the homestead, Omar sat on a rock in the yard, thinking hard. The nighthawks were already singing their melancholy song, and he felt defeated.

Would life ever change? Would he be violent forever? He had moved here to this mountaintop to get away from his anger, but it had followed him. He couldn't run away from himself.

Daisy was cooking his evening meal right now. She had not complained about this harsh lifestyle, and Omar didn't even show appreciation for her efforts. Milo was helping them eke out a living, but all the thanks he got was Omar's frequent anger. Omar had voluntarily put himself in "jail" in these Waslala mountains, but it wasn't helping. Was there any hope for him?

The next day Omar's mood improved, and even Daisy and Milo could smile again. After a day of hard work, Omar and Milo were resting in the yard listening to the radio while Daisy fixed the evening meal. Omar always tried to keep batteries on hand for his radio so he could hear if his family sent any messages.

Suddenly Omar and Milo heard a message from Miriam, announcing that she would arrive at Waslala the next day at noon. Omar and Milo cheered. Daisy came running out of the kitchen to hear what was going on.

"My mother is coming tomorrow!" Omar announced. "Let's go to town to meet her. I'm sure she'll have some cash along, so we can stock up on groceries. Do you want to go along, Daisy?"

Daisy beamed. "Sure! I haven't left this place for months. I'll be glad to get out."

"Let's leave very early, and we'll celebrate," Omar decided. "Since the dry season is slowly creeping in, the trails aren't so muddy."

Miriam's three-day visit brought much joy to the mountaintop. As Omar had hoped, she brought along groceries and cash, which Omar used to buy the things he desperately needed. While Miriam was with them, they ate like kings, and Omar began to think that maybe living on the mountaintop wasn't such a bad idea after all.

But Miriam brought along something else that was not so cheerful—news about Daisy's mother. The first afternoon as Omar and Miriam were standing alone in the orchard, Miriam told him, "Remember that I warned you to not bring Daisy back here? Well, I was right."

"What's up now?" Omar asked.

"Daisy's mother went to the law and made a real mess of things. I don't think the authorities will come way back in here to give you trouble, but if you ever set foot in Regadío again, it might get rough for you. For Daisy too."

"But Daisy chose to come on her own," Omar insisted. "What can the authorities do about that?"

"Somehow Daisy's mother got hold of your criminal record in the United States and got the authorities to believe some awful stories. When they found out that Daisy was living with a criminal, they allowed Wendy's father to get full custody of her."

"Does Daisy know this?" Omar asked.

"Not yet," Miriam answered, "but I think I should tell her. Apparently she has lost her baby forever."

"That's crazy!" Omar hissed.

"But wait!" Miriam said. "Wait till you hear what she told the authorities. Supposedly, you kidnapped Daisy by using witchcraft to bring her here by force. She claims that no normal woman would want to live with a criminal, and that Daisy's life is in danger if she stays with you."

Maybe she's right, Omar thought, with a twinge of guilt. *What if Mama knew how I treated Daisy just yesterday?*

Though Omar shrugged off the news, he did pity Daisy. "What a crazy mother she has!" he erupted, glaring at Miriam. "Daisy will be upset at what her mother is doing. Doesn't she know her daughter well enough to understand the truth? I've never pushed Daisy to live with me. It's the opposite—I've always tried to convince her to forget me."

Miriam was quiet.

"And, as you well know, I've never dabbled in witchcraft. Daisy stays here in this forlorn place because she loves me, that's all. Tell her mother that when you get back."

"I don't talk to that woman," Miriam retorted. "Even though we're neighbors, she hasn't talked to me in ages. She hates me almost as much as she hates you."

"Let's go in for a cup of coffee," Omar said. "We'll tell Daisy about this later this evening."

A couple of months later, Omar heard another radio announcement that pleased him. His dad Fermín was coming. Milo and Omar went to town to meet their special company, and Milo was delighted to find their brother Melvin along.

Late that afternoon, Omar ushered the visitors in through the trees surrounding the hovel. Even though the trails were dry now in the middle of the dry season, the four of them were tired from the long hike up the steep hill.

Though the shack they lived in was the poorest of the poor, Omar was proud to show his father what they had accomplished in the fields. The coffee groves were clean and well-kept, and the bushes were loaded with green berries, promising a good harvest. Omar and Milo had also planted bananas, tubers, and other food-bearing plants and vines.

As Fermín followed Omar around looking at everything, he grinned. "Son, it's a good thing I taught you how to work. Now I see the fruit of my labors." Omar just nodded, happy that his father could see how the mountaintop was flourishing.

That evening Daisy served a delicious chicken soup made from one of the young broilers. Along with hot tortillas and black coffee, all four men relished the meal.

Back out in the yard after supper, Fermín sat on an old stump and glanced shrewdly at Omar. "Looks like you're going to have a bumper coffee crop this year. But how are you going to shell the coffee beans? And after that, how will you haul your crop to town?"

Omar answered quickly, "My neighbor Jesús has agreed to let me use his coffee sheller for this harvest. But I don't know yet how we'll haul the beans to the sheller and then to town to sell. I guess if nothing else, Milo and I will haul the sacks on our backs."

"You need a horse," Fermín said, stroking his chin.

"That's the first thing I plan to buy with the money I make from the coffee this year," Omar answered.

"Omar, I have an idea. Recently I bought two donkeys, both jennies, and I want to resell them. Why don't you go fetch them over here to haul your coffee? Then you can pay me with money from the harvest."

Omar chuckled. "Nobody uses donkeys in this area," he said. "But they would sure be handy for hauling coffee."

Omar understood that Fermín was still dealing in cattle and horses, his main way of making money. But Omar could probably resell the donkeys for a good price when he was done harvesting coffee. So Omar hired his cousin Quintín to accompany Fermín back to Regadío and bring the donkeys to Waslala on foot.

Four days later, Quintín showed up, exhausted, with the two limping jennies in tow. He sat down to eat the good meal Daisy placed before him, swigging coffee as he told them about the trip.

He had used an old saddle to ride the larger jenny, and when she got tired, he had ridden the smaller one for short runs. Quintín chuckled. "For a while I thought maybe I should charge the spectators along the way to make some more money!" He had slept on people's porches when night fell, and some had given him food or coffee.

"Weren't you afraid they would hold you up or hurt you?" Milo asked timidly.

"Naw, people were usually friendly. Plus, I didn't have anything worth stealing. The only thing worth much was Big Jenny, and they were probably afraid she would kick the daylights out of them. It was a tiring trip, but it really did go well."

After Quintín left, Omar, Milo, and Daisy sat out in the yard and watched the sunset. Soon black clouds gathered overhead, and in the distance thunder rolled.

"Rainy season is here," Omar announced. "I wonder what rainy season in Waslala will be like. One thing for sure, it will bring in the storms and the mud. But it doesn't matter. We're all set. Now that I have the donkeys, I feel ready for the coffee harvest. After that, we'll finally have some money to eat decently and buy the things we need."

Daisy sighed. "It's May 15, over three months since we moved up here. Seems like a lot longer than that."

Omar just grinned. "Since we've survived for this long up on this wild mountaintop, we can surely make it from here on out."

38

DISAPPEARANCE OF A DAISY

OMAR STOOD ON the top of the coffee-choked knoll and stared. He could just see a corner of their yard below, where Daisy was sitting on a little bench, her face cupped in her hands, crying her heart out.

What should he do? Lately he had been suspecting that Daisy was homesick. Often she seemed pensive and troubled, even though she cooked food and kept the house like usual. Omar wasn't the type to baby a woman, so rather than trying to find out what was bothering Daisy, he went on with life full steam, hoping for the best.

Coffee season was almost over, and then, he hoped, life would slow down and Daisy could get back to normal. After two long months of the hard work, Milo and the two donkeys could hardly go anymore. The truth was, even Omar was weary. Getting the coffee picked, shelled, dried, cleaned, and delivered was a huge endeavor. Omar was hiring up to four people a day to help with the harvest.

Daisy was worn-out from cooking for the whole crew. Three times a day, seven days a week, she had to have plenty of food cooked and gallons of coffee brewed. There was no time for anybody to take a break and have a little fun.

But seeing Daisy cry like this filled Omar with anger. Daisy had known good and well that life here would be tough, yet she had begged him to let her come. Now she was trying to hide her longing to go home. Surely she was missing her little Wendy too. *Tomorrow,* Omar decided, *I'll make her go home. If she can't handle this life, she has no right to be here.*

The rest of the afternoon, Omar's mind whirled as he picked coffee with his workers. He felt satisfaction that the coffee harvest had gone well. But he still didn't have any extra money. Daisy still wouldn't be happy, and she wouldn't be able to cope with living this frugal life for another year.

As soon as he had sold enough coffee, Omar had bought a scrawny mare. From a distance, she looked white, but under the sheen of white hair, her skin was dappled. That's why Milo and Omar decided to call her Mil Colores.[21] It had been a wise buy; Mil Colores turned out to be a great packhorse. Now Omar could sell the donkeys and pay back his dad. But this purchase had wiped out most of the money left after paying the harvest crew.

There was more to Daisy's sadness than lack of money, Omar knew. Just the week before, he had caught Daisy crying as she looked at the photo in her hand. It was the tiny snapshot of Gema that Omar always carried hidden in his billfold. "Why were you snooping in my billfold?" he snarled. "That's what you get for not minding your own business!"

"You don't really love me," Daisy sniffed, tears streaming down her cheeks. "You only accept me because I cook for your hired men and take care of you and Milo. But you don't love me. You still love Gema!"

Omar had stalked off and worked off his anger while picking coffee. But now, as he stewed over the problem, his anger mounted again. *Daisy has to go. She's been a good companion in a way, but she's not happy. She can't stay here if she's not happy.*

In the evening, after the hired men had eaten and left, Omar confronted Daisy in the kitchen. "What were you doing out in the yard this afternoon?"

"Why?" Daisy asked nervously. "What do you know about my afternoon?"

---

21 Mil Colores: a thousand colors.

"I saw you from up on the hilltop. You were sitting out in the yard crying, weren't you?"

Daisy hung her head.

"You're homesick," Omar accused. "And you're missing Wendy, right?"

Daisy nodded.

"That's what I told you from the start!" Omar hissed. "I tried to warn you, but you wouldn't listen. Life up here on the mountain is tough. It's only for the strong and the brave. I want you to pack your bags and be ready to leave for Waslala by three o'clock in the morning so you can catch the five-thirty express bus. You're going home to your mama."

Daisy was shocked. She hadn't expected such drastic measures. "But I'm not asking to go home," she wailed, wringing her hands. "I think I can make it for a while longer. I'll try to be happy . . ."

"Nope, it's too late!" Omar snapped, turning to leave. "I won't have anybody on this farm that's pining to go home."

That night was cold in more ways than one. At three in the morning, Omar ushered Daisy outside, wrapped in her sweater. Mil Colores stood ready and waiting, Daisy's belongings strapped on the pack saddle. Soon they were wading through the mud as they slopped toward Waslala. Rainy season had done its brutal job on the trail, and the "staircases" were worse than ever.

As they neared the town, Daisy started to cry. "Omar," she sobbed, "I don't want to leave you! I have nothing else left in life. Please give me another chance."

But the more Daisy cried, the more Omar's heart hardened. "There's no second chance with me!" he spat. "The bus is coming, and you're going home to your mama where you belong. She hates me and she doesn't want you to live with a criminal anyway. And apparently, the way you've been moping around, you don't want to live with him either."

It was useless to try to reason with Omar when he was angry, so Daisy swallowed her tears, crawled on the bus, and cried all the way home.

Omar's thoughts were bitter as he traveled back up the mountain after buying supplies. *Daisy is right; I don't really love her,* he realized sadly. *I don't really love anybody, as far as that goes! I don't believe in Daisy—I don't believe in anybody. That's just the way I am.*

As Omar topped the mountain, he found he did miss Daisy just a little. If he would have allowed himself, he would have missed her a lot. But he steeled his heart and squelched his feelings.

Plodding on down the trail, bitterness gripped him. Here he was, alone again. Though he had determined not to be violent in his self-imposed Waslala jail, he still couldn't control his anger. He had chased away the brave woman who had begged to live with him and who had put up with him all these months. Would he ever change his ways?

Omar got back from Waslala around noon. That morning he had told Milo to inform the workers that the two of them would pick the rest of the coffee themselves since there wasn't much left and they didn't have a cook anymore.

When Milo came in, looking for lunch, Omar grinned sheepishly at his brother. "Well, Milo," he announced, "now we're on our own. That means we do our own cooking, wash our own clothes, and clean the house. I'm going to have to be Mama and Papa in this crazy situation!"

Milo just grinned back and nodded. "Bachelors we have become!"

Several weeks later, Omar and Milo were sitting in the yard one evening when they heard a shout from the path that meandered in through the trees. A little old man came traipsing across the yard. Omar recognized Indio Juan and began to grin.

Indio Juan was a friendly neighbor, outgoing and helpful as long as one stayed on his good side. Indio Juan came to stand right in front of Omar, folded his arms, and produced a toothy grin.

After chatting briefly, Indio Juan revealed the reason for his unexpected visit. "As I was coming through a thick stand of jungle today, I found a rare treasure. Since you're my neighbors, I figured I'd share it with you."

Reaching into the old leather pouch he carried, Indio Juan pulled out a handful of strange-looking moss. "This," Indio Juan explained, "is *paste caribe,* the best medicine in the jungle for snakebite."

Omar grinned, humoring the old man. Indio Juan was supposedly a healer who used herbs in his treatments. Omar wasn't superstitious, and he despised old wives' fables. Of course, he would never tell Indio Juan, but he didn't believe in the treatments that Indio Juan claimed would fix any ailment.

"This is what you do," the old man explained, lifting the ball of stringy moss. "You take a ball of this moss the size of a lemon, and you tie a piece of thread to it. Then you boil a liter of water and dip the ball of moss into the boiling water three times. Dip it in the water for only two seconds each time. After three dunks, the water is very bitter, and the tea is ready to drink."

"How much of the stuff should you drink?" Milo asked, interested.

"One big glassful," Indio Juan answered. Beaming, he handed the ball of moss to Milo.

Omar noticed that Milo was watching the witch doctor closely. *I think my brother actually believes that tale,* Omar chuckled to himself. *I wish I could.*

"So what makes you bring us this fantastic remedy?" Omar challenged, frowning slightly. "Do you think we're going to get bitten by a snake?"

"Well, you never know," the little gnome answered, his toothy grin fading. "There are a lot of poisonous snakes in the area. It's always good to be prepared."

After awhile Indio Juan left, and Omar promptly forgot about the *paste caribe.* But Milo didn't. He carefully hid it on a shelf in the bedroom where they kept their valuables.

After baching for about six weeks, Omar was very lonely. "I'm going to Estelí for a week," he announced to Milo one day. "Will you stay and take care of the place?"

Milo hesitated. Although he wasn't afraid, he didn't like to stay alone. However, with Omar gone, he could sleep later in the mornings—and he wouldn't have to work so hard. In the end, Milo agreed to Omar's plan.

In Estelí, Omar stayed with his cousin Luis, Andrés' brother. He sent word to his family in Regadío so they could come see him while he was there.

Miriam was the first to show up to see Omar. Her motherly heart was nearly breaking for her firstborn son. She really pitied Omar up there on the mountain with only Milo for company. "Omar," she said, "I want to talk to you about María Eugenia."

Omar's eyebrows jerked up. "What about her?"

María Eugenia was a girl from Regadío with whom Omar had had a brief relationship after he had come back from Costa Rica. In Waslala, the rumor had reached him that María Eugenia had a baby girl that she claimed was his.

"María Eugenia is lonely and still loves you," Miriam said. "She has no one to support her, and her life is difficult. Her baby is still small, but I think if you would take her back, she would go to Waslala with you. She would make a good companion in that lonely place."

Miriam convinced Omar to send word back to Regadío with her. Several days later, María met Omar at Luis's house. Since little Odalis was still small and María Eugenia wasn't ready to travel yet, Omar would go home alone, and she would come to Waslala later.

Several weeks later, Omar saddled Mil Colores and headed for Waslala to meet his new woman and his little baby. Omar's brother Melvin had accompanied María Eugenia to Waslala, and he also joined the little party on the mountaintop.

María Eugenia bravely faced the harsh climate and tough life in the hills, but Omar wondered how long she would last. Still not convinced that the baby was his own flesh and blood, Omar didn't allow himself to get too attached. But he enjoyed holding Odalis in the evenings, watching her coo and make funny little faces. This baby probably was his firstborn.

Omar didn't allow himself to get too attached to María Eugenia either. But she cooked his meals, washed his clothes, and did all the other house-work without complaining. She was easy to get along with.

During this time, Omar got into the horse-trading business with his dad. Fermín had discovered that horses were a notch cheaper in Estelí and Regadío than they were in Waslala. Omar had been able to sell the two jennies easily, making a nice profit. Since Waslala was a frontier town, horses and mules were in high demand. So Fermín began selling horses in Waslala.

Of course, Fermín didn't make the harrowing cross-country trips with the animals himself. Instead, he sent his sons—Milo, Melvin, and Alvaro. Fermín took the bus to Waslala and met the boys there.

Fermín was glad to have Omar's help to sell the horses. Omar seemed to have inherited a double measure of his father's gift of convincing folks to buy. He could sell the scrawniest nag for an exorbitant price.

They had a great arrangement. Fermín rented pasture from Doña Lidia, who owned a huge farm near San Pablo, Las Vallas. Every day, Omar would come down to meet his father and brothers. The men would saddle up a horse apiece and then spend the day in town. Omar soon knew the best hangouts for finding good buyers. Fermín and the boys would go to Fermín's brother Chema's place for the night, and Omar would return to his house on the mountain; María Eugenia was afraid to stay alone with her baby on that remote mountaintop.

Omar enjoyed his days in town with his dad's crew, all dressed in their cowboy best, riding fancy horses or good mules, eating in restaurants, and drinking beer. Soon the whole town knew about the cowboy gang that sold horses. Once the last horse was sold, Fermín would return to Estelí to start buying another batch, and Omar returned to the mountaintop to work on his farm. Those weeks of selling horses with his dad and brothers added spice to Omar's life.

But Omar still wasn't happy. He was restless and lonely, and he still had constant nightmares of armed men or the devil himself coming after him. Getting only a few hours of sleep at night made him anxious and angry during the day.

Omar ran the household on the mountain with an iron fist. His women learned to tiptoe around him and do everything they could to please the violent man they lived with. It was the only way to keep things going smoothly.

The poverty was hard on them all. Even after Fermín started bringing the horses, Omar often didn't have enough money to buy the groceries they needed. The constant hunger for something besides cooked green bananas and malanga was enough to make anybody irritated.

Omar was also bothered by guilt for the way he treated his brother Milo. While he and Milo had lived alone, they had gathered in the second coffee crop. Omar left for town with the money from the crop in his pocket. That night, he and his new buddies had drunk it all up in one long wild binge. He hadn't brought Milo so much as a piece of candy. All he brought back was a horrible hangover and a terrible temper that he took out on his poor brother.

The first morning after Omar had returned from Estelí, Milo failed to wake up at Omar's first command in the wee hours of the morning. Instead of calling him the second time, Omar had kicked Milo's bamboo bed to pieces.

"Is that the way I taught you to perform when I wake you in the morning?" Omar screamed, giving what was left of the flimsy bed one last kick. "Haven't I taught you to get up quickly when I call you? You know I hate lazy, useless chunks of human flesh. Get up immediately!"

It was no wonder that Milo decided to go back to Estelí with his dad, leaving Omar alone with María Eugenia.

So, life went on for Omar and his makeshift family. Though he had purposed in his heart to change his ways and to live in peace, it was becoming more and more obvious that he was not able to do it. The sense of failure dogged Omar every evening when he went to bed and every morning when he got up.

39

ONE DARK NIGHT

OMAR'S RUBBER BOOTS squished along the muddy trail in the pitch darkness. A storm was brewing swiftly, and the stars were smothered by the blackest clouds Omar had ever encountered in the highlands of Waslala. He couldn't see a thing, and he had forgotten his flashlight.

Omar was angry. He was mostly angry with his stupid mule, but he was also angry with the storm and the crazy circumstances he found himself in. If he had taken time to think about it honestly, he would have realized that, most of all, he was angry with himself.

This morning, María Eugenia had pled with him, "Please don't come home late, Omar. You know how frightened I am up here alone!" Omar had spent the day in Waslala with his dad and brothers, wheeling and dealing in horses. It had gotten late, but he had hardened his heart to María's fears.

Old Mil Colores was tuckered out, so Omar had left her in Doña Lidia's field with the horses they still needed to sell. Then he had saddled a handsome mule and ridden out of town at dusk, heading home.

It was July, the peak of the rainy season. Every day the heavens dumped tons of moisture, making the mountain trail almost impassable. The "staircases" were so deep that poor little Mil Colores had bellied out with every step on the way into town. *But,* Omar thought, *with this strong mule, I'll be home in a jiffy. He's so tough that he won't bottom out at all.*

But the handsome mule, coming from the much drier climate of Estelí, wasn't used to mud. Not only did he freak out as soon as they hit the mudflats, he panicked and stumbled and fell as if he didn't even know how to walk. Furious, Omar jumped off, tied the reins to the saddle horn, and chased the beast ahead of him.

Now, with darkness enveloping them, the mule kept going off the trail, seeking drier ground. Again and again, Omar used his quirt, swearing and getting angrier with every mismove the animal made. *This stupid mule can see in the dark. He should be my guide. But this idiot of a city slicker does everything wrong!*

Before they reached Palo Solo, the storm attacked in all of its fury. From then on, as the rain fell in torrents, the lightning flashed, and the thunder rolled, it seemed as if the storm and Omar were competing. Who was angrier?

The only light came from blinding flashes of lightning every few minutes. The mule took advantage of it, veering off into the bushes whenever he could. Screaming and cursing, Omar plowed through the mud until he found footing on the grassy edge. As he headed the mule back onto the trail again, he raged, "If only I had a pistol, I'd shoot this stupid mule, and then I'd shoot myself!" He meant it.

Omar suddenly stopped cursing and stood still in the middle of the trail. Mud-splattered and totally soaked, he shouted, "God, where are You?"

Crack! A powerful charge of electricity struck close by—close enough to make most men fall on their faces. But Omar didn't flinch.

"God," he continued, "kill me, please! Strike me with one of these lightning bolts. Make one strike my head right now! You know good and well that I deserve to die, so why don't You just get it over with?"

But God did not comply with Omar's plea, so Omar stumbled on. The mule was finally behaving well when they hit the deepest mudflat of all. As Omar floundered, one of his boots got stuck in the mud. When Omar applied all his strength to pull his foot out, his boot stayed in the mud and Omar fell forward, diving into the mess ahead of him.

Furious, Omar knew he had to find that boot. He couldn't make it home barefoot. So he swung around, searching in the mush with both hands. *Why is there no lightning now?* he fumed. Eventually he found the boot and forced it out of the sucking clay.

But his muddy foot went into the boot, as slippery as cooked okra, and it threatened to slip out again at every step. Again and again he lost one boot or the other. He spent more time fishing for boots than hiking ahead. Finally, too angry for words, he just carried the boots and plunged forward barefoot.

Out of the long mudflat at last, Omar put his boots on again. Then he climbed a knoll where a little cemetery lay quietly beside the trail. Most Nicaraguans were afraid to pass a cemetery after dark, especially close to midnight.

Stopping to catch his breath, Omar looked toward the cemetery, though it was invisible in the dark. He shouted, "Satan, where are you?"

God didn't answer my prayer, Omar fumed inwardly. *So I have a few things to say to the devil.*

"Demon, or whatever they call you, come out from your hiding!" Omar screamed, shaking the rain out of his hair like a dog. "I'm not scared of you, you fiend."

The only answer to Omar's challenge was another clap of thunder and torrents of rain that slashed at him from head to toe as he stood exposed on top of the knoll.

"All you dead folks!" Omar hollered, spurning the superstitious fear of the deceased that was part of his culture. "I'm not afraid of any of you, either! Come on out here if you dare. I don't know what fear is."

Still no answer.

Turning abruptly on the trail, Omar continued his seemingly endless trek. He was walking slowly now, barely putting one foot ahead of the other. The mule had ambled ahead. The storm was abating slowly, as was Omar's wrath. It seemed he had spewed out all of its vileness, until finally he was empty and exhausted.

Omar's mind had cleared enough to think rationally. During the next half hour of slipping and sliding up the last hill, Omar slowly came to his senses, thinking about things he had never dared consider before.

I'm paying for all my terrible sins, was the first thought that Someone drove deeply into Omar's heart. *God is punishing me. Every lightning bolt is God's way of telling me how bad I am—that He could kill me. This whole horrible night is just a little of the punishment I deserve for the wicked things I've done. But why doesn't God kill me, if I deserve to die?*

Omar reached the top of the last hill where the little gate opened toward the homestead across the field. Catching the mule, he led him through the gate and turned him loose before heading down the trail toward home. As he squelched through the grasses, he thought about his life. He tallied his worst sins, the awful things he'd done in uncontrollable anger—beating his mother, threatening to kill people, and actually killing Gema and Tony. He had damaged others by selling cocaine, by drinking, by swearing. And he had ruined the purity of so many young girls.

Omar shuddered as the cold wind on the top of the mountain jerked at his wet clothes. Deep in thought, he had missed the narrow trail that meandered through the grass. The wild night was still not done with its poor victim.

About the time Omar was asking himself what he could do to pay for his sins, he realized that he should have already reached the house. As he walked quickly toward what he thought was the hillside where the house was, he realized he was totally lost.

Omar lurched forward desperately, only to flounder deeply in a swamp. *This must be our malanga patch,* Omar guessed, plunging in water and mud up to his thighs and repeatedly losing his boots in the mud. Like a crazy man, he plowed in circles, grappling at the plants and wallowing in the mud. At last he floundered out of the swamp, and then he heard the Dalmatian bark. Omar discerned that he was at the foot of the incline to the house. In no time flat, he was standing at the door, hollering, "María Eugenia, open up!"

It had started to rain again just before Omar hollered, and María Eugenia didn't recognize Omar's voice in the roar. She had been terrified as the night sounds and the storm pounced on the little shack. The fierce winds seemed determined to jerk the hovel apart. Finally, when the second storm hit, she had accepted that Omar would probably not come home that night. So when she heard someone hollering and knocking on the latched door, she froze in fear. But during a lull in the storm, she was able to decipher Omar's angry words, "Open up!"

She opened the door, tears streaming down her frightened face. She shone the flashlight at Omar, who was soaked to the skin and lathered with mud from head to toe. "Omar," she croaked, "what happened?"

"Let me in!" Omar barked, pushing past her. "Can't you see that I'm finally home?"

In the living room, Omar lost no time stripping off his clothes. María Eugenia whimpered, "Omar, why did you come home so late? I've been terrified all evening!"

"Shut up!" Omar snapped, throwing his shirt aside. "Fear doesn't exist." He grabbed a towel and headed for the makeshift shower behind the house. "I'm the one who had a horrible night."

As Omar washed up, the rain finally stopped, and the crickets resumed their chorus. "What happened that you came home so late?" María Eugenia asked, standing outside in the dark. "And why are you so angry?"

"This has been the worst night of my life," Omar answered curtly, dipping bowlfuls of water out of a barrel and splashing them over his mud-caked body. "I was so lost that I didn't want to live anymore."

"Do you want me to heat up some food?"

"No."

Minutes later Omar lay in bed, exhausted. María Eugenia fell asleep quickly. With Omar's arrival, her fear had vanished. But Omar couldn't sleep. All his mind could do was run over the events of the horrible night. Was someone out there hounding him? Was someone trying to bring him to his knees? If so, was it God? Was it possible that God was actually interested in him? Or was it the devil taking over Omar's life because he had served him so long?

Omar's mind would not quit. *I've locked myself up in this prison called Waslala to separate myself from evil, but evil still follows me wherever I go. The devil is furious that I'm trying to change. Tonight he was desperate to kill me, but it wasn't my time yet.*

As Omar started to feel sleepy, thoughts of God gripped his mind. *It seems like a miracle that I couldn't die. Does God want to keep me alive? Does*

He have a purpose for me here? Omar sensed that something big was happening to him. He wouldn't rest until he discovered what it was.

Omar finally fell asleep just before the big red rooster crowed, and María Eugenia let him sleep. What the big rooster didn't know, what María Eugenia didn't know, what Omar didn't know, and what not even the devil knew, was that Omar's life had taken a turn in the right direction.

There was still a lot of work to be done in Omar's life, and a lot of time would be needed for the work to be finished. But now things could at least start to change.

María Eugenia stayed nearly six months on the mountain. Then she left for Regadío—peacefully, at least. She had discovered that Omar was showing interest in another woman, and she was tired of mountain life. "You don't really love me, Omar," she told him. "You know that as well as I do. I have no reason to stay."

Omar accepted María Eugenia's decision and took her down to Waslala on Mil Colores just like he had taken Daisy. But this time he wasn't angry. He knew it was largely his fault that she was leaving him.

Omar thanked María Eugenia for her work, kissed his little baby goodbye, and helped them onto the bus. He went to the public telephone and called Regadío to tell his mother what had happened.

Then he returned to his house on the mountain, alone and sad.

40

BITTER MEDICINE

OMAR STRAIGHTENED HIS aching back and used his hand-kerchief to wipe the sweat from his brow. Looking over the hillside that was fast being converted from a weed patch to a clean spot to plant potatoes, Omar grinned. When he and his brothers set their hearts to do something, they did it right!

Seeing Omar resting, Melvin and Milo risked stopping as well. Their opinions about this project weren't quite as positive as Omar's. When it was convenient for Omar to stop and rest, all was well. But Omar took a dim view of his brothers stopping to rest on their own. Melvin, still a teenager, took Omar's mastery better than Milo did. But all of them were exhausted from whacking away at the brush all morning.

"We need to get this quarter acre cleared by noon," Omar urged, glancing at the sack of potatoes waiting at the edge of the field. "I'd like to plant those spuds before the sun sets."

Milo glowered, taking his time to file the already keen blade of his machete. What was the rush? They had all week to get those potatoes planted.

After María Eugenia had left the mountaintop, Omar had asked his mother to send Milo again. Milo was reluctant, but since Omar needed him, he agreed to go. When Omar had called from Waslala to find out when Milo was coming, Fermín had announced, "Look, I have a sack of little potatoes that a friend gave me. It would make excellent seed. Shall I send it your way?"

Fermín realized that he was partly to blame for what Omar had become, and he assuaged his conscience by helping when he could.

"Sure," Omar had answered. "Anything grows on this fertile hilltop."

Fermín had not only sent him the sack of potatoes, but he had also sent Melvin to help plant them. So now Omar was desperately cleaning the hillside, wanting to get the little potatoes into the ground as fast as possible.

It was simple but strenuous work. Milo and Melvin used their sharp machetes to cut the foliage flush with the ground. The hillside was a tangle of plants—bushes higher than their heads, old banana clusters with stalks almost as thick as Melvin's waist, and a conglomeration of vines that were constantly grabbing at them and wrapping around their limbs as they worked. Omar's job was to grab the trash, shoulder it, and haul it to the edge of the field.

"Okay, boys," Omar hollered. "Time to get to work!" But as he bent over to embrace a thick chunk of banana stalk, he suddenly yelled in pain.

"Something bit me!" he cried, clutching his left hand.

Melvin had seen what happened. "A snake!" he cried, slashing its head off before it could slither into the brush.

Omar grasped his hand, moaning in pain.

Milo jumped into action. "Do either of you have a handkerchief?" he gasped. Omar pulled one out of his pocket, and Milo tied it tightly around Omar's wrist.

Melvin wailed, "Omar, you're going to die!"

"Let's head home," Omar retorted, clutching his hand. "And bring that snake along."

Milo sprinted ahead. Omar stumbled along, groaning in pain, and Melvin trailed behind, the headless snake dangling from the tip of his machete. In the house, Omar sat on the hammock that was stretched out in the living room. "Bring the snake," he moaned, nursing his hand.

Melvin dropped the snake at Omar's feet. "It's a coral snake!" Omar cried, staring at the snake's distinct red, yellow, and black rings.

"Will you die?" Melvin croaked.

"I guess we'll soon find out." Omar winced. "Where's Milo?"

Milo came in from the kitchen, carrying a small kettle of boiling water and a little chunk of moss. "How did Indio Juan say we should fix this miracle tea?" he asked.

"Three dips." Omar grimaced, shaking his head in misery. "I don't believe in that stuff, but anything is better than doing nothing. Look how my hand is swelling! Melvin, bring my razor!"

Milo dipped the clump of *paste caribe* in the boiling water three times. Then he gave a glassful of the brew to Omar.

Just before Omar started sipping the tea, he took the razor and slashed his hand at the spot where the snake's bite was clearly visible. Mercilessly, he squeezed the gash. Black blood, laced with poison, dribbled onto the ground.

For the next half hour, Omar alternately squeezed the gash and sipped the tea. "This stuff should surely be good for somebody that's dying," Omar joked. "It's the bitterest stuff I've ever tasted." Abruptly, he stopped talking and began to vomit violently.

In the midst of the chaos, two men called from the doorway and approached Omar, who was lying down in the hammock now, sapped of strength. "Hey, what's wrong?" they asked, sensing that things were amiss. Omar recognized Dennis, the local Pentecostal minister and his assistant, who trekked all over the mountain visiting people.

When he heard Omar's story, Dennis offered, "We're here to help." Turning to Melvin and Milo, he said, "Let's carry him out to the hospital on that hammock. Between the four of us, we can do it. If it was a coral snake, he'll be a goner unless he gets an antivenom injection."

"I'm not going anywhere," Omar answered weakly from the hammock. "If I die, I die here on my mountain. Don't worry about me. I drank that tea. If I live, I live. And if I die, that's just the way it'll be."

The two men looked at each other. They had heard about this fugitive on the mountain, and they knew he was a bad one—about as keen on religious people as he was on coral snakes. He'd as soon kill one as the other. The pastor and his helper had planned this first visit cautiously, with a lot of prayer.

Leaning over the hammock, Dennis asked hesitantly, "May we pray for you?"

"I don't care," Omar responded, lying pale and still.

The two men prayed out loud at the same time, practically shouting their petitions to the Father in Heaven. Even in his misery, Omar almost grinned. Several years ago, he would never have allowed a couple of preachers to pray over him. *But I've changed,* he admitted. *If God is out there, maybe He'll hear and answer. It sure doesn't hurt to let them try.*

After the men left, Omar promptly forgot them. He had no strength for anything but lying in the hammock, sicker than a dog and wishing he could die.

The two boys made a measly supper, distracted with worry for Omar. Omar didn't move from his hammock except to vomit, which was quite often. By the time the sun dropped over the horizon, Omar had almost dropped over the edge of life as well.

"What shall we do?" Milo wailed as darkness sneaked onto the mountaintop.

"Nothing except wait till morning," Omar insisted weakly. "Go to bed and sleep."

"But what if you die, and we're up here all alone?" Melvin whimpered as he crawled onto his bamboo bed.

"Like I said," Omar retorted, "just wait to see how I am in the morning."

Then everything went quiet. Only the night sounds could be heard as the long hours ticked away. Several crickets chirped incessantly, and red-eyed tree frogs clucked in the bushes surrounding the house. Dew dripped from the shingles on every side of the shack.

Omar slipped in and out of sleep during that long night. Turning over in his hammock for the hundredth time, it seemed to him that the pain might be lessening. *I wondered what it would be like to actually die,* he mused in his wakeful moments. *And after death, what then?*

The tropical kingbirds were the first to awake on the top of the world. Their cheery *tweek, tweek, tweek* roused Milo, who jumped up out of his hammock and slipped into the kitchen to start the fire and turn on the little radio. As the water heated to a boil, he tiptoed over to Omar's hammock and whispered, "Omar, are you still alive?"

"Sure am," Omar answered weakly. "I'm going to make it after all."

"Good news!" Milo chirped. "If you made it through the night, you'll live."

When the coffee was ready, Omar sat up in his hammock and sipped slowly. His hand and part of his arm were swelled to double their normal size. "Milo," Omar whispered, "make some breakfast right away, and then I want you to run to Waslala to tell the home folks that I got bitten by a coral snake. Maybe they can send someone to help out for a while. We really do need to get those potatoes planted."

Miriam traveled to Waslala immediately and found her son in bad shape. Omar could hardly eat, making him very weak with frequent black-outs to the point that he couldn't work. Even so, Milo and Melvin had finished planting the potatoes under Omar's direction.

Miriam convinced Omar to travel with her to Estelí to see a doctor. After a day in the Estelí hospital, receiving intravenous drugs and vitamins, Omar felt much better.

While Omar recuperated in Estelí for a week following his day in the hospital, Uncle Bato came to see him. "You know, Omar, you helped me in Los Angeles when I was down and out," Bato reminisced. "Maybe it's time I help you."

Omar was all ears.

"I just got back from the United States, and I have some money I want to invest. Maybe I can invest in Waslala and help you get on your feet."

In a short time, things changed drastically for Omar. Bato bought a nice house in Waslala, and Omar's cousin Donaldo and his family moved in. It provided a good base to stay when any of them needed it—Bato when he came to take care of his new ventures, Fermín when he brought in cattle and horses, and Omar when he needed to be in Waslala for business.

Next Bato bought 126 acres of land adjacent to Omar's mountain farm, with plenty of water and grass for cattle and several acres of coffee ready to harvest. Best of all, it had a decent house. Omar and Milo moved in, and

Omar started dreaming about which woman he could convince to come live with him next.

Bato stocked his farm with cattle and brought truckloads of mules and horses from Estelí to sell in Waslala. He let Omar do the wheeling and dealing, and Omar was able to make a little money. Bato also gave Omar a mule. Best of all, some of the cows gave milk, so Omar and Milo were able to add milk and homemade cheese to their skimpy diet.

Eventually Omar took on the role of Bato's manager and handled the Waslala affairs as if they were his own. He was able to buy better clothes, and he spent more time in town. That seemed to assuage his loneliness.

Soon Omar was back to riding bulls in the fiestas and drinking at the bars. He became known as an excellent cattle dealer, as well as being young, well-dressed, and handsome.

One day Omar was out with Quintín, buying cattle in the Jicaral area, several miles beyond Waslala. On the way back, as they rode up Papayo Hill, they stopped at Doña Ixolina's place for a drink. Quintín was a neighbor to this woman's family. Doña Ixolina had several things in her house that interested Omar—liquor and a pretty girl.

After the visit was over and they were back on the road, Omar asked Quintín, "Who's the girl that attended us?"

"Oh, that's Doña Ixolina's daughter, Maritza. Cute, isn't she?"

"Does she have a commitment with any fellow?" Omar asked.

Quintín chuckled. "Not that I know of. If you want to send her a message, I'll help you."

Omar grinned. "I just might, one of these days."

"Anytime," Quintín promised.

41

JOSÉ ADÁN

LOUD MUSIC FROM Bato's big CD player throbbed into the dark Waslala night. The little house where Donaldo and Doris lived fairly rocked to its wild beat. Bustling ladies filled the lean-to kitchen attached to the house, cooking a meal for the party.

Bato and Omar kept things lively with talk and laughter, while Doris's daughter Gloria and several other girls flirted with the men. Donaldo hung outside in the shadows, waiting until the food was ready, and the liquor ran freely. Doris and her neighbor lady were busy converting several scrawny chickens into a tasty soup. José Adán, Doris's sixteen-year-old son, was in his bedroom, trying in vain to finish his homework.

Omar was exhilarated. He had sent word to Doña Ixolina's pretty daughter, and that day Maritza had showed up at Bato's house in town. Omar had talked with the girl for an hour, and he felt sure that with a little more time, she would move up to the mountaintop with him. Though he had begged her to come to the party, she had declined, explaining that her mother didn't allow her to be out after dark. So even though his new prospect wasn't in the party, Omar was celebrating his upcoming success.

Bato was celebrating because he had bought another hundred acres of land. Although it had almost stripped him financially, he still had enough money to throw this party, and he had already bought his ticket, planning to head back to the United States next week, where he would make more money for future investments in Waslala.

Omar was intrigued with José Adán. Though just a teenager, the boy behaved like a mature gentleman. That night he and Bato both tried to get the young man involved in the party, but they were not successful. When the chicken soup was ready, José Adán came out of his room, smiling, to eat. But that was all. Try as they might, they couldn't get him to drink anything stronger than Coca-Cola.

When Omar asked him why he was so proper, José Adán grinned. "I have a goal to study and become a schoolteacher. If I start drinking, I'll never attain my goal." That's all they could get out of him. Though Omar's goals were totally different, he couldn't help but like and admire the boy.

After a while, Omar forgot about the boy and threw his whole heart into the party. *Once Maritza lives with me on the mountain,* Omar told himself, *I'll have to be good. I won't be able to cash in on these wild parties. So I'm going to make hay while the weather permits!*

After several weeks of wooing, Omar convinced Maritza to sneak out and meet him in town so she could move up to the mountain with him. Doña Ixolina was furious, and the neighbors were dismayed. It was as if Omar carried an irresistible magnet that few girls could resist.

During the third coffee season after he moved to the mountaintop, Omar harvested the coffee from both farms. He hired several dozen coffee pickers, and Maritza was extremely busy, cooking for them all, so he also hired a neighbor girl to help her. During weekly trips for the next three months, Omar used mules to haul over eighty *kintales*[22] of coffee off the mountain, making good money for both Bato and himself.

One day after the coffee harvest was over, Omar was at the house down in Waslala, chatting with Doris and her daughter Gloria. They served him coffee and urged him to stay for the evening meal. Omar declined, saying, "I need to get back before dark, or Maritza will have my hide."

---

22 *Kintale:* a hundred-pound measurement.

"How's she taking mountain life?" Doris asked sweetly.

"Not bad," Omar answered. "She's actually pretty tough. She worked hard all during the coffee harvest and now, finally, she has time to rest. And by the way, it was timed right. She's pregnant."

"How far along is she?" Doris asked, unable to hide her frown.

"Three months, supposedly," Omar answered, watching Doris's face carefully.

Looking around to make sure no one but Gloria was listening, Doris whispered, "Just like I thought. That baby is not yours."

Omar's face turned white and his lips curled. "Why do you say that?"

What Omar didn't know was that when Doris and Ixolina had been neighbors, they had become enemies. Doris couldn't stand Ixolina, nor her daughters. So now Doris had maliciously seized a chance for revenge.

"She was with another man just before she ran off with you," Doris lied, making a sour face.

Old memories came roaring back like a horrendous tidal wave, engulfing Omar's body, soul, and spirit—especially the memories of Gema aborting his babies. *Treason!* his heart screamed. Fury possessed him, and he snarled, "If that baby isn't mine, I'll never forgive Maritza. I'll shoot her dead!"

Even Doris was shocked at Omar's bitter response, but it didn't convince her to undo the smear campaign she had started. As Omar jumped onto his horse and headed toward the mountain, Doris grinned wickedly.

The long ride up the mountain calmed Omar's wrath, but still the battle raged in his heart. *We've lived together for three months,* Omar reasoned desperately. *That baby could be mine. What if Doris is just making it all up?* He knew that Doris's tongue was as long as the road up the mountain. But then again, what if Maritza *had* lied to Omar?

Back and forth his thoughts swung like a pendulum. How could he discover the truth? If she had deceived him, she would continue to lie to him. How could he trap her?

When Omar finally rode into the yard, he couldn't hide his suspicion and anger. As he walked up to the house, his face contorted in frustration.

Maritza was waiting for him on the porch of the new house, as pretty as a flower, her smile as bright as the noonday sun. When Omar stalked past without a word, she realized something was horribly wrong. She worried all evening as she served him his supper. She worried as he ate his food in silence, and she worried when Omar refused to talk to her during the whole long miserable night.

The next morning, Maritza couldn't contain herself anymore. As she served Omar his coffee, she said hesitantly, "What's wrong with you, Omar? Why are you so angry?"

Omar looked Maritza in the eye and growled, "Maritza, you'd better not be playing games with me!"

Maritza's heart froze. Though she didn't know the extent of Omar's crimes, she knew he was a criminal, and she had never seen him this angry before. But she couldn't guess what was making him upset. She was suddenly afraid of Omar.

"What have I done?" she gasped, clasping her hands together.

Nodding toward her middle, Omar hissed, "Is that baby mine... or isn't it?"

Maritza suddenly understood. "Omar!" she wailed. "Of course it's your baby! I've been up here with you for three months, and I'm three months along."

The argument that ensued was long and heated. Weeping, Maritza tried her best to make Omar understand that she had not had an affair before she came to live with him. But the more she tried to convince him, the less he believed. Maritza could see that Omar had been hurt in the past, and that this misunderstanding had opened the wound afresh in his heart.

The argument ended when Maritza blurted, "Do you want me to leave?"

"Absolutely!" Omar barked, turning and stalking out to catch his horse. "Be ready within the hour. I'm taking you back to Waslala!"

Though Omar provided the horse to carry Maritza and her belongings, he practically chased her down off the mountain.

On the way back home, Omar's mind worked in overdrive, thinking about the women who had lived with him on the mountain. Daisy had lasted a year with him. María Eugenia had lasted six months. And now Maritza had lasted only three months.

Bato was back again from six months in Miami. There he had managed a security guard company and made good money. Now, his pockets bulging, he wanted an excuse to party. Omar had done well with the coffee harvest in his absence and collected even more money for him. Both men were eager to spend some of their cash on a wild night of drinking and dancing. Rich smells from the kitchen promised a delicious meal. The three girls Omar had invited should be here any minute.

Omar had a malicious idea. "Bato, let's make José Adán dance tonight, shall we? I invited an extra girl just for that purpose."

Bato laughed, slapping his leg. "That will be the fun of the party tonight. It'll make Waslala headlines if anything does. Let's do it!"

When the girls arrived, Omar and Bato clued them in on the plans for José Adán. Giggling, the girls helped formulate the plan. Poor innocent José Adán walked into their trap when he came home from school.

Even before the meal, Omar and Bato tried to persuade him to dance. After the meal, things got really tough for José Adán. Omar instructed the extra girl to approach him and urge him to dance. When they challenged the foolish girl to kiss him, José Adán rammed his hand up between his red face and the girl's approaching lips, blocking her efforts. Then he fled to his room.

Everybody quieted down. Omar actually pitied the poor boy and wished he hadn't been so mean, trying to force the boy to do something he didn't want to do.

Later, in the kitchen, filling his plate, Omar asked Doris, "What makes José Adán so proper?"

"Well, there are several reasons," Doris replied. "First of all, he really wants to study. He fears that if he starts drinking, he won't be able to finish his studies right."

"But a lot of students party and still graduate."

"Not José Adán!" Doris insisted. "But there's another reason. José Adán has been friends for years with a group of people that are really different," she explained. "Ever since he was little, he attended their Sunday school. These people have somehow instilled in José Adán a desire to do what's right. He's not a member of their church yet, but he plans to join someday."

"Who are these people?"

"They're called Mennonites. Their missionaries have a church here in town, another one in Jicaral, and one in Kusulí. They also have schools and a clinic. They're very different from any of the other churches I know."

"I've heard about their clinic. But what makes them different?"

Doris didn't seem to know. "Maybe it's because they take their Christian life seriously. At least, José Adán has learned to stand up to bad things, hasn't he?"

Omar nodded, wondering what it would be like to be good, like José Adán. He almost envied the boy. What would it feel like to have a clean conscience from making right choices? *But that would be impossible for me,* Omar protested inwardly. *I'm much too wicked. I could never be like José Adán, even if I wanted to be.*

Omar returned to the living room, where things had quieted down. The music was playing softly as he plopped onto a chair.

"Let's have some stories," Gloria suggested, smiling. "You always have a lot of interesting yarns to spin, Omar."

When José Adán heard that Omar was going to tell stories, he came out of the bedroom. He couldn't sleep while the party was going on anyway, so he sat and listened attentively. For once, even Bato was quiet.

Omar told about his travels in Costa Rica, his drug business in LA, and his experiences on the mountaintop. Last of all, Omar told about being bitten by a coral snake. "I used to not believe in Indio Juan's remedies. But now I've changed my mind," he said.

"You take a little ball of *paste caribe* and dip it in boiling water three times. It becomes as bitter as gall, I swear, but it draws the poison right out through your gut. If it weren't for that tea, I'd be as dead as a dog, six feet under."

That night Omar had a hard time going to sleep. José Adán had made an impression on him. If he would make a firm decision like José Adán, could he, Omar, be good too? If he would determine to change his ways, was there still hope for a man like him?

42

NEW FRIENDS

AS THE EARLY morning fog settled into the valley, it was followed by a stiff breeze helping to push away the chill. Omar stood on the top of a knoll and scanned the field below him, perplexed. Where could his mule be?

The truth soon hit him—his mule had been stolen! Evidence indicated that a robber had roped the mule in the field and led him through the gate out to the main road. Omar's anger flared, thinking of what he would do if he caught the thief. But he had a problem—no gun. He walked back to the house, fuming.

Omar didn't have a gun, but he did have plenty of friends. Several days later a friend leaked the news about who had stolen Omar's mule. Leaving Milo to watch the farm, Omar headed off to Waslala on one of Bato's horses.

Along the trail, not far from town, a cluster of trees hugged a little creek where drunks, drug addicts, and sometimes robbers congregated. As Omar rode past the hangout, he happened to see Arista, the man whom his friend had accused of stealing Omar's mule. Because Omar still didn't have a gun, he didn't confront the robber on the spot. Instead, he headed to the police station and reported that Arista had stolen his mule and was at that moment hanging out with the druggies along the creek. Several policemen accompanied Omar to the spot and arrested Arista. Arista was furious. He insisted he hadn't stolen the mule.

Omar, though glad that the police had been able to capture the ruffian, also realized that he now had an enemy . . . and he still didn't own a gun. This bothered him. *What if they can't prove that Arista stole my mule?* he reasoned. *He'll be out of jail shortly, and then he'll come after me.*

A week later, when Omar rode into town, another friend informed him that a stolen mule that looked like Omar's was tied at the police station, waiting for confirmation as to who the owner was. By the time Omar got there, the police had let another farmer take the mule to pasture until the owner could be found.

Sure enough, it turned out to be Omar's mule. But the fellow who had put the mule to pasture was reluctant to let him go. "I like this mule," he told Omar. "I want to buy him."

Omar wasn't interested in selling his mule, but he changed his mind when the fellow said, "If you sell me your mule, I'll give you a revolver along with whatever money he's worth."

That afternoon as Omar rode home on Bato's horse with a gun tucked in his belt and cash in his pocket, he purred to himself, *That was a good deal—it was timed just right!*

Very soon after that, another friend stopped by Omar's house on the mountain with a new report. "Arista is out of jail. They couldn't prove a thing on him. He sent me to tell you to be on guard, because he's going to kill you."

Knowing Arista, Omar decided that his recently acquired pistol wasn't enough for a life-and-death situation. So Omar called Bato, who was back in the United States, and got permission to use some of the farm money to buy an assault rifle along with some ammunition that a friend in Regadío was selling.

The day Omar went to Regadío to buy the gun, he rode past the Regadío high school. Something he saw there caught his interest keenly. It was Yuri Blandon, a sixteen-year-old girl whose family he had known for a long time.

Yuri worked for her mother at the school's food stand. Omar knew her sad story. Because of problems at home, Yuri had run off with a fellow at the tender age of fourteen. Her distraught parents had sent the authorities after her and made her come back home. They had managed to keep Yuri at home, but as Omar suspected, she wasn't happy.

Two things about Yuri attracted Omar. First, she was pretty. Second, she was the positive type, always smiling. A friendlier girl could hardly be found in all of Regadío.

When Omar stopped at the food stand and chatted with Yuri that day, no one thought anything of it. As they visited and Omar listened to her natural bubbling laughter, a plan started hatching in his mind. This girl, who was as frisky as a wild doe, wasn't happy at home, and she had no child to hold her back. So she was free to leave home if she wanted to. *Hmmm. Maybe I won't head for Waslala right away, after all!* Omar decided.

After his first contact with Yuri, Omar used a different tactic. Since the girl was more Milo's age than his own thirty-two years, Omar started sending messages to Yuri through him. Milo would meet Yuri at the food stand and tell her what Omar was offering her, or he would deliver a letter that Omar had written to her. In less than a week, Yuri was ready to travel home with Omar.

Late that night after folks were in bed, Omar and Yuri left Regadío, heading toward La Naranjita, where no one would expect them to go. Early the next morning, they walked cross-country to Estelí and caught an early bus for Waslala.

As they traveled toward Waslala, Yuri revealed why she was so ready to leave home. "Ever since I tried to run away two years ago, my mother and grandparents harass me. They watch my every step. They hardly even let me go to the latrine by myself. Whenever I do an errand in town, they send somebody with me. They treat me like a baby."

Omar smiled at the girl. "Your father is seeing another woman, right?"

"That's right." Yuri sighed, wiping tears from her eyes. "And since that, my mother is never happy. It seems as if she takes all of her anger out on me."

Omar didn't make too many promises to his new sweetheart as they traveled into Nicaragua's interior. He knew he didn't have to. Anything would seem like paradise to this love-starved girl.

The next day Omar found that this was quite true. As Yuri rode Mil Colores, slopping through the mud all the way up the mountain, she just laughed. She loved it all, especially the freedom from her family that Omar was offering her. Yuri's cheeks got redder and rosier as they climbed the long mountain in the hot sun, but she didn't complain. She took it all in stride.

Just a mile before they arrived home, Omar and Yuri met Jesús, Omar's favorite neighbor, whom Omar had left in charge of the farm while he had been gone.

"What in the world did you find in Regadío now?" Jesús exclaimed. "I thought you were going to buy a firecracker, but I see I was all wrong!"

Omar laughed. Patting his backpack, he said, "You weren't mistaken, man. Here is where I carry my new firecracker."

"Looks to me like you found something better than a gun," Jesús insisted, staring at Yuri. "You found yourself a spring chicken, didn't you?"

Omar chuckled again. "Yep, I sure did. As pretty as a butterfly and as good as an angel."

"Well, I don't know about all that," Jesús drawled, shaking his head. "What I know is that you robbed a cradle somewhere!"

"Hey," Omar countered. "She's older than she looks. She's sixteen." Never mind that he was twice her age!

"She sure doesn't look it! But, then, I guess you're only fifteen yourself." Jesús roared with laughter at his own joke.

"Well, we'll see how she copes with life up here in the mountains," Omar said, smiling.

Yuri just grinned at the funny neighbor with his toothy smile and hung on for dear life as her mare jerked back into gear.

About a month after Yuri joined Omar on the mountain, Omar got a message on the radio from his dad: "Meet me in Waslala at noon tomorrow." Omar had no idea why Fermín wanted to see him, but the next day, he saddled up a horse and headed for town. Nothing prepared him for what he found.

First of all, Fermín usually came on the bus. But this time he had come in a borrowed pickup. In the back of the pickup was a handsome but ferocious-looking dog, heavily streaked with dark brown on tan. The dog, his eyes full of fury, looked as if he had eaten spikes for breakfast.

"I brought you a gift, son," Fermín began, forcing a weary smile.

Omar pulled his horse over to take a closer look at the large thick-chested brindle dog. He was taken off guard when the dog lunged at him, slamming into the end of his chain. Omar swore, reining his horse back. "If that chain weren't as thick as a logging chain," he said, "that beast would eat us both!"

"He's half Rottweiler and half pit bull," Fermín explained. "His name is Ranger, and yes, he's a vicious dog. But I know you're often lonely up here, and I thought you needed this dog."

Omar nodded. His Dalmatian had died several weeks before. "I do need a good dog."

"Look, it's no secret," Fermín admitted. "His former owners gave him to me to get rid of him. Now I'm doing the same."

"What does he do that's so bad?" Omar inquired, still staring at the huge dog.

"Mainly, he's just vicious," Fermín answered carefully. "His owners couldn't handle him or even get close to him. They had to use a long stick to retrieve his food plate and then push it back when it was refilled. Besides, he kills any animal that gets close to him. They were scared to death of the dog, and they told me the truth. But I love big handsome dogs like this, so I figured I could handle him. But that was less than a week ago, and I can't stand him anymore. He killed most of my chickens and some of the neighbor's pigs that sneak into our yard. And he killed my favorite Dalmatian. Now my neighbors are complaining."

"And I'm supposed to be patient with the beast and make him as tame as a kitten?" Omar frowned, scratching his head. "I'll probably shoot the mutt."

"That's exactly the deal!" Fermín chuckled as he sized up his son who was not afraid of anything. "I told everybody in Regadío that you would either make or break the beast. Either he shapes up, or he's a dead dog."

Omar swelled at his father's praise. Caressing the revolver at his belt, he chortled. "Of course I'll take the dog! Either he and I will get along, or one of us dies."

Suddenly Omar wanted to head back up the mountain. The business with his dad was done, and there was no reason to wait any longer. Omar had never even dismounted from his horse during the quick encounter. It was time for action.

Still on his horse, Omar opened the back of the pickup. Ranger lunged at Omar, but the chain was snubbed too short for him to do any harm, and Omar didn't flinch. Silently he rode to the front of the truck bed and reached in warily to loosen the chain. Dragging the dog off the truck, Omar rode around to the back, ready to face the battle. The dog had barely hit the ground when he attacked his new master. Lunging up at the man on the horse, Ranger was ready to kill.

But Omar was also ready. He merely pulled his leg up, high out of reach, realizing his good fortune to be riding one of Bato's tall horses instead of little Mil Colores. At every lunge, Ranger chewed viciously at the stirrup. But Omar spurred his horse, and soon they were dragging the dog down the road. Before the dog actually choked, Omar gave him a little slack. Suddenly, the dog was willing to follow. By this time, Omar had left his dad far behind. He didn't even look back to thank him for the gift. He wasn't at all sure Ranger was going to be a good gift, but he would soon find out. He rode on home through the mud.

Yuri was surprised to see Omar come home so quickly, and even more surprised to see the huge dog he was leading. Omar tied Ranger to a tree before he dismounted and went in to explain. "I want you to be extra careful with that dog," he warned, turning to look at Ranger, who now lay panting under the shade tree where he was tied. "He's dangerous. He has no scruples against attacking his master, much less strangers like us."

"What in the world are you going to do with him if he's so uncontrollable?" Yuri asked anxiously, staring at the dog.

"Don't worry." Omar laughed carelessly. "He'll either behave here, or he dies. It won't take me long to discover how this battle will end."

That evening Omar ran the first test of friendship by Ranger. The first thing he did was pull his pistol as he sauntered over to the dog. Ranger, spattered with dry mud, was still tuckered out from being dragged up the mountain and lay with his head resting on his paws, eyes shut.

When Omar approached, Ranger lifted his head. He opened his eyes wide and perked his ears. Sensing that the dog would be ready to leap at his throat as soon as he stepped within the range of his chain, Omar stopped just outside of that range and started spilling his thoughts out loud to the dog.

"You know what, Ranger? You and I are very much alike."

Ranger lay as still as if he were cut out of stone, but Omar knew he was listening. What Omar didn't know was whether or not Ranger liked what he heard, but he kept talking anyway. "Ranger, you and I both find ourselves hiding up here on the mountain because everybody hates us. Everybody is scared of us. Nobody trusts us. We're both alone in this world."

As Omar stood looking straight into Ranger's fierce eyes, he suddenly understood why those eyes were so full of fury . . . why the dog was ready to bite everybody. Out loud, he answered that question. "It's because of your past, Ranger. You've been hurt much more than you've hurt others. I admire your guts, man! Like me, you don't care if you live or die. I see in your eyes the reflection of my whole life. I understand your anger. You and I have so much in common, Ranger!"

Now it was time for the next part of the test. Omar, pistol ready, took one step closer and hunched down to the dog's level. Was he within the range of the chain, or wasn't he?

Omar placed the revolver, still gripped in his right hand, on his knee and took up his monologue again. "Ranger, we have to come to an agreement this evening. Are we going to be friends, or aren't we? I guess the decision is up to you. If you lunge at me, I will shoot you immediately."

Ranger didn't move.

"The truth of the matter is that you need me, and I need you. We both need a friend that we don't have. We're both too lonely. I can watch out for you, and you can watch out for me. Will you be my friend?"

As Omar talked in low friendly tones, the monologue began taking effect on the angry dog. Suddenly he wasn't so angry anymore. He lowered his head and rested it on his paws again. Though he didn't close his eyes, Omar knew that he was winning the battle.

"I'm willing to be your friend, Ranger. I'll give you a home. I'll feed you the best I can. Best of all, I'll give you love, something I doubt you ever had. The question is, will you be my friend?"

Omar understood perfectly when Ranger gave his startling answer. Ranger had only a stub where his tail was supposed to be. During the whole conversation, Omar had been watching that stub. When he saw that little stub wiggling back and forth, he knew the truth—he and the dog were going to be friends.

Omar rose to his feet, thinking, *I can't believe this! It looks as if this dog understands every word I say.* Of course, Omar knew that was impossible, but evidently the dog at least trusted the tone of his voice.

Acting bolder than he felt, Omar hunched down directly in front of Ranger. Risking his life, he stretched out his hand and patted Ranger on the head. Nothing of the dog budged except his stub, which by now was fairly bouncing up and down.

From that moment on, Omar and Ranger became inseparable friends. Ranger was strictly a one-man dog. Nobody else could manage him, but he obeyed Omar like an adoring slave.

Omar was pleased to discover that he had two new friends. Not only was Ranger a faithful friend, but Yuri hadn't been on the mountain long before he considered her a friend as well.

Yuri possessed several traits that helped her cope with the harsh lifestyle in San Pablo de Las Vallas. She was used to working hard without complaining. And not only was she used to hard work, but she was clean and thorough in her housework. Nor did she ask for comforts and fancy things. Omar was pleased with his new girl, though she was so much younger than he. She seemed to appreciate the little love he had to offer. Though Omar didn't expect Yuri to replace Gema, she was easier to please than others Omar had lived with.

Two friends made San Pablo de Las Vallas a better place for Omar.

43

RANGER TO THE RESCUE

THE MORNING BREEZES seemed to make the foliage on top of the mountain quiver with joy. The sun smiled down on the green countryside, bathing everything with a golden hue, and the sky served as a sapphire ceiling for a wonderful world. It was a breathtakingly lovely morning.

For once Omar felt almost happy. Yuri had offered to help him outside that day, claiming that she was bored with being cooped up in the house. Omar was delighted, and now they were busy fixing one of Bato's many fences on a wind-whipped hilltop. Yuri had little experience fixing fence, but she could hand Omar the tools and staples as he needed them.

Yuri's first year on the mountain had gone fairly well. Of course, there was always too much work and things that constantly worried Omar, but he was finally anticipating better days ahead. Recently, he had even been sleeping better, and his nightmares seemed fewer.

Another blessing for Omar was his dog. Ranger lay on the lush ground now, gleefully harassing the grass with his teeth and feet. *This dog loves his life up here,* Omar thought, smiling. It was true that they couldn't keep chickens anymore. But Ranger ran free across the hills, and he faithfully protected Omar and Yuri. Omar didn't think he could find a better dog.

When Yuri had discovered she was pregnant, she and Omar were both excited about having a baby. Omar began to dream again about the family he had never had. As they worked on the fences that morning, they talked freely about the baby and their future plans.

And yet, Omar was aware of the raw truth—he was still a violent man. That morning he told Yuri how just the day before, he had stood up to Carlos Picudo,[23] the toughest pistol-packing bully in Waslala. About a month before, Carlos had beaten up Milo and told him that he wasn't scared of his pip-squeak of a brother called Omar either. When Omar met the man, he forced him to swallow his words. Carlos Picudo quickly did so, sensing that if he didn't, he'd be a dead man.

Indio Juan had been giving Omar trouble with some line fences. One morning Omar had caught Juan in the act of tearing up a fence that he had just fixed for the umpteenth time. Omar was just about ready to throw some rocks and get rid of the man once and for all when Mil Colores, hidden in the bushes, snorted, and the man fled. Later, when Indio Juan threatened Omar's best friend Jesús, Omar had shot at him from a distance with his rifle. Once more, Indio had run like a scared jackrabbit, and he hadn't bothered Omar or Jesús since.

But today as he and Yuri fixed fence, Omar kept the gun by his side. "I don't trust Indio Juan," Omar confided. "I'm suspicious he might try to trick me someday when I'm back in the fields like this. I have to be careful."

Yuri wasn't exempt from Omar's violent anger either. Just a week ago, Omar had been in a horrible mood after a nearly sleepless night. Yuri, with her loving touch, had prepared and served his breakfast of refried beans and rice with fried plantain. But when he asked her for the second tortilla and she plopped it on his plate instead of placing it carefully, Omar had angrily thrown his plate of food across the floor, forcing her to start all over serving him again.

"I should never have taken up arms again," Omar acknowledged to Yuri, propping the gun against the fence they were fixing. "They only give me trouble. I lived up here the first several years without one gun, and I

---

23   Carlos Picudo: Carlos Big Snout. Soon after that, Carlos Picudo shot and killed a Waslala bar owner. Several years later, Carlos himself was gunned down as he left that same bar one night.

had less trouble than I do now. I've already almost shot two men. I keep wondering what will happen next."

But the morning was so lovely that Omar could almost forget his troubles as he basked in the warmth of the sun and his two faithful friends, Yuri and the mutt.

"Man, I wish Bato would keep better fencing tools up here for me!" Omar complained as he tightened the barbed wire and hammered another staple into a live fence post. "It's such a pain to cut the wire without a decent fence pliers."

"How do you manage?" Yuri wondered, holding an old tin can of staples and the meager tools Omar owned.

"I usually use the machete to cut a notch in the wire. Then I have to bend it back and forth till it breaks," Omar retorted. "But I have a better idea."

Omar stood the gun upright on its stock, holding the barrel with his left hand. Then he laid the barbed wire across the smooth metal muzzle with his right hand and said, "Yuri, hold the wire like this."

Omar's idea seemed bright. If Yuri held the wire across the edge of the muzzle as he whacked it with the hammer, it should pop the wire in two.

"What are you going to do?" Yuri asked, alarmed. "Are you sure there's no bullet in that rig?"

"It has plenty of bullets in the magazine," Omar explained impatiently. "But it doesn't have a bullet in the chamber. It's safe. Here, give me the hammer."

"Watch your face," Omar warned, as he raised the hammer. They both pulled their faces back as Omar struck.

BOOM! The beautiful morning was shattered by an awful bang. Ranger leaped to his feet, ready to fight a fiend. Yuri screamed, "Mama! Mama! I'm going to die!" and ran from the scene, clutching her arm.

Omar, confused, dropped the gun and the hammer, fearing for a moment that he had killed his woman. "Yuri!" he hollered, running after her. "Are you okay? Stop! Let me see!"

Yuri finally calmed down enough for Omar to assess the damage. He soon saw that she was probably not going to die after all. But he found several shrapnel wounds in her left arm—wounds that would leave permanent scars.

Distress flooded Omar. How could he convince anybody, especially the doctors at the hospital, that he hadn't shot Yuri intentionally? Everybody knew he was a violent criminal.

Omar soon figured out what had happened. The rifle had a bullet in the chamber after all, and when he struck the barrel's tip, it went off. But instead of shooting straight up into the sky, the bullet had been diverted by the head of the hammer. Picking up the hammer, Omar saw that the bullet had knocked a notch out of it, creating shrapnel. Omar noticed that he, too, was bleeding slightly from little pricks around his chest where tiny pieces of lead and metal had lodged into his flesh.

Once again Omar sought the help of his neighbor Jesús. It wasn't hard to convince Jesús that the whole thing was an accident, and he agreed to accompany them to Waslala. Maybe Jesús could help Omar convince the doctors that it had been an accident.

The emergency room doctor assured them that the wounds were not dangerous. Some of the shrapnel had gone through the flesh and come back out, and the rest would work its way out slowly with time. And the doctor believed their story about the bizarre accident, so there was no trouble at all. After Yuri's arm had been bandaged, the three pioneers hiked back up the mountain. That evening Omar and Yuri hashed over the details of the day.

"I'm getting rid of this rifle!" Omar declared firmly. "Guns only bring me trouble. I'll sell it as soon as I can."

"I tell you, Omar, I'm selling out. I can't trust anybody to be honest. Not even you!" Bato stood in the yard of his Waslala house. He was angry, and he wasn't hiding it.

Determined to not let his own anger get the best of him, Omar gulped. "Sure. Go ahead and sell. I'll even help you. But don't you dare say that I've been stealing from you!"

Bato quieted down, slightly scared of this nephew who had killed two people in anger.

"I've been helping you all these years, and all the thanks I get is a scolding," Omar threw in. "I won't have it. I haven't been stealing your money. You're out of your head!"

"But the figures don't match up," Bato complained, frowning deeply. "Something's not right."

"What do you or I know about keeping figures anyway?" Omar sneered, clenching his fists behind his back. "Since we both went through college, right?"

Bato didn't answer, and Omar looked him in the eye. "During the past six months while you were in the United States, we made a bunch of money, but we also spent a lot of it. You told me to buy that assault rifle, for example. The cash I handed over to you yesterday was all that was left over. Show me where I spent any money unwisely. But if you can't, then why don't you at least thank me for taking care of your place. Then shut up!"

Just like that, the Montenegro kingdom on the mountain crumbled. Omar helped Bato sell the cattle and the horses until all Omar had left was old Mil Colores. Then, for much less than it was worth, Bato sold the farm that Omar had worked so hard to fix up. He and Yuri packed their things and moved back to his own land.

Fortunately, Bato allowed Omar to cut and saw a few trees from his place to build a new house on Omar's property. It wasn't fancy, but anything was better than the hovel he had lived in before. The new three-room house had a tin roof and board walls.

Omar suspected that Donaldo and Doris were the guilty party in the mismanagement of Bato's investments. He rode in to Waslala one day and angrily accused the whole clan. "I just discovered that we have a rat in this house, and I hate rats! Get out immediately. Your pay for taking care of the place is the stuff you already stole."

Donaldo wasn't at home right then, but Omar kept watch while Doris, José Adán, and Gloria cleared out all of their things. When Doris gave Omar the key, he locked the house and headed back up the mountain. The only thing that gave him a tiny touch of remorse was how sad José Adán looked. Omar sighed, hoping José Adán hadn't been involved. He knew the boy wasn't really that kind of person.

Several weeks later, Omar met Donaldo on the street in Waslala. "Donaldo," he warned, "I'm so disappointed that I have to call you my cousin. Please ask God that you don't ever cross my path again. If you were worth the lead to pump you full of bullets, I would surely do it. But you aren't worth that much. I'll let you go, but don't you dare ever mess with me again."

Donaldo stood silently, knowing better than to offend Omar. Omar swung his horse around and cantered on down the road, seething with hatred for the man.

Omar was back on his own again. It was just Ranger, Yuri, and himself on top of that lonely mountain.

After the Montenegro kingdom collapsed, Yuri's second year on the mountain started out poorly. The coffee harvest was just as much work as usual, but the price was down. She and Omar almost killed themselves getting the harvest in, with hardly anything to show for it at the end. Only the joy of expecting a baby helped assuage the pain of their lonely existence and gave them hope for the future. Ranger continued to be a source of companionship and entertainment for Omar.

Toward the end of the coffee harvest, Omar lost his temper at the inefficiency of his hired help, and they all walked out on him. Suddenly, he had only Yuri to help him finish the last of the coffee picking.

One cloudy morning, despite being six months pregnant, Yuri helped pick coffee for hours. Just before noon, a heavy rain fell and soaked them to the skin. "Let's go home," Omar decided. "You need some dry clothes, Yuri, and we can eat lunch at home instead of out here in this weather."

Omar, Yuri, and Ranger set out in single file. Omar led the way, carrying a heavy sack of coffee. Yuri carried the baskets they used to gather the beans. Ranger came last, just as wet and cold and miserable as the rest. Even after the rain stopped, the wet bushes along the trail dumped their moisture as the trio pushed their way through.

As Omar entered the yard, dodging the drips from the surrounding orange trees, he was happily thinking about a fire on the hearth and some hot coffee with a tasty cooked meal. Yuri was shivering and thinking about dry clothes. As they approached the house, Ranger began to act strangely nervous, pushing past and whining a little.

What's wrong with that dog? Omar wondered, following him closely.

The main living area in Omar's new house consisted of an open-air porch under a tin roof. The two closed rooms lay at the end of the open area, and Omar and Yuri always locked both doors when they left the house. As Omar and Yuri rounded the corner and entered the open space, they saw Ranger sniffing under the storage room door, whining as if in distress.

Omar couldn't figure out what was wrong, but since he needed to open the storage room anyway to put the baskets away, he dropped the bag of coffee and marched over to unlock it. While Omar was finding the key and unlocking the door, Ranger whined at Omar's feet, digging desperately at the crack under the door. Yuri waited, the baskets in her hand.

No sooner had Omar unlatched the door, when Ranger crashed through, racing toward the bed at the end of the room where Milo usually slept when he helped on the farm. Ranger leaped up onto the bed, snarling. Before Omar's eyes even had time to adjust to the gloomy darkness, Ranger had attacked something that was coiled up on the pillow. Instantly the dog started yowling. To Omar's horror, Ranger bounced back off the bed, a five-foot fer-de-lance viper latched onto his face.

A horrible fight ensued. All Omar could do was croak, "A yellow jaw!"[24]

Although Omar had his *cutacha* handy, he couldn't enter the fray for fear of harming his dog, so he just watched in horror.

When Yuri heard the dreaded words *yellow jaw,* the terror of all tropical mountain folk, she felt trapped. No way was she going to go toward the storage room! She crawled up onto the woodstove and cried again and again, "Omar, what's going on?"

After a minute of fighting, Ranger shook the snake off his face. The dog pounced on the snake, grabbing it by the neck, right behind the head. He flung the snake back and forth until it was dead, and then he dropped it triumphantly at Omar's feet.

---

24   Yellow jaw: one of the common names for the fer-de-lance, a deadly pit viper.

Yuri wouldn't come down off the woodstove until Omar had pitched the snake over the hillside. Then she crawled down, pale and trembling. Omar, also pale and shaking, told her the horrible story, all the while petting his dog and constantly checking the cheek that was swelling fast. Kneeling down and caressing his dog tenderly, Omar whispered repeatedly, "Ranger, you saved my life! Are you going to die?"

44

FUGITIVE AGAIN

COLD WIND AND rain slashed at the mountaintop and screamed as it flung its gusty torrents down into the valley. The little house among the orange trees trembled with each blast. From outside, it looked deserted, except for a large brindle dog, whining and digging at the door of his master's bedroom.

Omar was lonely and miserable, lying in bed shivering with fever. At ten o'clock in the morning, he still hadn't gotten up—he was too sick. He had been dimly aware of Ranger whining at the door all morning, but he was mostly oblivious to the wind, the rain, and the dog.

A month before Yuri's due date, Omar had sent her back to Regadío so she could have the baby under her mother's care. Omar stayed all alone on the mountaintop to take care of the farm. Milo had left; he was done living on the mountaintop with its inhospitable conditions. No wonder Omar was feeling so sad and lonely that morning.

Ever since the snakebite, Ranger's health had been failing. He was shriveling up like a prune. And now, for the last twenty-four hours, Omar had felt like he was shriveling up too. He felt awful.

Toward noon Omar fell into a restless sleep, and Ranger became desperate. The floor of Omar's new house was hard-packed dirt, but Ranger's ferocious digging caused it to give way. Before Omar knew what happened, Ranger had dug his way under the door and surprised him by licking his face. "Master, what's wrong?" he seemed to be saying.

Omar stretched out his hand and weakly stroked his friend's head. "We need each other," he whispered. "We're both sick."

Ranger, content to know that his master was still alive, lay down beside the bed. Omar, feeling lonely and maybe just a little bit better, continued his monologue with the mutt. "You know what, Ranger? I saved your life. If I hadn't brought you up here, you would have been killed. And you saved my life when you killed the snake. So we take turns."

Ranger's stub tail bobbed as he basked in his master's attention. Omar caressed the dog as he spoke. "Now we're both sick. Not just our bodies, but we're also sick of life—sick of being hurt by people. The question we both have is, will we ever heal?"

Ranger whined a soft answer.

"When I moved up here, Ranger, I was running away from myself. I wanted to make sure I wouldn't harm anyone else. I've isolated myself from the rest of the world.

"This world hasn't been good to me, Ranger. It ruined my life, just like it ruined yours. At one time I thought this old world was the best one could find. But now I understand that the world is death. It brings only sadness, solitude, hate, hurts, evil, enemies, and failure. Nothing good have I received from this horrible old world.

"And now I realize that I only have two friends left—you and Yuri. And now even Yuri is gone."

The weather cleared the next day, and Omar got better. But Ranger didn't. While Omar was still all alone on the mountaintop, waiting to hear that Yuri's baby was born, Ranger died. Omar wept as he carried the lifeless dog to the coffee patch, where he dug a shallow grave. There, where no one could see the tears gushing down his face, Omar buried his friend. That day it felt like something in Omar died and was buried too.

Then one happy morning Omar got a message on the radio. "The baby is here!"

Omar packed his bags, left the house in the care of a neighbor lady, and headed for Estelí. Leaving behind the sad memories of his dog, Omar rushed toward the two people he still needed, and who needed him—Yuri and the baby she had named Karen.

In Regadío, Omar discovered how much he had missed Yuri. But what made him the happiest of all was to finally have his own little baby girl to hold and to love. His bond with Yuri doubled as he held his little daughter.

Afraid that little Karen would pick up mountain leprosy,[25] a common malady in San Pablo de Las Vallas, Omar and Yuri stayed in Estelí for three months. After Karen was strong enough to face the harsh mountaintop life, Omar and Yuri returned to Waslala.

Omar planned to live in the safety of his mountaintop for a long time. Though he felt freer and freer to travel to Estelí and Regadío, he still thought that San Pablo de Las Vallas was the safest place in Nicaragua for him to live for the time being.

It was midnight. Clouds raced across the sky ahead of a stiff wind. A full moon peeked between the clouds, watching a drama unfold on the top of the mountain. In the little house, half hidden under the orange trees, Omar had fallen into a deep sleep.

Milo and his cousin Gustabito were sneaking up to the shack. "Don't you dare get close to that house before you identify yourself," Gustabito warned. "Omar will shoot to kill if he gets it into his head that we're robbers."

"Naw, Omar knows me well, and I know how to handle him," Milo bragged. Then, as Gustabito took refuge behind an orange tree, Milo walked boldly across the moonlit yard and knocked on the door.

Instantly, Omar was out of bed. Snatching up the pistol he kept under his pillow, he leaped to the door. Through the crack at the side of the door, he spotted a man standing in the shadows. The moon held its breath and a cloud covered its face as Omar aimed the pistol through the crack toward the intruder's heart, his index finger ready to pull the trigger.

"Omar! It's me . . . Milo."

---

25   Mountain leprosy: leishmaniasis, a parasitic infection spread by sandflies.

The quiet night erupted as Omar flung open the door. He leaped out onto the yard snarling, "Milo, you crazy brute! I almost shot you!"

Speechless, Milo stood still in the moonlight, his head bowed.

"What in the world brings you up here this time of night?" Omar hissed. He was startled when Gustabito stepped out of the shadows.

"Omar, they're out looking for you," Gustabito said urgently. "They came to Estelí and questioned Fermín and Miriam separately."

"Wait a minute!" Omar barked. "Start over. Who's looking for who?"

"The authorities," Milo gasped, wringing his hands.

"The gringos from Los Angeles! The FBI from the United States!" Gustabito added earnestly.

"Humph, they might be looking for me in Estelí and Regadío, but they won't find me here in these boonies." Omar glanced toward the house where Yuri stood in the doorway listening.

"Don't be so sure," Gustabito rejoined. "Guess what they told Fermín and Miriam both? They said, 'We know Omar is hiding in the mountains of Waslala, and we know he was here on a visit just last week.'"

Suddenly the mountaintop seemed cold. Omar glanced around, as if the FBI was about to pounce. "Come on in," he suggested quickly. Inside he asked, "What do my parents think I should do?"

"Run!" Milo declared.

"But where to?" Omar wailed, running his fingers through his hair. "I seem to have killed all my options. I can't go to the United States. I can't go to Costa Rica. I can't leave the country. What does Nicaragua have to offer me?"

"Look," Gustabito said, "the folks back home are suggesting Managua. There among the multitudes they won't find you. They won't even think of looking for you there. That's the best they can come up with."

Omar nodded slowly. "They're right. I must pack my bags right now. I need to get to Waslala in time to catch the three o'clock bus. Yuri, can you pack my clothes?"

"What will the baby and I do?" Yuri moaned, her face full of fear. "Karen and I can't stay up here alone!"

"You and Karen go back to Estelí with Milo and Gustabito," Omar ordered, looking from one person to the other. "Tomorrow, Milo, you arrange things around here. Go see if the neighbor lady can come take care of the place temporarily. But the best thing for me is to get out of here as fast as I can. Those FBI agents could be working with the local Waslala police and could have this house surrounded even before daylight. The local police who came here to investigate for marijuana know where I live, so they could easily come up here again, especially if the FBI pays them."

The little house hummed with action now. Lighting a couple of lamps, they all pitched in and helped get things ready. By two o'clock in the morning, Omar was hurrying down the mountain, carrying a heavy knapsack. The air was cold, and the moon was dipping toward the west. Yuri and the men had stayed at the house, trying to get some sleep.

After the arrangements were made the next day, Yuri and the two men abandoned the mountaintop. As they fled, Yuri wondered if she would ever come back to San Pablo de Las Vallas again.

The meeting in Estelí was a serious one. In the living room of Omar's cousin Luis, Yuri was surrounded by folks who were concerned for both her and Omar—siblings, cousins, and her mother Maura. What would be best for Yuri and Karen under the circumstances?

Omar's family reasoned that Yuri should stay in Estelí to wait for Omar. "Omar didn't abandon Yuri as if he were separating from her," his sister explained. "He just had to run, to who knows where. But as soon as he gets settled, he'll want Yuri and Karen to join him."

Maura, concerned for her daughter's welfare, wanted her to come home to Regadío to live with her parents where she belonged.

Yuri didn't know which to choose.

"If Omar didn't abandon my daughter, then why is he not here to prove that he'll take care of her and this tiny baby?" Maura argued hotly. "And anyway, Neftalí, her father, told me to bring her home."

"It's easy to understand why Omar had to flee," Cándida replied, piqued at Maura for wanting to take Yuri home. "The FBI carried a huge folder on all the crimes Omar committed in Los Angeles."

Yuri was suddenly all ears. She knew, of course, that Omar had lived a wicked life in the United States, but she didn't know many details except that he had been into drug trafficking. She suspected that he had killed someone, but she had no idea who or how.

"Mama says the FBI interview was awful," Cándida continued. "They had photos of the crime scene, including one of Gema after she was dead. When Omar heard about all the proof they had, he had to run. But he won't abandon Yuri and Karen. He'll come back for them."

Maura shrugged. "I guess it's your decision, Yuri. You're his wife."

The horrible story about Gema's death helped Yuri make up her mind quickly. "I'll go home with my mother," she answered quietly.

Everyone accepted Yuri's decision, and the meeting dispersed.

Omar's cousin Armando in Managua seemed glad to take him in and hide him. But Omar was restless, holed up in the city with nothing to do. After his active, productive life on the mountaintop farm, he felt useless and hedged in. Even Waslala, which had sometimes been a nightmare for him, now seemed attractive compared to hot, stuffy, boring Managua.

Sometimes he was tempted to return to dealing in narcotics. He knew he could get a false passport and travel to Mexico. There his business could grow and flourish. But, no, that wouldn't work. He would only end up in the same old frenzy of making money and a name for himself. Then he would kill someone again. He'd better stay where he was and make the best of things.

Omar missed Yuri and especially little Karen. But for now, there was no way to get close to Estelí. And though Omar would never have told anyone, his heart ached for his dog Ranger.

After hiding in Managua for a month, Omar worked up the nerve to travel to Waslala and ask his two uncles to help him sell his farm. Waslala, he was sure, would never be a safe place for him to live again since the FBI knew he had been hiding there.

A month later, Omar went again to Waslala and sold his farm for much less than it was worth, along with the rifle that Yuri hated. This time, he stayed in Waslala for a week, trying to sell old Mil Colores.

The old mare had two good selling points. She was a strong, tough animal for hauling cargo, and she had thrown some beautiful foals. In fact, right now she had a beautiful little mule foal that trotted beside her like a shadow wherever she went. Little Jack was a sight to behold, head lifted and stepping high, speckled in white and red.

That week, while Omar tried to sell Mil Colores and her offspring, he rented pasture from a lady named María who lived up on top of Papayo Hill. Omar respected María, knowing that she was a member of the church José Adán had joined. He was intrigued with her friendliness and the modest way she and her daughters dressed.

During the day, Omar led the mare into town and tied her up with her foal at a strategic place while he whiled away the time, waiting on a sale. In the evening he led Mil Colores up the hill and turned her into María's pasture.

By the time the week was almost up, Omar was feeling desperate. In spite of Little Jack's cuteness, Omar was having no success at selling his animals. *I'll try one more day*, he decided. *If Mil Colores doesn't sell tomorrow, I'll take her out to Don Chema's and rent pasture for a month and go back to Managua.*

As he led the pair up Papayo Hill one last time, a white Land Cruiser careened down the hill and passed him. Omar chuckled when he saw how the people didn't even notice him, staring instead at the funny little mule. The driver actually stuck his head out as they passed, almost running the vehicle off the road. Ridiculous! Everyone loved to gawk at the cute little jack, but no one was buying.

The next morning when Omar arrived at María's place to catch the mare to head out for Waslala one more time, María came out to greet him. "Good morning, Omar," she said. "Yesterday, when you were coming up the hill, the pastor of my church saw you leading your mare up the hill, and he liked that little mule."

Omar smiled, realizing it was probably the man who had almost driven off the road, staring at the mule. "Does he drive a white Land Cruiser?" he asked.

"Yes," María answered, smiling. "He really liked that mule and asked if you could take it to his farm today for him to see it."

Omar's hopes leaped. "Sure! Where does he live?"

María gave Omar directions, adding, "If you have any problem finding it, just ask anybody where the gringo lives. Everybody knows Pastor Pablo."

The gringo's place was back a zigzagging lane, off the main street. As Omar led the mare and its offspring in the lane, he spied a spacious yard and the house with its front covered with ivy. Feeling a little timid, Omar hesitated. These people were probably rich and might have big fierce guard dogs. He'd better signal to let them know someone was coming.

"Morning!" Omar shouted.

Several children and a middle-aged man stepped out onto the porch to see who was calling. When the man saw Omar hesitantly waiting in the lane, he hollered, "Come on in. The dog is tied."

Omar led the mare into the yard and tied her to a fence. The friendly pastor smiled as he shook Omar's hand. "My name is Pablo," he said, "and it looks like María told you that I'm interested in seeing that cute little mule."

Omar answered, "My name is Omar Montenegro, and, yes, I want to sell this mare along with her foal."

"I'll tell you the truth," Pablo said, stepping closer. "I'm not really interested in buying the mare. But my brother-in-law Luis from Managua is here. He has a little farm up on the mountainside. I knew he'd like the little mule and might buy it. I'll call him so he can see this delightful little jack."

In a matter of minutes Pablo was back with a whole row of people in tow. All of Pablo's six children followed him, plus Luis and his two children. Everybody's attention was drawn to the little jack.

"That's one cute little jack!" Luis announced in English, appraising the foal standing grandly beside his mother. The little mule, as fuzzy as a teddy bear and as speckled as a bird's egg, held his head high and pointed his long ears straight up like a jackrabbit's as he tried to hide behind his mama. His black eyes sparkled, watching the gaggle of people staring back at him. "So cute, but its mama is as ugly as a hyena."

Pablo chuckled and answered Luis in English. "I knew you would like the mule. Man, if I'd have the money, I'd buy him without batting an eye. But I can't afford it right now."

"How much does the guy want?" Luis asked, still staring at the jack.

Pablo turned to Omar and reverted to Spanish. "How much?"

"Seven thousand córdobas," Omar answered, grinning as the gringos discussed the mare and the baby. What these people didn't know was that since he had lived in Los Angeles, he understood some English.

"Whew! Does he think that mare is made of gold?" Luis exclaimed. "Isn't that way too high for that nag?"

"Yes, it's high for the mare," Pablo answered. "But just think what that little mule is going to be worth in a year from now. The mule alone will be worth that much."

"Maybe in a year from now," Luis agreed, chuckling. "But that's not today."

"The ugly mare is worth about three thousand," Pablo acknowledged, "and the baby is worth about two thousand. Why don't you make him an offer?"

"I want to talk with my wife first," Luis answered and disappeared into the house.

Would these gringos ever get around to buying Omar's mare?

Minutes later Luis came out again, his wife and Pablo's wife with him. Again, Omar had to hear all about the ugliness of his mare and the cuteness of the little mule. Finally Luis said, "Pablo, offer him five thousand for the pair."

"I can offer that," Pablo answered, "but he won't sell for that. I'd offer him at least six."

"But six thousand is too high!" Luis retorted. "Man, I wish there were a way to buy the mule without that ugly mare. I don't even want that mare. So it's like I'm paying all that money for just the colt."

"But remember, Luis," Pablo insisted, "once the mule is weaned, the mare is still worth something. That's the way he figures. Maybe you could sell her then."

"Boy, I'm just not so sure..."

Eventually everybody except Pablo and his son Jacinto got tired of the wheeling and dealing and went back inside. Pablo turned to Omar and confessed, "Luis doesn't like the mare, but he does really like the mule. So he doesn't want to pay more than five thousand córdobas."

"I can come down a little," Omar answered, "but not that much. That would be a giveaway."

Pablo nodded. "What shall we do?" Pablo asked his son in English. "Luis wants the mule, but I don't think he'll pay what this man wants."

"Yeah, I don't think they'll make a deal," Jacinto answered. "Luis is just too tight."

"But we have to give this fellow an answer," Pablo replied. "I'm sure he's tired of waiting. I'll go see what Luis says."

After a whole hour and several trips in to talk to Luis, Pablo finally came to an agreement with Omar. Luis paid six thousand for Mil Colores and the cute little jack.

Pablo apologized for the delay. "It's just that Luis can't stand that mare," he admitted.

Omar just chuckled, and as he walked out the lane with the money in his pocket, he almost laughed out loud. If only those folks knew he had understood most of what they had said in English, they would have been shocked!

When Omar got back to María's place, he told her about how the gringos had said ugly things about the mare but had loved the mule. He hoped María would tell those gringos what all he had heard. Maybe that would teach them to be more careful about what they said!

The next morning Omar left Waslala the way he had first come, riding high on the pipes of an old IFA and hanging on for dear life. Looking out over the familiar, picturesque countryside, he felt sad. *I'll probably never be back*, he realized.

What did his future hold now? He had no idea. He would just have to live one day at a time.

45

EIGHT PROMISES

OMAR HAD LIVED in Managua for two months when he finally found courage to make a secret trip to Estelí. As far as he knew, the FBI had not made further attempts to find him. Once in Estelí, Omar sent word to Yuri to come see him. Despite her father's warnings, she sneaked off and spent several days with him. It was a good time of bonding for the little family. Omar loved his little Karen, and it tore at his heart to see them leave again.

Miriam and Milo also came to see him in Estelí. Milo was eager to share his news with Omar. "Bato is helping me go to the United States," he explained. "I need money to go. Now that you've sold your place, I wonder if you would loan me the money."

"I'll think about it," Omar answered.

"I'll pay you back as soon as I get a job up there," Milo promised, smiling at his older brother. "Remember how you wanted to go to the United States so badly? Now it's my turn."

In the end, Omar did loan Milo money to go to the United States. It was still several months before Milo would be ready to travel, but Omar was glad to help the brother who had stuck with him through thick and thin in the Waslala mountains.

Bato, apparently forgetting his Waslala grievances, also approached Omar. He had invested his Waslala money on a remote farm in San Ramon, twenty miles from Matagalpa. "Omar, San Ramon is even safer than Managua. Why don't you move onto my new farm and help take care of it while I go to the United States?"

Omar was so tired of Managua that he consented immediately. Before moving out to the beautiful farm where the cool climate and the coffee groves reminded him of San Pablo de Las Vallas, he sent for Yuri. He hoped they could be a happy family again. But Yuri refused. Omar was still a fugitive, and Yuri's father Neftalí didn't think it wise for Yuri to get back with him again.

Omar took care of Bato's farm for only a month when a new situation brought an abrupt change of plans.

On the San Ramon farm, Omar had no way of communicating with his family unless Bato showed up. One day when Bato had come to the farm, he hinted that Omar's mother was having trouble with her health. Alarmed, Omar pressured Bato until he reluctantly admitted that Miriam had been to the hospital and had her gall bladder removed.

"Is she okay now?" Omar inquired anxiously.

"Oh, yes," Bato lied, wanting Omar to stay on the farm. He was soon to leave for the United States and couldn't afford to lose Omar. "She's recuperating well."

Omar sighed in relief. He was sorry his poor mother had been ailing, but he was comforted to think that Miriam had always been healthy, working hard and serving others unselfishly, especially her children.

Unexpectedly, a new feeling washed over Omar like a tsunami after an earthquake. He realized how deeply he missed his mother, and he regretted that because of the way he had treated her, she had no idea how much he loved her.

Believing Bato's story about his mother's health, Omar made a quick trip to Waslala to collect some kettles, pots and pans, and other things he had left behind. Forced to stay overnight in Waslala and wanting to catch the early bus, he asked for permission to sleep in a storage building close to the bus stop. That evening, Omar nestled down early among the sacks of corn and beans and went to sleep, hoping he wouldn't have a nightmare.

At midnight he awoke suddenly, sensing a presence beside him. It was so dark that he could barely see his hand in front of his face, but his hair stood on end, and his flesh crawled. Fear coursed through him as he imagined a shadow passing by his side.

Was a robber creeping up on him? Or had an evil spirit come to torment him?

Omar sprang savagely at the dark being, grappling for its legs to bring it down. But all he embraced was thin air.

Rummaging through his belongings, Omar finally found his flashlight. But when he shone the light around the room, nothing was with him in the huge storage room except dozens of sacks of corn and beans.

Trembling, Omar flopped back onto his bed of bean sacks, but sleep had fled. Troubled thoughts haunted him. *Something terrible must be happening somewhere,* Omar surmised in anguish. *Or is something terrible going to happen to me?* Why did he have this heavy foreboding feeling? Was someone going to die?

He was gripped by the strong realization that Bato had lied to him about his mother. Something bad was happening to her. While he waited for the bus to leave that morning, his heart screamed, *I must find out what's happening to my mother. Tomorrow I must go see her.*

When he arrived back at the farm in San Ramon, Bato was there. Without ado, Omar announced, "Bato, I'm leaving. I have to go see my mother. I have a feeling she isn't well."

"What do you think you can do?" Bato sneered. "Are you a doctor that you can heal her? Are you God that you have some special touch?"

Without a word, Omar turned on his heel and left. In his heart he snarled, *That beast! To him the farm is more important than my mother!*

What Omar didn't know was that Fermín had come to the farm in San Ramon two days before with a message. "Tell Omar his mother is asking for him. She wants to say goodbye to him before she dies."

When Omar reached the road at the end of the lane, a pickup truck came by, and Omar signaled it to stop. As if sent by God, the driver of the pickup not only confirmed that he was going to Estelí, but also offered Omar a ride to Uncle Gustavo's place in Estelí.

"How's Mama?" Omar demanded when he arrived in Estelí at the home of his mother's uncle.

"Why didn't you come quicker?" Gustavo asked, frowning. "She's been very sick. She's been asking especially for you."

"I didn't know!" Omar cried.

"Didn't Bato tell you that her operation went bad, and she's dying?" Gustavo asked. "I sent word with your father for you to come."

"Bato didn't tell me anything!" Omar stammered, confused. "But I had a nightmare. I knew something was wrong, and I came right away. Where is Mama?"

"Be brave," Gustavo admonished, seeing Omar's distress. "Your mother is in the hospital. They operated on her gall bladder, but something went wrong, so they had to open her up again. Things are still not good. Go see her quickly. She's been calling for you desperately."

Omar took off for the hospital at a run. After a few blocks, he caught a taxi. "I need to see my mother," Omar gasped to the guard at the hospital entrance. "She's dying, and she's calling for me." When the guard saw Omar's tears, he had mercy and let him in immediately.

Omar hurried down the corridors and finally found his sister Jáqueling at the doorway of a hospital room. "Oh, my brother!" Jáqueling cried. "Our mother is dying!"

Omar ran into Jáqueling's arms, and they cried together. "I've been such a wicked son," he wept on his sister's shoulder. "I've made my mother suffer so much!"

Pulling away from his sister's embrace, Omar turned to go see his mother. "Try not to cry," Jáqueling warned. "It might not be good for her emotionally. She is very weak."

Omar tiptoed into the gloomy hospital room. Nothing could have prepared him for the sight of his mother lying gaunt and pale on the hospital bed. Miriam had been reduced to a mere skeleton, attached to tubes running everywhere. His mother's expression told him that she had been watching for him.

"Son, how are you?" she whispered.

"It doesn't matter how *I* am," Omar answered, tears filling his eyes. "I'm okay. What matters is how *you* are." Strong emotions flooded over him again, and he started to cry—he just couldn't help it.

"Son, don't cry. Didn't your uncle tell you that I was sick?"

"No! I came only because I felt something strange in here," Omar answered, laying his hand on his chest. "Bato hid the truth from me. I'll never forgive him!"

"Omar, do forgive your uncle," Miriam admonished kindly. "What's important is that you're here now."

Unable to contain himself any longer, Omar knelt beside his mother's bed and held her frail hand. "Mama," he sobbed, "don't talk, because I can see it is difficult for you to speak. So just listen. I've come a long way to tell you this."

Tears trickled down Miriam's face.

"I've come to tell you that I'm sorry for being such a wicked son. I've quit my bad ways, and I'm sorry for the way I made you suffer. I promise I'll stay by your side until you get out of this hospital."

Omar's mother, Miriam.

Miriam was in pitiful condition, with a tube down her throat and a catheter bag hanging on the side of the bed. She looked so pale and weak. Only a miracle from God would get her out of this hospital. "Mama," Omar said, grasping for hope, "God's going to get you out of here."

"Don't worry, son, I feel the same way. I have faith that God is going to heal me."

Later that day, the surgeon who had operated on Miriam came out to the waiting room to report to the family. Omar listened impatiently, along with the others, but the doctor's explanation made little sense. The doctor clinched the report, saying, "Be strong, family. There is nothing more we can do for your mother. Only your prayers and a miracle from God can save her now."

The family looked at each other, horrified. No sooner had the doctor left than Omar turned to Miriam's brother Reinaldito, who had studied medicine. "Reinaldito, did you understand that report?" Omar asked. "It didn't make sense to me."

"You're right," Reinaldito agreed. "Something's fishy. That surgeon didn't explain why they had to operate on Miriam twice and why there's nothing more they can do now. Look, I have connections here in this hospital. I'll check this out, and I'll be back."

A half hour later, Reinaldito was back with another doctor in tow. "We were right. I found this colleague who studied medicine with me and works here. He happens to know the case." Reinaldito turned to his friend and paused.

"Say on," Omar barked.

"During Miriam's first operation, the doctor made a serious surgical error and unknowingly punctured her intestines," the young doctor explained. "By the time they cut her open the second time, she was full of infection. The truth is, they don't know how to repair the damage. That's why she's dying."

A profound hush fell over the waiting room. Omar looked from face to face. What should they do now?

Reinaldito continued, "If you'd like, my friend will help you. But first you must ask the hospital here to release Miriam and transfer her to Managua immediately. Managua has better doctors and more experienced specialists. If you agree, I'll help start the paperwork right now!"

"Yes, please help us!" Omar exclaimed. "We want to do all we can to save our mimita."

Raising his hand, the doctor asked for one favor. "Please don't tell anyone that I told you this story, because I could get into big trouble."

"Don't worry," Omar replied quickly. "All we care is that we get Mimita to better hands in Managua. We won't cause any trouble here. And we all thank you very much for your help!"

The next day Miriam was transferred to the Managua hospital in an ambulance, and her family followed. As soon as Miriam arrived, she was wheeled to the operating room for her third operation.

Three and a half hours later, Omar's sister Selene came out to the waiting room to report. "What the doctor in Estelí told us was true. They had severed the urethra and punctured the intestines. Worst of all, they didn't repair the damage; they just sewed her shut.

"These doctors here in Managua did all they could. They repaired the damage and cleaned her internally. But they aren't sure she'll make it. They told us to pray, because only God can save her now. If she lives, they'll know God helped them during this operation."

While Miriam remained in intensive care, the family waited. Anytime, they might receive news of Miriam's death. All of Omar's brothers and sisters had arrived in Managua except for Milo, who was in the United States. Omar kept him informed by phone calls, and Milo started sending money for the hospital expenses from his U.S. wages. Miriam's children wept as they suffered with their mother. They felt so unworthy of their mother's love. Slowly, Omar's mass of emotions transformed themselves into a prayer. How could he, such a wicked son, pray to a holy God? And yet, as both doctors had said, God was the only One who could help them now. Omar could tell that his siblings were praying too.

In his desperation and pain, Omar's heart cried out to the God who loved him and had been waiting for this moment for many long years. As he sat outside on the hard cold *pollos,*[26] weeping, the cry of his heart changed to an audible prayer.

"Father, we are not worthy of the mother You gave us. All these years we have not appreciated what we had—not until now that we're losing her." Omar burst out crying again. It seemed as if that was all he could do lately. The heart that had been as hard as a stone was finally softening.

That evening when the family gathered, Omar had a serious message for them. "Look, we have to trust in God," he said. "That's all we have left. Let's be honest. We've all been bad sons and daughters. I know I've been the worst. I caused our mother so much suffering. But not anymore."

---

26 *Pollos:* cement seats set up out in the open in the public parks and hospital yards.

The rest of the family nodded in agreement and listened quietly as their older brother shared his heart, tears streaming down his face. "Let's promise to change," Omar urged his siblings. "Let's seek God and change our ways. Maybe if we promise to stop our wickedness, God will hear our prayers and let Mama live. I, for one, promise to change. If Mama comes out of this hospital alive, she'll discover that she has a brand-new son. From this day on, I'll never touch liquor again."

Omar was overcome with emotion. "Maybe, just maybe, it's not too late to show our mother that we can be better children."

Again, the siblings agreed.

"Let's all eight of us make a solemn vow to God and to our mother," Omar suggested. "This vow must be from the bottom of our hearts. Each one of us will be responsible to make it happen. If God gives us our mother back, we will thank Him with our lives. We'll change, and she'll be the happiest mother alive."

His brothers and sisters nodded in agreement, and Omar escaped outdoors to be alone. Never before had he made such a serious speech about spiritual things. As sunset settled over the sprawling hospital grounds, Omar found his favorite *pollo* and lay down. He was overwhelmed by his own little sermon.

Omar closed his eyes, his head thrown back over the hard armrest. *Oh, Lord, show me the path to You, and I promise that I will follow it. I promise that I'll change. I promise to be a better son for Mimita and also for You. I won't make Mimita suffer again.* And then as an afterthought, Omar threw in, *And I promise to change so* You *don't have to suffer so much watching me live in such wickedness.*

The grackles were cackling their good night as they settled into a huge laurel bush. But for once Omar didn't hear their loud racket, because the man who used to have such a hard wicked heart was still praying. *And Lord,* Omar squeezed out between sobs, *I promise I won't leave this hospital until I can leave with my mother alive and well.*

46

HOME AGAIN

AS THE LONG shadows of evening extended across the huge hospital complex, Omar strode purposefully down the long corridor. He swung in to one of the rooms and made his way toward bed number 233 nestled in the far corner.

Miriam was waiting for him, smiling weakly. "Good evening, my son," she whispered.

As he had been doing every evening, Omar knelt beside the bed and lifted his mother's pale hand. "Good evening, Mimita. How has the day been for you?"

After they had caught up with each other's news, Miriam whispered, "Son, you need to go home and get some rest!" She patted Omar's hand. "It's been several weeks now that you've been faithfully helping me here in this hospital."

Omar smiled. "No, Mama. Remember what I vowed. I won't leave this place until you can come with me. It's taking a long time, but thank the Lord, you're finally getting better."

During the first two weeks of Miriam's hospitalization, the family feared she would never get better. But then she had improved just enough to be moved out of intensive care. Jáqueling stayed with Miriam day and night. When she occasionally went home for a day, one of the other girls took her place. Whenever food or medicine was needed, Omar was the errand boy, ready to run for anything at a moment's notice.

At first the family encouraged Omar to go home to rest once in a while, but they finally gave up. To Omar, his vow was chiseled in stone, and staying near the hospital door had become his mission. "This is where I belong!" he said. "I don't mind sleeping on the porch. It's the least I can do for our mother!"

On the big porch beside the emergency room door was a U-shaped set of concrete benches. Here relatives sat and waited, often twenty-four hours a day, for news about the loved ones they had brought in. Omar had claimed one of the benches, and his life had taken on a strange routine.

One of Omar's sisters brought food to the hospital for Miriam and Omar. Every day Omar went in to see his mother during visiting hours. After they had chatted, Omar used the bathroom in the hospital room to take a shower. His sisters took his dirty clothes home to wash, leaving Omar a set of clean clothes every day.

Every two weeks Milo sent money from his wages in the United States. Milo had wanted to come home, but Omar, knowing how hard it was to get to the United States illegally, had convinced him to not spurn his opportunity. Besides, Milo's financial support was a godsend.

While Miriam recuperated, Omar had a lot of time to think. What would he do with his life once his mother was well? He couldn't forget about Waslala, and it appeared as though the FBI had forgotten him. Surely in Waslala, he could find work that he enjoyed. Omar was tired of being a fugitive. Maybe he should return to Waslala—and if the FBI caught him there, so be it.

One happy day, after Miriam had been in the hospital for a month, the doctors announced, "We're impressed at how your mother is recuperating. Every test shows improvement. Maybe in about four days we'll allow her to go home. Her healing is truly a miracle from God!"

Four days later, Omar waited at the hospital door as his frail mother came toward him in a wheelchair. She smiled, and he burst out crying, but this time his tears were tears of joy. His prayers had been answered by the Lord God Almighty.

Omar and Jáqueling took Miriam to her brother's place in a taxi. "Omar," Miriam whispered, "while I was sick in the hospital, I often asked the Lord to save my life for the sake of my children. I believe my children still need me."

Yes! Omar cheered under his breath. *We eight siblings must prove that our vows were serious—we must live changed lives.*

Omar stayed with his mother in Managua for a week. When Miriam was strong enough to travel, Omar went to Regadío to fix up her little house so it would be ready when she got home. His brothers Alvaro and Melvin helped with the repairs. Miriam returned to Regadío, safe and sound, and Omar made sure she was in good hands and well taken care of. He promised to visit her regularly.

During Omar's last week in Regadío, he urged Yuri to accompany him to Waslala again. Yuri was agreeable to giving it another try, but it was hard to convince her parents that Omar was changing. At last they agreed to let her go.

As Omar and his little family bounced to Waslala on the back of the IFA, Omar shared his Waslala dreams with Yuri. "Since Milo doesn't have to pay hospital bills anymore, I hope he'll start paying back his debt to me. Then I can buy a lot to build a house for us. Meanwhile, I'll rent a house to live in."

Yuri liked when Omar told her about his plans, but she seldom gave suggestions. She was shy, and Omar usually had concrete plans figured out on his own. "Sounds good," she answered, smiling at Omar.

Omar and Yuri located an old house to rent close to the Waslala River. Omar found work shoeing horses. Horses abounded in Waslala, and Omar was good at the job, but the income was meager.

Then one day Fermín arrived in Waslala with good news. Alvaro and Melvin were coming cross-country again with a string of horses and mules. "We're depending on you to help us sell the horses," Fermín told Omar.

"Sure!" Omar exclaimed. "I badly need the work!"

For the next several days, the four men made a splash just like in the old days, riding through town to sell the animals, dressed in their best cowboy clothes. When only two horses were left, Omar stayed at home one day to do some shoeing while Alvaro and Fermín went to town to sell the horses. That day Alvaro came home with a story.

"I sold that big red gelding to a gringo today," Alvaro told Omar.

"Oh, I know that gringo!" Omar answered, chuckling. "Did he give you a hard time making the deal? When I sold old Mil Colores to his brother-in-law, I met the gringo and his family. But that was one of the toughest deals I ever made." Omar told how he had understood what the gringos said about his ugly nag, and how they had adored the little mule.

Alvaro laughed. "Well, I was prancing down the road, showing what Old Red could do," he said, "when the gringo stopped me and asked if I was selling him. Guess what? He thought I was you and claimed they had bought old Mil Colores from me. I cleared that up quickly. I guess we do look a lot alike."

Omar chuckled in agreement.

"Once it came down to it," Alvaro said, "Pastor Pablo wasn't sure he wanted to buy the horse. But your old friend, Heriberto Rodriguez, was hanging around, and he helped me out. In about fifteen minutes he convinced Pastor Pablo that since he's such a big man, he needs a big horse." Alvaro laughed, slapping his leg.

"Did he drive a hard bargain?" Omar asked, smiling.

"Not bad. I asked for seven thousand córdobas, and he paid me six thousand. I still made a nice profit on the horse."

Early one morning Omar was out in town buying tortillas for breakfast. A small group of people was waiting to catch the five-thirty express bus to Managua. As he approached the group, he recognized Pastor Pablo, who had a suitcase beside him. Omar was going to walk past without saying anything, but the pastor stepped out of the group and hailed him. "Señor!" he said, smiling and shaking Omar's hand. "Are you the man that sold me the red horse?"

"No, that was my brother Alvaro," Omar answered, smiling back. "I'm Omar."

"Look, I don't have time to talk, or I'll miss my bus," Pastor Pablo said, seeing the bus rolling up the street. "But I need somebody to train a couple of mares, and you fellows are cowboys. Could you do that for me?" Pastor Pablo glanced at the bus as it screamed to a stop.

"Sure!" Omar replied quickly. "I need some work right now."

Pastor Pablo was already pushing his way toward the bus, but he smiled and hollered over his shoulder, "I'm on my way to the States. I'll be back in two weeks." Then he disappeared into the bus, and all Omar could do was nod and wave goodbye.

Later, as Omar and Yuri ate their tortillas and beans, he told her what had happened. "This is exciting!" he exclaimed. "That gringo has a farm, so maybe he has other work for me. That sure is what I need right now."

Two weeks later, Omar took Yuri and little Karen with him to Pastor Pablo's farm. As Pablo stepped out of the house to talk to Omar about training the mares, his young daughter came out to meet Yuri. The young girl picked up little Karen and led Yuri off toward a pond where they had a monkey on an island.

Omar and Pastor Pablo headed in the opposite direction to see the horses in the barn. Omar agreed to train them for a thousand córdobas apiece. He would come daily to catch and ride them and then bring them back to the farm for the night. As they parted, Omar said, "Okay, Pastor Pablo, I will be here tomorrow morning to give the biggest mare her first ride."

"Great!" Pastor Pablo said, shaking his hand. "This is just what I've wanted for quite some time—a cowpuncher who can train my mares so that I can ride them myself."

Omar and Yuri walked out Pablo's lane together, both talking at once. "That was one nice girl!" Yuri gushed. "Her name is Cynthia."

"Pastor Pablo is also a nice fellow to deal with," Omar said. "He already has a hired man, so I won't get that job. But if I can train his horses and help him with his cattle, it will be a good start. You know how much I love that kind of work."

"Cynthia invited me back anytime," Yuri marveled. "I can see she loves children, and she fell in love with Karen's curls. She took us to see the monkey and their scarlet macaw. I saw her mom from a distance, but I didn't talk to her."

"I'm starting to train the horses tomorrow," Omar interrupted. "They call them Ilana and Flicka. Strange names—they must be English. But both mares have some good blood in them. I really look forward to training good quality horses."

That night Omar and Yuri both felt a touch of hope. Might their lives actually improve back here in Waslala? These gringos were nice people, and something about them made Omar think of God. Maybe if he vowed to seek God, the pastor would help him find Him.

That night Omar dreamed—not a nightmare, but a beautiful dream. He and Yuri and little Karen were standing beside Pablo's pond, and the moment was peaceful and joyous. When Omar awoke, that's all he could remember. But it was enough. His sleep was sweeter than it had been for a long time.

47

TO LIVE AGAIN

A WEEK HAD passed, and Omar was enjoying his new job. In front of Pastor Pablo's barn stood a triangle of almond trees, and under the almond trees, one of the hired boys was sitting on his horse, ready to lead. Omar was preparing to mount Ilana, the handsome bay he had been hired to train. Omar grinned as he observed Pablo's whole family watching from the ivy-covered porch of the house. It tickled Omar that they wanted to see the rodeo. Were they secretly hoping that Ilana would buck on her first ride? Omar relished giving them a show.

Omar tied Ilana's halter rope to the other horse's tail and snubbed her close. Then he fished his big red bandana from his hip pocket and tied it around Ilana's head, blindfolding her. In one smooth movement, he swung up onto the saddle, nimble as a monkey.

Omar motioned, and the hired boy spurred his horse forward. Ilana followed, tame as a lamb. Omar grinned as they rode out into the bright sunshine and waved goodbye to the bystanders. He was doing what he loved most—working with horses.

The next week went by quickly. Omar was fast becoming friends with Pastor Pablo and his sons, Jacinto and Kenny. Yuri was also becoming good friends with Cynthia, who convinced Yuri to come to church one Wednesday evening. Of course, Omar went with her. Although it was totally new for both of them, it seemed right to go to the house of prayer. The rest of the church people were just as friendly as Pablo's family.

One day when Omar was out riding Ilana, he met a man everybody called Venganza.[27]

"What a lovely mare!" Venganza gushed. "Is she yours?"

"Nope, she's the gringo's," Omar answered. "I'm just training her. But yes, she's good quality, isn't she?"

Venganza chuckled, pointing to the bulge on Omar's waist. "Let me see your pistol."

Omar pulled out his .38 caliber and handed it over. Venganza was captivated by the gun. "What do you want for this pistol?" he asked.

Omar smiled and tucked his gun back where it belonged. "It's not for sale."

"Come on," Venganza drawled. "I'll make you an offer you can't turn down."

"Go ahead. That doesn't mean I'll sell."

"I have an empty lot at the other end of Waslala that I want to get rid of. It's worth more than the pistol, but you could have it for the gun and some cash. You could build a house on it."

This was not an offer to take lightly. Omar really did need a lot where he could build a house for his family. "Come to my house tomorrow and we'll talk," he told Venganza.

The next evening Omar was relaxing in the hammock in the yard just before the sun went down. He was grinning as he patted the head of his new hound dog. Pastor Pablo had given him the pup along with his pay for training his horses. Pablo's wife had gotten tired of the mutt tearing up everything he got hold of.

Omar surmised that Pablo didn't know how much a hound dog like this was worth to deer hunters. His ears hung longer than his snout. He was spotted, with the build of a champion—a perfect deer hound. Omar was sure the dog would soon be worth almost his weight in gold.

---

27   Venganza: revenge.

At that moment, Venganza walked up to Omar and shook his hand. Omar sat up in his hammock, ready to cut a close deal. Omar pretended at first that he had no interest in selling his pistol. When Venganza caressed the beauty, Omar knew he was gaining ground.

Venganza had been watching the hound dog hanging around Omar's hammock. "Omar," he said, "if you give me the .38 plus that mutt, you can have the building lot."

Omar gulped, hardly believing his good luck. The dog had basically cost him nothing. This was a better deal than he had imagined! In thirty minutes, the deal was settled, and Omar and Venganza made plans to go look at the lot the next day. By the following evening, Venganza had his pistol and his dog, and Omar was excited to own a lot in town. Besides that, Omar's friend Heriberto had offered him an old house, rent-free, adjacent to his new lot.

"Imagine, Yuri!" Omar exclaimed. "We can live right beside my lot while I build the house. It's the perfect arrangement."

"And I'm happy that Old Pedro and his family will be our next-door neighbors," Yuri threw in. "They're such nice people."

"Before we move," Omar said, "we should go to Regadío one more time to see Mimita. As soon as we come back, I'll go up the mountain to get lumber from my friend Jesús."

That evening, Omar's heart was happy. For some reason, things seemed to be falling into place for him. Was it because he had promised God to seek His face?

Regadío was in a wild mood when Omar and Yuri arrived the next week. The town had just started its annual fiestas, and Omar was sorely tempted to join his drinking buddies. But remembering his vow, he first spent some quality time with his mother. Then, avoiding his cronies, he went to the fiestas with Yuri and Karen instead.

Omar remembered Bato's advice, "Don't drink when you ride bulls." Bull riding was one thing he could do without drinking, and he offered to compete with the best bull riders at the rodeo. He took on the strongest bulls and won first prize. When Omar wasn't riding, he performed in the ring. With his red cape, he danced around as an angry bull tried to knock him flat. When the bull attacked, Omar held the cape in front of the bull's face, then sidestepped just before the horns gouged him.

Among the spectators were Yuri and little Karen, who was now almost two years old and as sharp as a tack. During a lull, Omar stepped over to the corral fence to talk to his woman and daughter. His heart swelled, proud of little Karen with her head full of golden curls framing her lovely face and sweet smile. Safe in her mother's arms, she watched her daddy adoringly.

Omar dreamed of the day Karen could dress like a cowgirl and learn to ride horse with him. He couldn't wait till she grew up. Yuri beamed, proud of the way her man could handle the bulls. "Karen loves to watch you perform," she said. "Every time you sidestep and the bull rushes by, she laughs."

But when Miriam discovered that Omar was going to the fiestas, she moaned, "Omar is back to his old life. I so hoped he would change."

"Don't be so sure," Cándida replied. "Haven't you heard about Omar's vow?"

"What vow?"

"Oh, Mama, Omar isn't the same man since your sickness. He hasn't gotten drunk once. You see, while you were hanging between life and death, he made us all vow that we would be different. He thought maybe if God saw that we were going to change, He would hear our prayers and heal you. One of the things Omar vowed was to never touch liquor again."

"I'm glad to hear that," Miriam said. "But it's really hard for me to believe he won't come home drunk tonight."

"Let's wait and see," was Cándida's quick response.

At dusk, Omar came by with his little family, as sober as could be, but his family was worried when he disappeared into the dark later that evening. But soon Omar was back, with Alvaro and Melvin in tow. Miriam met them, concern written all over her face.

"Mimita, these boys were down at Jenny's bar, drinking," Omar announced. "I got there just in the nick of time, because Alvaro was getting ready to fight with another drunk. Let's make them stay at home the rest of the night so they don't get into trouble."

That night Omar and his mother both went to bed with a prayer of hope in their hearts. Maybe, just maybe, Omar Montenegro could change after all.

The trip back to Waslala was long and tiring. Omar and his family caught a bus to Matagalpa, and then rode on the IFA truck from Matagalpa to Waslala. Little Karen was sick, fighting fever off and on all day. When they got back to Waslala, Yuri gave her some acetaminophen, and soon Karen seemed better.

Omar was relaxing in his hammock in one corner of the living room when Karen started cutting up. At first, when she ran in from the kitchen and threw herself on the floor, Omar didn't catch on to what she was doing. But Yuri, standing in the kitchen doorway, laughed. "Omar, look. Karen is fighting the bulls in the ring!"

Karen popped up off the floor and started twirling again. Bouncing around as if dodging the bulls, she flung herself onto the floor as soon as the imaginary bull had rushed past.

Soon Omar was egging her on. "Dodge that old bull, baby!" he cheered. "Watch out, baby! That bull will get you!"

Every time Karen hit the floor, Omar roared with laughter.

After the funny little episode, Omar picked up his innocent little girl and held her tight. She was his own flesh and blood, and Omar sighed as he held her against his chest. He loved her so much!

But a little later, Karen's cheeks turned red with fever again. Yuri and Omar stayed up with the crying baby most of the night. Around 3 a.m., her fever soared dangerously high, and she began to convulse. She threw her head back, rolled her eyes, and slumped into unconsciousness. Omar grabbed his baby up into his arms and rushed out the door, calling back to Yuri, "I'm taking her to the hospital!"

Fortunately, the house Omar and Yuri were renting was only a few blocks from the Waslala hospital. Omar ran like a gazelle through the dark, panting with love for his little girl. What if Karen died?

A frantic prayer burst from his heart, "God, take my life and give my daughter's life back! I'm wicked and deserve to die! She's pure and good, and she deserves to live. God, please spare her life and take mine instead!"

Just as Omar flew through the hospital gate, his little girl gasped for breath. "She's still alive!" Omar exulted. "God is answering my prayer!"

Minutes later, a doctor had Karen hooked up to an IV drip and was giving her something to bring her fever down. Yuri arrived on the scene, her face pale and tearstained. She and Omar stood and watched, swallowing their tears as little Karen stabilized.

Love and relief washed over Omar. Under his breath, he whispered, "Thank You, God! You gave Karen's life back, and you didn't take mine. It's like we both got our life back again. Thank You, Lord!"

48

JESUS LOVES YOU

IN PABLO'S HOUSE, surrounded by early morning sounds, the pastor himself was savoring his first cup of coffee along with his predawn prayers. He was praying for Omar.

"Morning!" Omar called, breaking the silence.

Pastor Pablo walked out onto the porch and offered his hand. "Good morning, Omar! What can I do for you?"

Overcome by emotion, Omar stood mutely, a huge lump in his throat. Surely this kind pastor would help him. Regaining his composure, Omar opened his mouth. "My daughter is sick in the hospital," he choked. "Could you pay me some money ahead for training your mares?"

"Sure," Pastor Pablo replied. "How much do you need?"

"Six hundred córdobas."

"Okay!" Pablo replied and disappeared into the house.

Omar's heart flooded with gratitude. This man barely knew him, but he was willing to fork out money for Omar's need. This man was a real friend!

When Pastor Pablo returned, money in hand, Omar choked up again. Embarrassed by his display of raw feeling, Omar turned and walked behind Pastor Pablo's vehicle. Pablo followed him. Could this man sense what was in the bottom of Omar's heart? Could he somehow detect that Omar was sick and tired of life and wanted to seek God?

"What happened to your little girl?" Pastor Pablo asked softly.

"We don't know," Omar answered, wiping his eyes. "All we know is that little Karen is very sick. Mostly she's had some high fevers . . . and this morning I thought she had died." Omar told the pastor about their scare that morning.

"Would you like if we'd come pray for your daughter this evening during visiting hours?" Pastor Pablo wondered.

"Yes, please!"

"We could also sing for you," Pastor Pablo added.

That evening in the simple hospital room, Yuri sat beside her daughter's crib, stroking her pale brow. Omar stood beside Yuri, head bowed and hands folded. Pablo's family and some others stood in a half circle around Omar's family, singing in four-part harmony. Omar sensed deeply the love shining from the singers' hearts. The words of the last sacred hymn they sang touched his hard heart.

"Jesus loves you; He really cares.

He knows your problems; He sees your tears;

And when you need Him, He's always there.

Jesus loves you; He really cares."

While Pablo's family sang, Omar's heart asked, *How can Jesus love me? I've been such a wicked man. If Jesus does love me, what can I do but give Him my heart in return?*

As the singing continued, Omar just stood there and sobbed while the Lord worked in his heart.

After the songs, Pastor Pablo prayed for Karen, and the two families left. Omar wondered if the singers had any idea what the song had done to his heart.

At the crack of dawn the next day, Omar arrived at Pastor Pablo's house again. "Pablo . . ." he stammered. "Pablo, could we talk privately?"

Pastor Pablo led Omar back into an orchard where they were hidden among the trees. Omar's words came out in a torrent. "First of all," he said, "my daughter is much better this morning. I think we can take her home later this morning. Thanks for praying for her!"

"Praise the Lord!" Pastor Pablo exclaimed. "God is so good."

"The other thing I want to say is that the song you sang last night, the one that says 'Jesus loves you,' really broke my heart. I've been a wicked man. Slowly God has been changing me. Slowly He's been showing me what is bad in my life, and I've been getting rid of the wickedness."

Pablo stroked his bearded chin and listened carefully.

Then Omar told Pastor Pablo about his mother's sickness and how he had vowed to stop drinking. "And then, recently, I got rid of my firearms. I used to not be able to sleep without a gun under my pillow. But now that's gone.

"Last night I felt clearly that only one thing remains for me to do, and that is to give my life to God. There's nothing more to hold me back. Can you help me? What do I have to do to be saved?"

Pastor Pablo started slowly. "Well, Omar, there's a lot more to sin than just drinking and guns. Sin is a heart problem. You sin because you're a sinner. That's why you need to be born again. Obviously, you sense that you're a sinner."

Omar nodded vigorously. In that, Pablo was absolutely right!

"Are you married?" Pastor Pablo asked, watching Omar's face closely.

"No, Yuri and I are not married," Omar answered, hanging his head. He hadn't thought about that.

"Well, I really do want to help you give your heart to the Lord, Omar. That's the best thing you can do. But we have to make sure that you understand what you're doing and that you do it right. There's no use in doing a halfway job, right?"

Omar agreed again. *That's the kind of man I am,* he asserted to himself. *If I do something, I try to do it right.*

"If you're not married, you're living in fornication," Pastor Pablo told him gently. "So you have to get that taken care of. Has either of you been married before?"

"No," Omar answered. "But I think Yuri would agree to get married, so that wouldn't hold us back."

"Look," Pastor Pablo urged. "If you're agreed to do this right, go home and talk to Yuri. Taking up the cross of Christ is not easy, but it's a wonderful life to live. You need to be born again."

Omar listened carefully, wondering what it meant to be born again.

"We have a lot to talk about, Omar," Pastor Pablo said. "Have you ever heard of restitution?"

Omar shook his head.

"That means that as you come to God, you are willing to not only confess your sins to Him, but you want to clear things with your fellow men. For example, if you have an enemy, you'll go make things right with him. If you stole something, you go pay for it."

Omar nodded. "That makes sense. I would be willing to do that."

But even as Omar spoke the words, his mind flew to two things that would be very hard to make right—his murders, and his part in the attack on his cousin Andrés. Would he be willing to clear those things?

"I really do believe you're ready for this," Pastor Pablo assured him. "As far as your marriage, either you and Yuri should separate until you can get married, or you should get your paperwork done first."

Omar was thinking hard. "Yuri is young and doesn't have her citizenship card yet. That might be a problem. As a minor, she might have to have her mother's signature to get married."

"Well, you go home and talk to Yuri about it. Meanwhile, we'll be praying." Then, as an afterthought, Pastor Pablo suggested, "Let me pray for you right now."

As the pastor put his arm around Omar and prayed for him, Omar could almost feel virtue seep through him. Emotion filled his heart as he cried out silently to God along with the man he knew loved him.

I know this man is full of God, Omar concluded. *If there's anybody on this earth that can help me be a Christian, it will be him. And yes, now I know for sure that Jesus loves me!*

During the next week, Omar and Yuri moved to Heriberto's house next to Omar's newly acquired lot. Janie, Pastor Pablo's daughter, helped move their things over in Pastor Pablo's jeep. It was a rickety little shack, but good enough for the time being. Omar had traveled up to the mountaintop to talk to his friend Jesús. As he expected, Jesús gave him two trees to saw for lumber for a new house on his lot.

Omar and Yuri traveled to Estelí to get Yuri's citizenship paperwork started so they could get married. Then they traveled on to Regadío to wait until it was ready.

Omar and Yuri stayed at his mother's place for the night, but during the day, Omar spent time with his family and Yuri with hers. Omar excitedly told his family about the new church and the kind people they were associating with. He told them of his plans to give his heart to the Lord, and that he needed to get married. His family was happy for him and grateful to anyone who could help Omar abandon the wicked road he had been traveling.

Omar wondered how Yuri really felt about their new friends in Waslala. Neither Omar nor Yuri had known much church life except the Catholic church, and neither of them were active there. So far, Yuri seemed to appreciate Cynthia and the rest of the church folks. But Omar had no idea what she really felt deep in her heart.

Omar didn't realize that Yuri had told her family how he was so taken up with the gringo missionaries. Lacking the spiritual thirst that Omar had, Yuri didn't have convincing answers for her family's questions. Before long, Yuri's family was totally against what Omar was planning to do. They told Yuri that Omar's choice was not realistic.

When the week was up, Omar was ready to pick up Yuri's citizenship card on their way home. He was shocked when Yuri announced, "Omar, I'm not traveling back to Waslala with you. I'm staying in Regadío. My mom found a job for me at the tobacco factory. Go on back to Waslala and join that church if you want to."

Omar was devastated. For a half hour he tried to convince Yuri that he sincerely wanted to follow the Lord and that if he did, life would change. He also told her that they were made for each other, and how important it was for Karen's sake that they stick together. But Yuri was unmovable as stone.

Brokenhearted, Omar caught the next bus out of Regadío. As the bus traveled toward Waslala, the battle in his heart raged. *I can't back out of my commitment to God!* he cried in anguish. *Yet how can I live without my little Karen? What will my future hold without a wife? What will the men in the Waslala brotherhood say?*

There was only one thing for him to do—go and find out. The faith that was born in Omar's heart did not die. Even if that same heart felt split in two, Omar knew what God wanted him to do. So, weeping like a child, he went ahead and did it.

That evening he stopped by Pastor Pablo's place and blurted out the sad news. At the end, Omar sighed. "Pastor Pablo, there is no reason left to not give my heart to the Lord. I guess we can say He cleared the way. You have been explaining to me what it means to be born again, so now the time is here to do it."

The two men knelt under the trees in the orchard. Omar confessed his sins, and the Lord Jesus washed them away.

After the prayer, Omar told Pablo about some of the restitution he needed to do to clear his life. "I need to ask María Eugenia's mother for forgiveness. I can't talk to her personally because she is in the United States. But I could give her a call. And I need to apologize to poor Maritza. I really gave her a rough time. That one's easy because she lives here on Papayo." But Omar didn't mention the murders or what he had done to Andrés.

Pastor Pablo went with him to make things right in Waslala. After they were done, and Omar's eyes were shining with peace, Pastor Pablo asked him a question. "Omar, don't you think the time has come to make another vow?"

"Like what?" Omar asked eagerly.

"It looks like you have cleared everything out of your life so you can serve the Lord. Wouldn't now be the time to make a commitment to never touch a woman again unless she is a born-again Christian and you marry her God's way?"

Omar understood perfectly. Nodding, he answered, "And I'll add to that. I will not marry a woman unless she shows by her life that she is genuine and unless she dresses modestly and wears a prayer veiling."

"Praise the Lord!" Pastor Pablo cheered. "Now I know that you're saved!"

Omar grinned. "Even if I need to live alone the rest of my life, I'll be a bachelor for the Lord."

"It won't be easy, Omar," Pablo warned, "but the rewards are out of this world!"

49

A SINISTER CONFESSION

A HUSH SETTLED over the congregation as Omar took a seat toward the front of the chapel. He was dressed in a long-sleeved white shirt that he had managed to iron. His blue jeans were tattered but clean. His face was clean-shaven except for a mustache, and his hair was trimmed short and combed neatly.

A young man dressed much like Omar walked to the front of the chapel. Standing behind the pulpit, José Adán smiled and said, "Good morning!" Omar had heard that José Adán had joined this church. Omar admired this young man who chosen to eschew evil and had never gotten scarred by sin like he had.

Omar's heart swelled as José Adán led the congregation in four-part, a cappella singing. The God-filled words reached deeply into his heart and spoke to its needs. While Omar worshiped with the congregation, his bleeding heart healed just a little.

After several songs, José Adán announced, "Open your Bibles to Psalm 23 for a meditation this morning." Pages rustled as everyone found the passage. Omar opened the Bible Pastor Pablo had given him the day before, but he had no idea how to find anything in it. He had never read the Bible, and he didn't know where the Psalms were.

A brother sitting beside Omar reached over and gently paged through his Bible until he found Psalm 23. By then José Adán was almost finished reading the psalm. Omar listened as José Adán explained how the Good Shepherd supplies all our needs when we follow Him. Great joy filled Omar's heart. He understood what the Scriptures were saying! An overwhelming desire to obey them fused with his understanding.

During the sermon Pastor Pablo expounded on the New Testament teaching of restitution, and Omar again understood. Zacchaeus's story riveted his attention.

Zacchaeus had been a rather bad fellow—heart set on riches, proud, stealing, and all the rest. But Jesus took special interest in him, and even announced that He wanted to come to his house that day. In spite of his failures, Jesus loved Zacchaeus!

And now Jesus has taken special interest in me as well, Omar realized, overwhelmed.

When Zacchaeus jumped up and declared what he was willing to do to change his ways, Omar felt like also jumping out of his pew and declaring, *I am willing to do anything, just like Zacchaeus, to get my life back in shape!*

Jesus had answered Zacchaeus, "This day is salvation come to this house." Omar's head dropped, and he rested his forehead on the bench in front of him as he wept. This was almost too good to be true!

Omar had always worn blue jeans and a sleeveless shirt to his work at Pastor Pablo's farm, which made his tattoos clearly visible.

"Pablo, this tattoo bothers me," Omar announced one morning, slapping the big one on his upper arm. "Do you know if there's a way to get rid of it?"

"Yes," Pablo answered slowly, "there are ways to remove tattoos. But I think it would be very expensive. I have a much easier solution for you."

"What's that?"

Pastor Pablo grinned. "Wear a shirt with sleeves. Not only would that hide the tattoo, but it would be more modest."

Omar's mouth dropped open as he stared at Pablo, "Well, sure! I never thought of that. That will take care of it."

Since Yuri was no longer with him, Omar lived alone. He cooked his own meals and washed his own clothes. He stayed busy sawing the lumber on Jesús' farm and hauling it down the mountain on the back of an old one-eyed mule he had borrowed from Pablo. He asked a neighbor to help him, and every weekday they hauled two loads down the muddy mountain trail. *As soon as I get that lumber down to a truck access,* Omar dreamed, *I can start building my house. Just maybe Yuri will come back to me again, and we can get married.*

Omar was astonished at how friendly and accepting the church brethren were. Once the lumber was hauled down closer to Waslala, Alvino Miller sent his truck to take it to the house site. But Omar wondered, *What would these people do if they knew who I really am?*

Pablo and Omar sat on the little wooden dock, deep in conversation. Lily pads floated in the murky pond water, and a green frog croaked before diving into the depths. Dragonflies zipped around, and a little green heron stood motionless on the opposite shore, waiting for a fish.

Omar's face was pale, and his lips trembled. "Pablo, the time has come for me to be honest with you," he said quietly. "I haven't been a good man."

"Well, you told me that you were a great sinner, Omar," Pastor Pablo answered. "What else do you need to tell me?"

Omar swallowed deeply. "I used to be a criminal. If you would look up my name on the Internet, you would be shocked at what you found."

"Why would your name be on the Internet, Omar?"

"I lived in Los Angeles for a while," Omar answered. "That's where I committed my crimes, and that's why I'm a wanted man. I came to Waslala as a fugitive. But I've decided I'll never run from the law anymore."

"So what were you involved in?" Pastor Pablo asked innocently.

"I was into trafficking drugs and all that goes with it," Omar responded. "The worst is that I . . . I . . . shot and killed my girlfriend. Like I said, I'm a wanted man."

Pastor Pablo stared pensively at the young man before him. "Yes, you *are* a wanted man. The law wants you. But Somebody else out there badly wants you as well—the Lord Jesus Christ. Yes, you are a very wanted man!"

Omar's head dropped, and tears sprang to his eyes. Staring at the place in the pond's surface where the frog had disappeared, he listened intently to Pablo's encouraging words.

"Omar, if you have truly repented of all these sins, God has forgiven you, and you're free! Maybe the law still wants you, but before God you're not a fugitive anymore. Jesus found you, and you are free!"

"I want to confess this to the brethren, Pablo," Omar said soberly. "I feel bad coming to church and everybody taking me in without knowing who I really am. At the next service I want to tell the brethren the truth. Do you think they'll still accept me?"

"Absolutely they will!" Pastor Pablo confirmed. "Just like me, they understand God's forgiveness. The brethren will be just like Jesus—more than happy to accept you and help you go straight!"

"What about restitution?" Omar asked hesitantly. "If I would turn myself in to the United States, I would probably go to jail for life."

"I don't know what to say about that, brother," Pablo answered. "I have had no experience with such situations. For now, rest in the fact that you're free before God. He has forgiven you. Let's pray about it. If God wants you to do restitution to the United States, He'll show us."

"I also shot a man in Costa Rica," Omar whispered. "I probably killed him, though I never heard for sure." Then Omar told Pastor Pablo that story.

"I want to tell you everything, Pablo," Omar stated. "I want to be free. I don't want to hide anything."

Again, Omar felt the nudge to confess what he had done to Andrés. But he pushed the thought aside. *Andrés is in the United States, and I can't reconcile with him now anyway. I'll cross that bridge when I get there.*

On Wednesday evening after church, the little office cubicle in Alvino Miller's bookstore was packed with people. Jacinto sat in the office chair in front of the computer, with Omar sitting beside him. Pastor Pablo and his nine-year-old son Kenny had joined them, along with two of Alvino Miller's sons.

They all stared at the computer screen as Jacinto typed "Fermín Omar Montenegro" into the Google search page. Though Omar himself had never tried it, he knew that the news had been full of his crime after it happened, and he suspected that he was still a wanted man.

The computer blinked, and then a page full of titles appeared. The first title confirmed what Omar had suspected:

WANTED: Montenegro, Fermín Omar—Los Angeles Police Department

MOST WANTED PROFILE

Do you have information on this person?
Fermín Omar Montenegro

The suspect was involved in a domestic dispute with the victim.
The suspect shot and killed the victim.

WARNING: THIS INDIVIDUAL IS CONSIDERED
ARMED AND DANGEROUS. DO NOT ATTEMPT TO
APPREHEND SUSPECT YOURSELF. IF SEEN, CONTACT
YOUR LOCAL POLICE STATION ASAP.

CRIME INFORMATION

Suspect: Montenegro, Fermín Omar	Hair: Black
Alias: Salazar, Omar	Eyes: Brown
Sex: M	Date of Birth: January 14, 1974
Descent: Hispanic	Estimated Age: 26
Height: 5'7"	Weapon: .22 caliber revolver
Weight: 170 lbs	

You could have heard a pin drop in the overwhelming hush that filled the little office. Jacinto turned to Omar. "Shall I go on?"

Omar nodded.

Jacinto clicked on the web title, and what showed up next, nobody in that room was prepared for.

Stunned, everyone just stared at the photo, then silently read the web page. Pastor Pablo sighed deeply as reality hit each of them.

Overwhelmed by awful memories, Omar dropped his face into his hands and burst out crying. His body shook like a leaf in the wind, and immediately Pastor Pablo and Marcos Miller put their arms around his shoulders to comfort him.

Little Kenny announced, "That's not Omar!"

Slowly Omar regained his composure and raised his tearstained face. Pointing at the photo, he sighed. "Kenny is right. That man died! That's not me anymore!"

"Let's pray," Pastor Pablo suggested. "God has forgiven you, brother. This is an awfully tough reminder of your past. But God can take those memories away and make you free."

The next Sunday morning Omar gave his testimony in church. He openly confessed his crimes and then shared how it had affected him to see his crime report on the Internet. With tears streaming down his face, he spoke of the joy he now felt in serving the Lord.

"One thing that has really changed," Omar testified, "is that now I can sleep. I used to be haunted by constant nightmares, but now I sleep like a baby." Omar ended his testimony by requesting prayer for Yuri and Karen.

Omar soon joined the Bible class for baptism that Pastor Pablo and Daniel Muñoz, his co-pastor, took turns teaching. But most of all, Omar loved to study the Bible on his own, driven by a lifelong thirst for something that satisfied. He read his Bible as if trying to make up for lost time, and his changed life was the obvious fruit of that passion.

But one question haunted Omar after a Bible class on loving one's enemies. *Will I, who have always been such a violent, angry person, be able to do good to those who want to hurt me? Will it actually be possible for me to love my enemies?*

Omar guessed God would have to test him to find out.

50

IN SEARCH OF A THUG

OMAR AND HIS uncle Bato stood looking out over the pictur-esque scenery from the second story of the Rio Lindo Restaurant. The second story was open to the north, protected only by metal bars to keep out prowlers. Holding onto the bars, the two men surveyed the farm spread out before them as they waited on their food.

"It's a nice place," Bato stated, gesturing toward the lush pastureland just across the Waslala River, hedged in by living fencerows. The hillside resembled a patchwork quilt, done in various shades of green.

"Yes, Pastor Pablo's farm is nice," Omar agreed, though his mind was not on the beautiful scenery or the cattle wandering down toward the river for a drink. He was wondering what Uncle Bato wanted with him now. "Do you still have your farm in San Ramon?" Omar inquired.

"Sure do," Bato replied, turning toward the stairway where a waitress was coming up the steps with two plates of food. "But let's eat now."

Bato had showed up in Waslala that day and asked to take Omar out to eat that evening. Omar expected that Bato wanted a private word with him, and he wasn't mistaken. But Bato wanted to eat first.

Like usual, Bato ordered the best food. Rio Lindo's special was steak done on flat iron platters that the waiters carried to the table using leather hot pads, the meat still sizzling. That, and a plate of rice, fried plantains, and a salad, made a meal worth drooling over. But the two men didn't drool long; they just fell to. They weren't disappointed—the food was delicious!

It wasn't till after they were done and had pushed back their chairs and were sipping coffee that Bato said, "Omar, I came to Waslala because I need your help."

Omar nodded. *This man makes me feel weird,* he thought, staring out over Pablo's fields again. *He's up to no good; I can just sense it.*

"You know, Omar, I really like my farm in San Ramon, and I sure would hate to sell." Bato paused. "But right now I'm between a rock and a hard place. I either have to sell the farm or do something about my unhandy neighbor, who is making my life impossible."

"What's the trouble?" Omar inquired.

"He's the most unhandy varmint that ever existed," Bato complained bitterly. "The other day we had it out with words, but we'd both like to get rid of the other." As his uncle continued to talk, Omar was horrified. Did his uncle believe he was still that kind of man? Did Bato think he, Omar, would be willing to sneak over there with an assault rifle and take another life? Did Bato really think that was the solution to all his troubles?

Slowly Omar shook his head. "I can't do that, Uncle Bato."

Omar knew exactly what was coming next. Bato pulled a big wad of money from his pocket and held it where Omar could clearly see it.

"I brought this wad of dough along for you, Omar. You can't tell me you don't need it. I want to pay you for the little cleanup job."

Omar held up his hand and answered carefully, "Uncle Bato, the thug you came to Waslala looking for doesn't exist anymore. He died, and a new Omar was born. Uncle Bato, I've been born again. I serve Jesus. I would never do what you're suggesting."

"Oh, so now you've turned chicken, eh?" Bato sneered, fingering the wad of money. "You used to be a man."

Omar shook his head. "It's hard for you to understand, Bato. But when I found out that Jesus loved me and gave His life for me, it changed my life completely. I have received His salvation and given my life back to Him. I'm a changed man. The old criminal is gone forever."

"But look at this!" Bato insisted, thrusting the wad of U.S. dollars at Omar. "You need this. I know you do."

Omar shuddered, eyeing the money. Bato knew his weak spot, and right now, Omar was totally out of money. In the past, when Omar had occasionally asked Bato for a small loan, Bato had always just given it to him. Maybe he could at least ask for a loan.

But a still small voice whispered, *Don't accept anything from this man. His intentions are evil. You will be beholden to him, and you must stay free. You don't want anything to do with this perverse person!*

Lifting his head high, Omar said, "I'm sorry, Uncle Bato, but I can't help you. I'm a Christian."

Suddenly the meeting was over. Bato got up and stalked down the steps, Omar following. Bato paid the restaurant bill, but Omar knew that his uncle was disgusted that he had spent the money in vain. Though it had been hard, Omar was glad he had done what was right. The peace he felt was more important than any amount of money in his pocket.

Later that afternoon, before Omar could even tell his story, a brother from the church slipped a 500 córdoba bill into Omar's hand. "Just to help out a little," the brother whispered. "I know you're going through a tough time financially."

"Pablo, both of your mares are trained and ready to ride," Omar announced with a broad smile. "I suggest that you ride Ilana, since she's larger than Flicka."

"Great!" Pastor Pablo answered. "Why don't I ride her this morning?"

A half hour later, Ilana was saddled and ready. Pablo's family followed him out to the barn to watch him ride his favorite mare for the first time.

"She's as gentle as can be," Omar bragged, holding the reins while Pastor Pablo approached.

Pablo took the reins. Then he placed his left foot into the stirrup and hefted himself into the saddle.

Omar had seen Pastor Pablo ride his stallion Ébano. Although Pastor Pablo claimed he wasn't as agile in the saddle as he used to be since he had gained some weight, he could still ride fairly well. Omar expected every-thing to go well.

But as Pastor Pablo swung into the saddle, Ilana started off down the little downgrade toward the house. Pastor Pablo leaned forward into the saddle, trying to regain his balance. At that moment, Ilana pulled a trick on her master. She decided that she didn't like the extra weight of her new rider, and she started to buck.

Pastor Pablo had no chance to prove his riding abilities. Before he was able to straighten up in the saddle, he was pitched right over the horse's neck and hit the ground rolling.

In seconds, Omar was beside him. "Are you okay?" Omar yelled, ready to help him up.

But Pablo popped back onto his feet, laughing. "I'm okay. Didn't hurt me a bit."

When Pablo's family saw that he was okay, they all burst out laughing. "Wow!" Jacinto joshed. "That was a free show!"

But Omar was anxious. He felt responsible since he had trained the mare and had declared her ready for Pablo to ride. *What if Pastor Pablo gets mad?* Omar worried, watching the man's face.

But Pastor Pablo wasn't upset at all. He was unhurt, laughing along with the rest. "What do you think got into that mare?" he asked, still chuckling.

"It was probably the extra weight that she didn't like," Omar explained, shaking his head. "But I don't know why she bucked when she never bucks for me."

"I'm a stranger to her," Pastor Pablo explained. "Well, all I can say is that she did a good job of getting rid of me quickly. Some other day I'll ride her, and she'll have to accept it. My riding days surely aren't over yet!

"Don't feel bad, Omar. It's not your fault. She would never do that to you."

"You mean, Omar wouldn't fall off so easily," Jacinto ribbed, and they all joined in the laughter. "That mare barely tried, and you were flat out!"

As Omar walked back home, he felt amazed that even after Pastor Pablo's tumble, this family still loved him. Even though they knew who

Omar was and the crimes he had done, they still trusted him. How could they trust him—especially the girls? They treated him as a brother in the church and a friend. Next chance he got, Omar would ask Pastor Pablo about it.

Omar's new house was going up slowly. After the lumber was on the spot, things sped up. One day the brethren came and helped put the roof on. That was the day Omar learned what a frolic was, and he loved it.

Once the little house was finished, Omar often wondered, *Will I ever live in this house with Yuri and Karen? What do I have a house for if I don't live in it?*

Meanwhile, Daniel Muñoz had invited Omar to move in with him. Daniel was Pastor Pablo's bachelor co-minister. Omar still had to wash his own clothes, but he and Daniel bought groceries together and shared the cooking. Daniel often went to eat at his mother's place, and Omar was always invited.

"Omar, our neighbor has a bunch of cattle he wants to sell," Omar's cousin Osbaldo told him one day when Omar was visiting his uncle Juan in Guabo. "Why don't you buy them and sell them for a profit?"

Omar grinned. "You know I don't have any money. I couldn't buy even a little steer; how do you think I could buy a herd?"

"Look," Osbaldo explained, "Serapio is a kind old man. I think he would give you time to pay. Meanwhile, you could be selling them."

"But how could he trust me? He doesn't even know me." A frown grew on Omar's face.

"If you go with me," Osbaldo explained, "he'll trust you. We're great friends with Serapio, and I know you're in a tight spot financially. Buying and selling is something you do well. You learned it from your dad, selling horses all over town. Let's give it a try."

Osbaldo finally convinced Omar to try the business venture. But as they rode down the road toward Serapio's place, Omar had second thoughts. *How does Osbaldo think that this man will trust me? Yes, he knows Osbaldo well, but Osbaldo isn't buying the cattle—I am. There's no way this man will trust a stranger.*

As their horses trotted down the road at a slow pace, a thought struck Omar. *Tell Serapio the truth, Omar. People trust those who are honest. Tell the truth and trust Me for the rest.*

That must be from the Lord, Omar realized.

A half hour later, old Serapio was showing Omar a strange assortment of cattle milling around in his corral. But before they got down to business, Omar announced, "Look, Don Serapio, I want to buy your cattle, but I don't have any money. If you don't trust me and would rather not deal, that's perfectly fine. If you trust me, I'll sell them as I can and pay you when I get paid. Once I've paid, you can extend me the bills of sale."

Serapio didn't bat an eye. "That's fine," he assured his new friend. "Take them and sell them as you can."

After a bit more dealing, Omar announced, "I want to take two cows right away. I think I can sell them to the local butcher. I can bring the money tomorrow and take a few more animals."

The next day Omar returned to Guabo with the money in hand, and both men were happy. In less than a week, Omar had sold all seven animals and paid Serapio fairly. Omar was able to buy some groceries and a little steer for himself. Eventually, he could sell that steer at a profit, and maybe soon he would have a business going.

That evening Omar cooked a meal in Daniel's bachelor den. Ever since he had worked in Tacos Mexico, Omar had enjoyed cooking. He had bought a few pounds of chicken and cooked up a soup fit for a king. While he and Daniel enjoyed the meal, Omar told Daniel about the cattle sales, and Daniel shared his happiness.

Omar concluded, "Daniel, let's thank the Lord tonight. God is helping me make my living. It shows that He loves us and cares for me. I want to serve Him the best I can."

51

THE TEST

THE AFTERNOON SKY was riddled with clouds, but the cheery sun smiled down between breaches in the clouds. The horse's shod hooves clacked rhythmically on the hard Waslala street as Omar trotted toward Papayo Hill. His heart was happy.

Even though Omar missed Yuri and little Karen, he was glad he could follow the Lord instead of living in sin. The new peace he had found was indescribable. Why hadn't he thought of finding God long before? He could hardly believe what he had missed.

One reason for Omar's happiness was that he had found a job. Marcos Miller had asked him to manage his brother Jonathan's dairy because Jonathan and his family were in the United States for three months. "The dairyman we had was stealing money from the milk sales," Marcos explained, "so Jonathan said I could ask you to take over till he returns."

Omar had readily accepted the job, and the dairy was blossoming under his care. He also agreed to train one of Jonathan's horses—the horse he was riding now. Jonathan was appreciative of Omar's work, and Omar was eager to meet the man who had married one of Pastor Pablo's daughters.

As Omar approached Evelio Salina's little eating place on the way to Jonathan's farm on Papayo Hill, he remembered that he was hungry. All he had eaten for breakfast was bread with coffee, and food was cheap here. *I'll stop and get a bite to eat,* he decided.

Omar left his horse on the street, but he tied the reins to a sturdy almond tree, leaving the rope hanging limp across the sidewalk. He had barely walked into the restaurant when a voice rasped, "Whose horse is this?"

Omar popped out of the restaurant faster than he had stepped in. On the street, a half-drunk stranger was cursing and pointing at Omar's horse.

"What's the problem?" Omar asked.

"Is that your horse?" the drunk yelled. "Do you own this restaurant, or what?"

Omar's hackles rose. "What's the problem?" he asked again. "That horse isn't bothering anybody."

But the drunk was not dissuaded. He edged closer, and the stench of his alcohol breath enveloped Omar—a smell that Omar hated and avoided if at all possible. What could he do now?

"Don't you see that you can't tie your horse there, you stupid idiot!" The drunk spat, stepping closer yet. "You don't own this place, so go tie your horse somewhere else."

Omar's anger began to boil as he slowly backed away from the drunk. He narrowed his eyes to slits, but just before he retorted, "Is your name Evelio Salina? Do *you* own this restaurant?" Omar remembered that he was a Christian now. He heard, as clearly as if someone had spoken audibly, *Love your enemies, bless them that curse you.*[28]

Keeping his mouth shut but wailing inwardly, Omar untied the horse's reins and continued backing away. In the past, he would have knocked this drunk down with one stroke. Omar had never before allowed a human being to treat him like this. If this man had known what kind of person Omar had been only several months ago, he wouldn't be doing this to him!

To Omar's horror, the drunk drew a knife. By now they were both out on the street, and Omar was still backing away. Seeing the flash of the blade, Omar realized he had two options. Either he could lay the drunk over with one swift kick, or he could run.

---

28   Matthew 5:44

Omar slipped around the back of his horse, popped nimbly into the saddle, and clattered away, leaving the drunk muttering and brandishing his knife to the wind.

As he spurred his horse on, a battle raged in Omar's heart. One voice shouted, "Go back and beat the life out of that coward!"

But another voice won the battle. "Don't do it. Just don't do it. You are a Christian now!"

Just before Omar left town, he stopped at the last store and bought a soda to assuage his hunger and thirst. He was surprised to discover he was trembling all over. His heart was still boiling hot. He wanted to gallop right back down that hill and give the drunk what he deserved. Instead, he jumped back on his horse and rode on, sipping his drink to cool his fury.

Halfway up Papayo Hill, Omar turned in at the gate to Jonathan's farm. He dismounted and stood alone under the huge tree in the barnyard. There he burst out crying, giving vent to the strong emotions he had reined in for the last twenty minutes.

Oh, God, Omar prayed, *please forgive me! You know my flesh badly wanted to beat up that man. Why was it so hard on my pride for people to see me run away from a powerless drunk? Why am I such a violent man? When will I ever change?*

At two-thirty Omar headed down Papayo Hill toward the chapel, feeling troubled. He wanted to be at the chapel in time for the scheduled Bible class for baptism, but his newly restored conscience was telling him that he had failed his Lord miserably. *The Bible says I should love my enemy, but I sure didn't love that awful drunk.*

After the Bible study, Pastor Pablo gave the students opportunity to give a testimony or share a prayer request. This was Omar's chance to unload his burden. While the rest of the class listened, he poured out the whole story. The tears flowed, and again Omar found himself trembling.

"Brethren, what can I do to change?" Omar cried. "I feel contaminated because I got so angry. And, oh, how I hated that awful, stinky man. In my heart I knocked him over a thousand times. But the Bible says that I should love my enemy. Please pray that I can find peace. I do want to love my enemies."

"Omar," Pastor Pablo said, "There's something you've totally missed. Yes, I will pray that God will cleanse you from all bad feelings toward that old drunk. But I want you to know that today you have won a great victory! Christ won the victory in you."

Not comprehending, Omar raised his tearstained face.

"Just think what this little meeting would be like if you were telling us that you knocked out that man's teeth. Or what if this afternoon I would have to go see you in jail because you nearly killed the man? Look at it for what it was—a great victory."

Suddenly Omar was smiling through his tears. "I guess you're right. I didn't really do anything to him except run away. That was better than doing what my old man wanted to do."

"Right, Omar. You've been violent in the past. So allowing Christ to keep you from beating up that mean man was definitely a victory. See, God needs to test you, and He knows exactly how much you can handle. So that test was just your size. I sincerely believe that the day will come when you'll be able to control even your feelings toward a person like that. But today it's enough to know that you were able to control those fists, don't you think?"

The rest of the class was nodding. Omar understood, and he was smiling again.

"What you want to do now to make this victory complete is pray for an opportunity to meet that man so you can witness to him. Hopefully he won't be drunk next time."

The very next Sunday Omar shared his story again during testimony time. The congregation was hushed as Omar told what had happened in front of the restaurant. He finished by saying, "I'm praying for an opportunity to tell the man I forgive him and to tell him about Jesus."

Almost every Sunday, Omar shared with the congregation the things he faced that week as he learned to walk with the Lord. Every time Omar made yet another restitution or discovered a new truth in God's Word, the brethren rejoiced.

The sun was drooping toward the horizon, splashing the western sky with color. Omar stood on the top deck of a ferry, staring across the choppy waters of Lake Nicaragua as the boat plowed its way toward Ometepe Island. To the east, two volcanos reared their tips from the heart of the island into the darkening blue. The taller Concepcion volcano was perfectly cone-shaped. The shorter Maderas volcano resembled a regular mountain peak, dressed in the greenest of jungles.

The deck was full of tourists on their way to the island. A few of the passengers were in the Bible class with him, and Omar knew them well. A few were from other Mennonite churches in Latin America. They were headed to a mission church on the island. As Omar compared this experience with the wild parties and drug dealings on Long Beach in LA and Jaco Beach in Costa Rica, he felt very fortunate. What a joy to be living a clean life, surrounded by wholesome brothers, serving others!

Omar especially admired Jonathan Miller, the leader of the group, whom everybody called Jona. Jona and his family had recently returned from their stay in the United States, and Jona had thanked Omar for rescuing the situation at the dairy.

Jona was married to Pastor Pablo's daughter Jéssica, and they had a little girl called Patricia. Omar watched them with interest. What intrigued him the most was how Jona and Jéssica wanted to serve the Lord and raise their family for God. *That is precisely my dream too.* Omar sighed wistfully.

Soon after Jona's return to Nicaragua, the Waslala churches had decided to send a small crew to help with building a small chapel for the new mission in Merida, a small town on Ometepe Island. Milton Alvarado and his family from the church in La Estrella, along with Geovanni Paniagua, were currently living in Merida, trying to get the mission going.

That evening, they gathered in Geovanni's living room, and Omar started telling stories of his life in LA and his recent conversion. "What has been really hard," Omar confessed, "is that as soon as I decided to serve the Lord, my woman left me and took my darling daughter to live in Regadío, my hometown."

The head cook for the group, Ivania Laguna from Jicaral, was touched by Omar's story. She, too, had suffered when her first man had abandoned her years before, leaving her with a tiny daughter to raise by herself. "Now," Ivania told Omar, "my daughter is what I live for. But you don't even have your daughter to live for!" Ivania asked Omar more questions about his recent life. Deeply moved, she promised to pray for him.

Early the next morning, the single men met on the beach. A stiff breeze wafted over the waters that were still pink from the dawn. Flocks of cattle egrets flew past on their way to the fields. Local fishermen were throwing in their lines, hoping to catch tilapia.

A young man from the Kusulí brotherhood led out in some precious sharing time. Omar was amazed at how this young man from a very poor family could be a spiritual leader. Their time in prayer was the preparation the men needed for the day of work facing them.

After the framework of the new chapel was finished, Jona and Omar put on the roofing while the others prepared to pour a concrete floor. It was backbreaking work to mix the cement by hand and pour the floor. The men sweated like workhorses in the blazing sun, but they enjoyed working together, and the job was done well.

The Waslala brethren also participated in a church service on the island, experienced sweet fellowship, enjoyed a huge fish soup, and made memories that none would forget.

As the ferry plowed the deep waters of Lake Nicaragua on its return, Omar rejoiced. Everything he had enjoyed on this excursion was so different, so much more meaningful than anything he had experienced in his former life.

As they rode the ferry back, Omar again watched Jona's little family from a distance. His friendship with Jona had been thoroughly sealed on this trip. It was a true friendship that would last for a long time.

52

DOUBLE JOY

THE SKIES WERE dumping rain the morning after Omar returned from Ometepe Island. Wrapped in a raincoat, he walked rapidly toward Pablo's place. Jona had asked Omar to train a colt for him, so Omar had decided to ride him rain or shine. But as he passed Pastor Pablo's porch, Pablo called him over.

Omar turned and entered the porch, shaking off the rain and stripping off his coat. Then he faced Pastor Pablo expectantly. These meetings on Pastor Pablo's porch were fast becoming a daily ritual. As usual, Pablo had set out a chair for him and a cup of black coffee to boot.

"Omar," Pablo began eagerly, "while you were gone, I got a call from Yuri. She says she wants to serve the Lord."

Omar gasped. "What did you tell her?" He leaned forward in his chair.

"Well, I wasn't sure what to say, but I did tell her that *you* went all the way with the Lord. And I told her about your vow."

"Was she shocked?"

"No, she said she wants to come back to Waslala to go straight with the Lord. She said, 'I'm not calling because I'm desperate to get back with Omar.' She claimed, 'I want to serve God.' Then she told me how bad things have gone for her in Regadío."

"If we could just be sure she's truly repentant," Omar mused. "It would sure be nice if this were genuine. You know how I miss little Karen."

"I have an idea," Pablo suggested. "You call her and tell her the truth. If she can prove her sincerity living apart from you, then you'll be willing to pray about marriage. But if not, she shouldn't expect you to take her in."

Omar called Yuri and told her that he had promised God he wouldn't touch a woman again unless he was married to her. And the woman must be a born-again Christian. When Omar was finished, Pastor Pablo talked to Yuri, explaining to her what repentance meant. "Think about it for several days," Pastor Pablo suggested, "and then I'll call you back. Meanwhile, I'll tell my church brothers here in Waslala about your desire to serve the Lord."

The brothers were unified in inviting Yuri to come to Waslala to seek God. She could live in Omar's new house, while Omar would continue living with Daniel. Omar would provide for Yuri financially until they could see what her real intentions were. Then if her interest were genuine, they could consider marriage at some later date.

Pastor Pablo called Yuri back after several days, and he was delighted to inform Omar that Yuri had accepted all of the requirements and seemed broken and repentant, wanting to serve God. A week later, Omar, Pastor Pablo, his son Jacinto, his daughter Cynthia, and another Nicaraguan girl from church traveled to Estelí to bring Yuri home.

Omar was glad to give the group a tour of his beloved hometown of Regadío. Pastor Pablo and his son Jacinto were excited about the story of Chema Briones and his immense plantation as they toured the dilapidated old ranch house that still stood on the outskirts of town.

But the best part of the trip for Omar was introducing his new church family to many hometown friends. His mother seemed especially warm toward the Waslala folks and welcomed them to have a service in her house that evening.

Quite a number of Omar's family and former neighbors came to the service. Even Yuri and curly haired Karen came to listen. Jacinto led a few songs and then Pastor Pablo preached a message that everyone could understand.

At the end, Omar gave his testimony. With tears streaming down his face, he confessed, "My heart was as hard as stone toward God. But up on the top of that Waslala mountain, God dealt with me. You know what a violent person I used to be. I was angry at everybody. But through suffering and crises, God humbled me and slowly broke my heart."

Then Omar told how Karen had almost died in his arms and how he had prayed that God would take his life, but spare Karen's. Omar's family listened intently to Omar's testimony, although they weren't totally convinced. Miriam sincerely hoped that her son would be changed into a new creature, just like Pastor Pablo had preached.

The next morning, Pastor Pablo and his group were ready to travel back to Waslala, and Yuri and Karen joined them. Once again, Omar was grateful to see how Cynthia took Yuri into her heart and befriended his little Karen.

During the next three months Yuri gave her heart to the Lord and proved quickly that she was sincere. Very soon she joined the Bible class for baptism and threw her heart into learning about God. Omar continued to stay at Daniel's place, but Yuri prepared his meals from the groceries Omar provided.

After Omar and the whole church were convinced that Yuri's conversion was genuine, she and Omar started having occasional dates, meeting in a thatched roof gazebo in the yard behind the CAM[29] nurse's house. They enjoyed these times of sharing.

"It seems really strange," Omar told his pastor, "to have dates with a woman I used to live with. But I know it's a good idea. We talk about our goals and how to raise our family for the Lord."

"Praise the Lord!" Pablo cheered. "Yes, though it seems strange, keep it up. If you can come to an understanding, hopefully soon you and Yuri can get married."

"What I really wish," Omar said longingly, "is that Yuri and I could both go back to start our lives over and do this courting right, and then get married in the Lord. You brethren don't know what a great blessing you have when you do things the Lord's way from the start."

The morning came when Pastor Pablo and his wife Euni accompanied Omar and Yuri to the judge's office to take care of their civil marriage. Marta, a sister from the Waslala brotherhood, and Jona, Omar's best friend,

---

29   CAM: Christian Aid Ministries, a conservative Anabaptist organization based in the United States that does relief work and distributes Gospel literature in various countries of the world.

went along as witnesses. Everything went smoothly, and by eleven o'clock, Omar, Yuri, Pablo, and Euni were returning toward the center of town.

"Now," said Pastor Pablo, smiling, "you finally have a wife of your own, in God's will."

Omar's eyes were filled with tears as he whispered, "And praise the Lord, she is a Christian! But we will wait to unite again till after the church ceremony on Sunday. Then I'll finally have the Christian home I've always longed for."

The Waslala chapel was full and running over. Omar and Yuri sat on the front bench. Omar wore a long-sleeved white shirt and black pants. Yuri wore a snow-white dress that Pastor Pablo's daughter Janie had given her. Little Karen sat on the bench between them, her curls as blonde as straw in the sunshine.

Bishop Tim Schrock had preached a powerful message on baptism, and Pastor Pablo baptized Omar and several others while Tim held the bowl of water.

Yuri wasn't to be baptized yet, but she was delighted to be taking the Bible class for baptism with her best friend Cynthia. She was also happy that her mother had come all the way from Regadío to be with them on this special day.

After the baptism, Pastor Pablo preached a second message on marriage, and then he married Omar and Yuri. Though everything was so new for Omar and Yuri, they appreciated the way these Waslala brethren loved God and tried to obey the Bible. After so many years of not having close friendships, and not loving or trusting anybody, the brotherhood was like a dream come true for Omar, a little piece of Heaven on earth.

About a week after Omar and Yuri's marriage, they traveled to Managua where Alvino Miller and his wife Edna were temporarily stationed at CAM's headquarters. There they spent a delightful week at CAM's lovely guest-house, and Alvino and Edna took them to see interesting places in Managua.

Omar and Yuri rejoiced, because their relationship was finally becoming what it should be, following the Biblical pattern. They now were married in the Lord, and they could look forward to serving the Lord together.

One morning as Omar walked briskly down the street in Waslala, he recognized the man coming down the other side of the street. He crossed the street to meet him, whispering to himself, *Here comes the answer to my prayer.* Omar stood there on the street, smiling, with his hand outstretched. "Hello, my friend! How are you doing?"

The man looked startled, but he was forced to stop. He shook Omar's hand and stuttered, "I-I-I'm doing okay."

Omar kept the man's hand in his grip. "Do you remember me?"

The poor man's lips trembled slightly. "Yes, I sure do." It was the man who had raged in a drunken fit at Omar when he tied his horse at Evelio Salina's restaurant. But today he was sober—and scared.

"Well, I just want you to know that I forgive you for the way you treated me the day you were drunk. I used to be a very violent man, but I've been converted. I'm a Christian now, and I'm learning to love people instead of getting angry at them."

The man was relaxing, but the fact that Omar didn't turn his hand loose unnerved him. He just nodded numbly.

"You see, I've given my life to the Lord Jesus, and that's what I want to recommend to you. Seek God. He can forgive your sins and help you become a man who is free and useful here on this earth. He can help you stop drinking. He can give you peace and joy."

The man was still speechless.

"I've been praying for this opportunity to witness to you."

Omar finally turned his new friend loose, and as he headed on down the street, he smiled. What a pleasure it was to be able to witness to people instead of beating them up!

On a vast open plain, Omar was running for his life as a volcano erupted behind him. Loud rumbles blasted his ears. Lava and fire spewed into the sky. Rocks were thrown around like toys. Omar ran like he had never run before.

Suddenly Jacinto appeared in the middle of the plain, smiling fearlessly. Gasping for breath, Omar continued his desperate dash for safety. Why wasn't Jacinto afraid of the deadly eruption?

Then it happened.

A red-hot streak of lava caught him right across his back, like a lash from a horsewhip.

Omar screamed and leaped as hard as he could. He landed beside the bed, running, like he often did when he had such nightmares.

"What's wrong?" Yuri cried, sitting up in bed. "Are you having another nightmare?"

Controlling himself, Omar returned to his bed, trembling like a leaf. "Yes!" he gasped. "And it was awful!" He bowed his head and buried his face in his hands, praying.

Omar sat on the edge of his bed, thinking hard. He hadn't had one nightmare for months since he had been converted, nor had he had trouble sleeping at night. God had surely done a wonderful work in his heart. So why had his nightmares returned now? The answer flashed into his mind. *I must confess what I did to Andrés. God is clearly telling me I need to make restitution with him.*

Although it was only 1 a.m., Omar didn't sleep the rest of the night. He told Yuri his dream, concluding, "What surprised me most was that Jacinto wasn't afraid. He didn't run. He didn't need to. He was actually smiling—he was ready to die."

Omar spent time in prayer and read his Bible. Before the birds opened their beaks in praise, he was walking fast toward Pastor Pablo's place, knowing that Pablo got up early to pray.

Very shortly Pablo was with him, finding chairs for them both. *Pablo is getting used to the fact that I need to talk often,* Omar realized. *I wonder if he gets tired of me.*

"Pablo, I had a horrible nightmare last night!" Omar began slowly, telling Pastor Pablo about the dream. He also confessed that he thought the dream was meant to show that he needed to make restitution with his cousin Andrés. For the first time, he told his pastor the story of the awful crime that he and his uncle Bato had committed.

Bowing his head, Omar sighed. "I was hiding the truth, Pablo. God does not allow that. That's why I came right away to confess. I know what I have to do. I was not the author of the crime, but I helped, and I am to blame."

"That *was* a serious crime," Pablo agreed. "Does Andrés suspect that you were involved?"

"No, he doesn't. But he did suspect my uncle Bato, and he knows we hung out together."

"After Andrés got better," Omar explained, "he bought himself a pistol for the first time and declared, 'If I ever find out who did this to me, I'll kill him!' "

Pastor Pablo raised his eyebrows. "Are you willing to face him?"

"Yes, I am," Omar stated firmly. "Especially since that nightmare last night. But there's a problem—Andrés lives in the United States. However, I heard he wants to return to Nicaragua soon. What should I do?"

"This is a touchy restitution, Omar, and it must be done carefully. Though I agree God wants you to do it, I would give it time. First of all, it must be done personally, so we will have to wait till Andrés comes back to Nicaragua. Will you pledge to God that you'll do this as soon as you have the opportunity?"

Omar readily agreed to face Andrés as soon as he could. He didn't know that it would end up being a year until he could keep his promise. But the moment he made the pledge, peace flooded his heart. For now, he had done what he could.

"Once Andrés is back, I will go with you to talk to him," Pablo promised. "God will make it be a beautiful thing! Meanwhile, you are free."

The scene around the large table was a happy one. Pastor Pablo's family had invited Omar's family for a meal after a Sunday morning service. The two families were enjoying chicken and rice with iced tea. Cynthia was holding little Karen, whose curls bobbed happily. Omar was telling stories of the recent happenings in his life. Yuri was quiet, answering questions when asked. They all laughed and talked as the delicious food disappeared.

After the meal, Yuri helped the ladies wash the dishes, and Omar and Pastor Pablo settled into their usual spot on the front porch. As they talked and sipped black coffee, Omar told Pablo about several things that were bothering him.

"Pastor Pablo," he began, "I told you that my brother Milo owes me a lot of money."

Pablo nodded. "Yes, you said you loaned him money to go to the United States."

"That's right, and he promised to pay me back as soon as he could. He did send money all during the time Mama was sick, and I appreciate that. But whenever I call him and ask about my money, he makes a lot of promises, but never sends me a cent. What should I do?"

"Well," Pastor Pablo answered slowly, "there's really not much you can do if you aren't going to fight it with the law. And I don't recommend that. I don't think it's wrong for you to remind Milo, but it's not worth fighting over or losing your peace."

Omar nodded quickly. "The money I loaned Milo was money I made selling drugs in Playa Jaco," he said. "It's dirty money. So maybe it's just as good I don't get that money back."

"That's a good thought, Omar. Pray about it. If God doesn't soften Milo's heart to pay you, you can assume it's His will that you don't get that money back. You can be satisfied knowing that what you have accumulated honestly is good money. You've earned it by the sweat of your own brow."

Omar sighed and changed the subject. "I keep thinking about my pending legal situation with the United States. Have you felt any direction as to what I should do?"

"Look, Omar, I really appreciate your willingness to do anything along the line of restitution. I have a feeling that the day will come when you'll be faced squarely with your legal situation. I get these mind pictures where I'm calling that telephone number on your web page. But I'm not sure that now is the time."

"Yeah, I feel the same way," Omar mused. "We'll wait and pray. At least I'll never run again. The authorities know I'm in Waslala. If they want to come arrest me, I'm right here."

Omar sighed again. "I have another question, Pablo. How can you and your family take me in like this when you know I was a criminal?"

Pablo smiled at Omar. "It's not a problem at all, brother. You see, we understand how God changes a man. We believe in forgiveness and reconciliation. We believe that a genuine convert is a new person in Christ. When I'm with you, I do not think of you as a criminal. I know you are my brother in Christ."

"I can hardly believe how your daughters trust me as if I were a brother," Omar confessed. "It means a lot to me that we can all be together today as one big family, even with my past. Even when they see how I've changed, a lot of people would never trust me."

"You're right," Pablo acknowledged. "But you've changed. The way you're willing to face your past and make restitution has convinced us that you're genuine. And so, why *shouldn't* we trust you?"

As Omar walked home with his little family, he told Yuri about the conversation. "I have found a real family at last," he said with tears in his eyes. "It's the family of God!"

53

NUEVA ARMENIA

THE TROPICAL NIGHT hugged the rustic cabin in its sultry embrace. Bats fluttered past the open windows, snatching up beetles that had been enticed by the light from the candles flickering in the main room. Fireflies flitted across the yard, blinking their good nights. In the distance an owl hooted eerily.

This cabin was a bachelor's haunt for the week, and it looked it. Several hammocks in the spacious main room hung above the mats on the floor. The sheets were rumpled, and clothes hung from nails pounded into the bare studs. The room contained little else except for backpacks and several pairs of rubber boots, soiled with fresh dust.

Omar, Pastor Pablo, and Julio Lopez, a convert from the Jicaral congregation, had traveled together to southern Nicaragua. Bishop Marcos from Costa Rica had joined them, and they had bussed into the remote town of Nueva Armenia. The fledgling church there was holding a week-long Bible conference. The two speakers were Marcos, who was teaching a series on child training, and Pablo, who was teaching about the time God had destroyed the earth with a great flood.

Every afternoon the brethren from Nueva Armenia congregated for the joyful time of singing and Bible study in their rustic wooden chapel. The weather was hot, and the sweat ran, but hearts and souls were stirred by the teachings from the Good Book.

Now, the men who had traveled together were conversing seriously in the cabin where they were lodging. Julio and Omar recounted their stories of how the Lord Jesus Christ had wooed them—the drama that thrills the heart of every born-again Christian. Omar and Julio were not in competition; their stories were simply amazing testimonies of God's mercy on wicked men who heed His call. The way God had restored their shattered lives was nothing less than miraculous.

During that week, the teaching on child training reached deeply into Omar's heart. On the third day, Omar was surprised to see Marcos stride up to the pulpit with a thin switch in his hand. Showing what the Bible had to say about applying the rod, Marcos gave practical teaching on how to use it in training children to learn obedience.

Since Omar had trained horses from his childhood, this made a lot of sense. He had just never heard that the system worked on children. But the more Marcos explained and shared about his own experience as a father, the more Omar was impressed. The bishop's emphasis on using the rod with love, not anger, struck home for Omar.

As the week progressed, strong bonds formed between the visitors and the locals. Those evenings in the bachelor's cabin, Omar marveled, "I have never seen anything like this! In the world we never made friendships so quickly. We were always wary of each other and never quite sure what was going on.

"Here I feel as if I have known and truly loved these brethren for years." Omar looked at Marcos, smiling. "Most of all, I enjoy your teaching on child training, and I can't wait to get home to put it to practice."

On the way back to Waslala on a night bus, Omar shared his plans with Pablo. "Pastor Pablo, up till now I've left the child training up to Yuri. Now I see that's a mistake. As the leader in the home, I need to step in and take responsibility for these important things.

"My sweet Karen has a tender conscience, and I know she won't be hard to train. But understanding what I do now, I know she needs more attention. Marcos says you can do a test to see if your child is obedient. I want to ask Karen to sit on a chair for a certain amount of time and see if she obeys. I'm sure she'll jump off the chair as soon as we put her on it."

Pastor Pablo encouraged Omar in his new vision.

Then he dropped a bomb. "Omar, guess what? I think God is giving us some direction about turning yourself in to the U.S. authorities. Marcos talked to me privately the last day, and I knew I needed to share it with you."

Omar gave Pablo his full attention.

"Marcos knows about an experienced Christian lawyer in the States who has been involved in situations like yours," Pastor Pablo began, his voice husky with emotion. "He suggests that it's time you look into settling with the United States. He thinks we should start by getting advice from this lawyer."

Omar was quiet for a long time, thinking hard. *Has the time come? Is this from the Lord? What if I have to go to jail?*

Finally he answered, "Pastor Pablo, we've been praying about this. I have a lot of confidence in Marcos. If he believes this is the time, I'm ready."

"Praise the Lord!" Pastor Pablo responded. "I knew you'd be willing to consider this, but I also realize how hard it will be."

"Yes, that's what I've been thinking. What if I have to go to jail? But yet, I am responsible for my crimes, so if God wants me to, I'm willing to pay my dues. Yes, I really do want to take care of this."

By now Pastor Pablo and Omar were both shedding tears. It was a huge step, and they both knew it.

"This would be much easier," Omar acknowledged sadly, "if it weren't for Yuri and Karen. And now my wife is expecting again. But the Lord knows even that."

"Rest assured," Pastor Pablo said, "that the church will take good care of your family if you go to jail. The important thing is that you be free before God."

After discussing this new twist in his life, Omar turned to another topic. "Pastor Pablo, I've learned so much this week that I can hardly contain it. One thing I realize I need to work on is my relationship with my wife.

You know that it's been hard for me to really love Yuri. Since I've heard the teaching on love at home, I understand that I need to make some changes."

Pastor Pablo was listening intently, and the bus tires hummed on in the darkness as Omar struggled with his emotions.

"You know how I always said that I would never find another woman like Gema? I know now what I must do. I need to renounce that false idea. I need to ask God to rip away that tenacious claim she's had on me for so many years—so that I can truly love Yuri. If I don't, I'll never love my wife as I should."

Omar put his head down on the seat in front of him and wept. Pastor Pablo reached over and comforted his brother whose shattered heart was healing.

"Who's going with you tomorrow?" Nathan Yoder asked. Omar had just told Nathan, a young brother from church, about his plans to travel the next day.

Omar smiled. "Just me. Just me and the good Lord."

"I think it would be nice if someone would go with you," Nathan suggested. "That's a big job to face all alone. How are you going, and what time?"

"I leave at five-thirty tomorrow morning on the express bus, Lord willing."

The next morning as the express bus slammed to a stop on Main Street, Omar was pleasantly surprised. There stood Nathan, backpack in hand, ready to accompany him to Estelí.

After the trip to Nueva Armenia, when Marcos had suggested that Omar face his legal issue with the U.S. authorities, Omar had lived out some tense, yet thrilling moments. The Waslala brotherhood had agreed that it was time to seek advice and pray about Omar's encounter with the U.S. government.

Pastor Pablo had contacted the Christian lawyer from the United States that Marcos had suggested. The lawyer referred Pastor Pablo to a Christian organization that helped prisoners reconcile with folks they had hurt with their crimes. This organization was sympathetic to Omar's case, but they clearly explained that they didn't know how to handle a case where the criminal was still on the loose, wanting to reconcile with the U.S. government.

When the help from the States' side stalled, the Waslala brethren suggested that Omar seek advice from the local authorities. So Omar was making this trip to Estelí to meet with two of his uncles who held government positions.

Later, in Uncle Tabito's living room, the four men engaged in serious conversation. When Miriam's brother Eric heard his nephew's story, he responded, "Well, Omar, you're facing a delicate situation. I knew you had committed crimes but had never heard the details. My advice is that you don't touch anything that has to do with the U.S. authorities. It's been almost ten years since you committed the crime. Let the thing rest."

Uncle Tabito agreed. "Omar, you don't know what you might get yourself into if you face the FBI. If a vicious dog is sleeping, it's always best not to wake him up."

Omar waited awhile before answering slowly, "Well, uncles, I see what you mean, and I appreciate your advice. But ever since I was converted, my pastor and I have been praying about this. I believe God wants me to make restitution for the crime I committed. Plus, I've decided that I'll never be a fugitive again. I need to face this thing head-on."

Eric stared at Omar. "Well, if that's the case," he answered carefully, "the first thing you'll need is a high-powered lawyer with connections to the government."

"Wait!" Omar announced, raising his hand. "I don't need a lawyer. I already have one."

The two uncles stared at Omar, wondering.

"My lawyer's name is Jesus Christ. That's the only lawyer I need."

Eric stroked his chin, and then he stammered, "Well . . . if that's what you say . . ."

Tabito shook his head, astounded. "So what can we do?"

Eric spoke again. "Let's go talk to Estelí's top judge. He's probably the one who'll hear your case when you turn yourself in. He's my personal friend, and I'm sure I can get an appointment this evening."

That evening they met in the living room of Estelí's top judge, who listened carefully to Omar's story, with Eric and Tabito adding some explanation.

The judge cleared his throat. "First of all," he said, "the FBI is going to try to get you to go to the States for trial. There they would sock a life sentence on you in no time flat. But here is where you can thank Nicaragua for its non-extradition law. According to our country's laws, you need not be tried in the United States. You will be tried right here in Estelí."

"Right," Eric agreed. "Under the non-extradition law, the city of LA must send their lawyers, their witnesses, and their detectives to Nicaragua, and you will go to trial here."

"Meanwhile, we can pull some strings." The judge winked at Eric. "Things shouldn't go too badly for you, Omar, if we let Eric help you out a bit."

Suddenly Omar realized, *With the help of these three men, I wouldn't have to go to jail for a minute. But that wouldn't be right.*

Omar swallowed deeply, willing the judge and his uncles to understand. "Look, that's not really what I'm looking for. I-I really did commit a crime—a horrible one. I killed an innocent woman. So I'm guilty, and I really should pay my dues. Right?"

Silence. You could have heard a pin drop.

"What I want to know, sir," Omar added, looking at the judge, "is what jail time would I get if you judged me fairly and squarely here in Nicaragua?"

"Fifteen years."

"That's what I wanted to know," Omar answered, bowing his head. "That's about what I expected."

"I really don't know why you would do that," Tabito threw in, getting to his feet to indicate that the meeting was over. "But I can respect your decision."

Eric got to his feet as well.

The judge raised his hand and continued, "If you decide to contact the FBI, make sure you set it up to turn yourself in voluntarily here in Estelí. That will be to your favor in the trial."

Omar stood up. "Thanks a lot, my friends. I think you understand what I want, and I know I can count on you all once the time comes. If it does, God's will be done."

"I admire you," the judge said, handing Omar his business card. "Here's my phone number so you can call me at any time."

Omar couldn't wait to get back to Waslala to tell the brethren what he had found out. When he met with Pablo, he said, "Pastor, it's just like I expected. Fifteen years is a long time, I know. But through good behavior I can whittle it down to maybe seven or eight."

Pastor Pablo nodded.

"I've already decided that if I go to jail," Omar stated, "it's because God wants me to give my testimony there. Have you thought about it, Pastor Pablo, that they'll lock me up with the worst criminals?"

Pastor Pablo was overcome by emotion. "That's right, Omar! If you go to jail, we as a church will lay hands on you and commission you to preach the Gospel to criminals like you used to be. God will take good care of you, and the church will take good care of your wife and children until you get out. May God's will be done!"

Omar and Pablo were quiet for a moment. The hush spoke of God's presence, and they knew they were walking on holy ground. God in Heaven smiled down on the man who had once been obstinate and violent, but now was subject to God's plans.

Neither Omar nor his pastor knew what the future held, but God did. In that confidence, Omar rested.

54

VIDEO OF CONFESSION

ON THIS SUNDAY morning, the gazebo's thatched roof gleamed in the sunlight, and the brackish pond nearby simmered in the sun. Two flycatchers tried to out-tweet each other from the immense tree spreading its verdant branches over the cheery scene.

Omar sat nervously in one corner of Pablo's gazebo, and Yuri sat at the opposite end, calm and collected as usual. She was holding Karen, dressed in pink, her curls subdued by a twin set of braids. In another corner stood Pompeyo, a local Waslalan, with a video camera in his hand, poised and ready.

Pastor Pablo stood facing Pompeyo. When everything was ready, Pablo nodded, and Pompeyo raised the camera to play it on Pastor Pablo's face.

"Good morning to all who hear and see me. My name is Pablo Yoder, and I am pastor of the Waslala Christian Brotherhood. It's been my pleasure to serve as a missionary here in this remote place called Waslala, Nicaragua.

"Among the many experiences I have had here in Waslala, one has been leading to Christ a man who is now my brother in the Lord."

Stepping over to Omar, Pastor Pablo placed his hand on his shoulder and continued, "This is Omar Montenegro, and he has some words to share with you today.

"It's a blessing for me to introduce my brother. Although much of his life has been sad, today he is happy." Pablo sat down beside Omar and placed his arm across his shoulder. Then, nodding, he indicated that it was Omar's turn to talk.

As part of his restitution for the crime of murder, Omar had planned with Pastor Pablo to make a video of confession to send, not only to the U.S. authorities in LA, but also to Gema's daughters and others of Gema's family.

As Pompeyo directed the video camera at Omar, Omar felt his heart pounding. His mouth was dry, but he knew what he had to do. He started carefully.

"First of all, I want to thank the Lord that I am here today by His mercy. Yes, I have some things to share with you, my listeners.

"I want you to know that repentance has come to my life. I have given my life to God. In my former life, I did many wicked things. I committed many ugly sins, and they tormented me. For many years, I was plagued by nightmares and horrible dreams.

"All this came upon me because, in a crazy fit of fury and jealousy, I took the life of a woman who was very special to me. I did not want her to step out of my life.

"All my life, I had longed for a home and a family. The family I finally acquired was this woman Gema and you two, Daiana and Noemi, Gema's daughters. When I met this family, I was recovering from having lost my family in Nicaragua. My parents had separated, and I was devastated, roaming around in the world all alone. So when I finally found this family, I was very happy. Even though I was not living right, I always longed for what was good."

Omar continued, confessing how he had murdered Gema and then planned to take his own life, but how God wouldn't let him pull the trigger. He told of his years as a fugitive, suffering guilt and remorse, knowing that his wicked crime had deeply affected Gema's young daughters.

"I have felt remorse all these years, thinking about you, Daiana and Noemi," Omar said.

"Today I want to ask you for forgiveness. That's what this video is all about—to ask you, Daiana and Noemi, to forgive me for my awful crime.

Daiana, today you are seventeen years old, and Noemi, you are fifteen. I remember so well how we used to go play in Huntington Park. We had so much fun. We used to go to Long Beach, and we were just like the family I had longed for."

Then Omar asked for forgiveness from other members of Gema's family. "Matías, you knew me well. You remember what I was like with Gema and the girls. Can you forgive me?

"Ramón, would you please forgive me?

"Doña Juana, can you forgive me for all the damage I did to you—for hurting you so cruelly? I am so sorry!

"Even as I hurt you all, I was destroying my own life as well.

"This video is also to declare that I am willing to pay for the damage I did to all of you. I plan to turn myself in to the authorities here in Nicaragua. I invite all of you to come to my trial. Bring your lawyers, your detectives, or whoever else you want. I am here, and I am willing to pay my dues to prove that I have repented of my sin.

"Even if I turn myself in and pay my penalty, I realize this will not bring your mother's life back, nor erase the horrible crime that I committed. There is no justification for what I did. All I can do is repent and at least try to pay what I deserve to pay. If you can forgive me, that's wonderful. If not, I leave it all in God's hands. Only God can help you forgive me. I know that God has forgiven me. He sees that my heart is not the same as before. He knows I am willing to serve Him to the end.

"I realize how hard it is for you to forgive me, but with God everything is possible. I invite each one of you to seek God. If any of you are Christians, you will understand that what God has done in my life is huge!"

Omar dropped his head and wept.

Controlling his emotions, he continued, "I can't understand how God could even pay attention to me. But as you can see, I am here today because He loves me. For five years I tried to run away from myself. Attempting to stop my violence and not damage people anymore, I isolated myself from humanity, suffering all alone. While I was up on the mountain, many terrible things happened to me. All along I knew I was paying for my sins. When repentance came, it did not come easily. It came shrouded in pain.

"Today you will see my family. I have three children and my wife Yuri. I want to give them love—the love that I never had.

"I finally repented when my little Karen—"

Pompeyo turned the video camera over to Yuri and Karen. Karen looked like a doll, dressed in her Sunday best. Omar called little Karen over to him, and her pigtails bobbed as she ran to her daddy. She jumped up on his lap, sucking on a lollipop Yuri had given her.

"This is Karen," Omar whispered, taking her into his arms. "One night she became sick with a high fever. Then suddenly she convulsed like a person who is dying. In a panic, I picked her up and ran toward the hospital. I was sure she had died and that I was paying for all my wickedness.

"As I ran toward the hospital, I cried out to God, 'Please take my life and not hers! I deserve to die because I am such a bad person. But save Karen's life, because she is pure and good.' When I decided to give my life in exchange for hers, she breathed again.

"You know, that's what God wanted—for me to give up and repent. God didn't take my life after all, and He gave my daughter's life back. I recognized God, and He gave me new life in Christ Jesus my Saviour. I thank Him today for the peace He gave me. My life is so full of love and so many good things that God gives me daily. But I really do feel remorse about all the people I hurt, and I am willing to ask forgiveness from everyone I have offended.

"I ask forgiveness from all the people I sold drugs to. All I cared for was making money. But I thank God that all those vain ambitions died. All I want now is God's peace.

"I ask forgiveness for everything bad I did in the United States. I also ask for forgiveness from you, the U.S. authorities, for doing wrong when I had the opportunity to work and to change my ways. Unfortunately, I spurned that opportunity. I address you, the detectives who are overseeing my case. I am here in Nicaragua. I will never be a fugitive anymore. I am ready to face justice and to accept my punishment."

Then, turning to his pastor, Omar choked, "Pablo, that's all."

Pastor Pablo got up and addressed Omar. "God bless you, brother! I bless you for proving your repentance with more than words, and for your willingness to turn yourself in to the U.S. authorities. It is one thing to say,

'Forgive me, but don't stick me in jail.' It is quite another thing to say, 'I am sorry, and I am willing to accept whatever God dictates through the legal authorities.'"

Turning to the camera, Pastor Pablo explained that the Christian brotherhood at Waslala had committed themselves to helping Omar and his family during this tough time of restitution. As Pompeyo turned the camera on Yuri, Pablo introduced her as Omar's wife. He explained that Omar and Yuri were now members of the brotherhood.

"Since the day Omar confessed his crimes to me," Pastor Pablo continued, "we have been praying, waiting, and asking God for this opportunity to do what we are doing today. Right from the beginning, Omar said, 'I am willing to face the authorities.' Now the time has come.

"Omar is already free in Heaven, but now he will also be free here on this earth. God has forgiven him. You can see the peace of Christ on his face and sense the joy of the Lord in his heart.

"Omar and Yuri are expecting another baby soon, and he wants to be a free, true Christian father to his children.

"May God bless this family and help them to face their uncertain future. We don't know if Omar will go to jail for one year or five years or ten. All he wants is God's will.

"Thanks for watching this video, which is a vital part of Omar's liberation process. God bless you. In a minute we will also be showing some scenes of our congregation in a Sunday morning service."

It was a touching service that Omar and his family celebrated at their chapel after they finished making the video of confession. The Waslala congregation felt a little nervous as Pompeyo filmed them, but they were glad to allow whoever saw the video to get a glimpse of Omar's church.

Omar led the songs that morning. Of course, one of the songs he chose was "Jesus Loves You," and he dedicated it to Daiana and Noemi.

As the congregation sang, Pompeyo zeroed the camera in on Yuri and Karen. Little Karen opened her mouth wide and sang along, but since she was too small to know the words, she was several words behind everybody else.

When Omar took his seat after leading the songs, he was overcome with emotion. He had made his confession to Gema's family and to the U.S.

authorities. He had shared a picture of the church that he loved so much. Now, as Pastor Pablo got up to preach, Omar put his head down on the bench in front of him and wept. Pompeyo recorded the touching moment.

At the end of the service, Pastor Pablo asked Omar and his family and several of the other brethren to come forward as he sealed the occasion with prayer.

The service was ended, and the video of confession was finished. One question clung to Omar's mind. *How will God get that video into the hands of the right people?* He didn't know, but he trusted God and felt a deep peace.

God, in His wisdom and strength, would make sure that sooner or later, the video would make its way to the right people. God knew who needed to hear Omar's confession. Omar realized that this event had been another step in his liberation process. What a miracle!

Omar stared at the drunk sitting on Pastor Pablo's porch. The man's hair was long and unkempt, and he hadn't shaved in a week. His clothes were tattered, and his hands were stained black with grease and burned motor oil.

Questions darted through Omar's mind. *This man claims that he wants to become a Christian?* Omar was thinking. *He's probably having all kinds of troubles, sinner that he is, and wants help now that he's drunk. But as soon as he's sober, he'll forget it all and keep on downing the booze.*

"I talked to Pastor Pablo," the man said slowly, "and I have decided that I'm going to serve the Lord. I'm tired of sinning and serving Satan."

Omar eyed the man closely. He did not sound terribly drunk. What if he really were sincere about changing?

Everybody in Waslala knew Tomás Garcia, the best chain saw repairman in town. He could even fix chain saws that others had given up on. When sober, Tomás was useful and well-liked. But when he was drunk, he was useless.

The evening before, Tomás had come to Pastor Pablo, hopelessly drunk, asking for help to be saved. Pablo had taken the time to pray for Tomás and told him to come back the next day sober, so he could help him find the Lord.

Today Tomás was back, and Pastor Pablo had prayed for him again. Tomás admitted that he had had a terrible hangover and had drunk two shots of booze before coming, but he claimed that he still wanted to be a Christian. Pablo told Tomás to come back the next day totally sober. Then he invited him to church that evening.

Since it was still several hours till church time, Pablo had brought Tomás to the porch where Omar was sitting and suggested that Omar give him some good advice. Then Pablo disappeared inside to get ready for church. Omar listened doubtfully to Tomás's story.

Hesitantly, Omar gave Tomás his own testimony and then explained to him what he could do to be saved. The more Omar talked, and the more Tomás listened, the more sober he became, and the more Omar believed him. By the time they walked to church together, Omar was starting to believe that maybe Tomás was serious after all.

After the service, Pastor Pablo invited Tomás up to the front and told the brethren his story. "Tomás wants to be saved. This morning he still drank two swigs of alcohol because of a horrible hangover. But he promised God to not drink again, ever. I promised to go to his house tomorrow at 5 a.m. to pray for him so that he doesn't drink. At two o'clock tomorrow afternoon he plans to come to my house to be saved. Let's pray right now that this might happen."

So Pastor Pablo prayed for Tomás. Although most of the brethren wondered if Tomás would really come through, they all saw he was sober now. Omar especially cared for this man who had been gripped by the devil of drink for so many years. *Oh, I hope that Tomás can become free through the Lord Jesus Christ!* was Omar's prayer.

A holy hush hung over the Waslala church. Pastor Pablo's family sat in the front on one side and Timo Miller's family sat in the front on the other side. The rest of the people from the Jicaral and Waslala congregations filled the chapel behind them. In front of the pulpit stood a small table with two brand-new, identical Bibles resting on it. Bishop Tim Schrock stood behind the pulpit, explaining to the congregation what was happening.

"Brethren, the time has come for God to choose which of these two families will be elected to move to Managua to start an outreach in the city. No man or woman on this earth knows which of these Bibles has the lot in it. But God does, and He will direct these two brethren to take the book He wants. Let's pray."

Omar was enthralled. It was the first time he had witnessed a casting of the lot. For the first time he was hearing how the apostles had cast lots to choose an apostle to replace Judas Iscariot after he hung himself. Omar was impressed by how the church took all these things so seriously and sincerely wanted God's will. This solemn ritual was refreshingly free from political interest or trickery.

Timo Miller had been ordained to minister to the little flock in Jicaral before Omar had come on the scene. But now that the Waslala brotherhood felt a call to start an outreach in Managua, Pastor Timo was willing to move to the city to preach there. Timo confessed openly that he felt a call. Pastor Pablo and his family were also willing to move to Managua to minister to the needy people in the city. They were ready to drop their financial investments and go if God called them.

Someday, Omar whispered in his heart, *I also want to be willing to leave all to go preach the Gospel! I wonder if this stirring I feel in my heart isn't a call to preach already.*

After Tim's prayer, the hush hanging over the congregation was amplified. Omar watched and prayed silently. Timo got up first and took one of the Bibles, and Pastor Pablo took the other one. Tim Schrock opened Timo's book and found the lot.

The brethren didn't even try to suppress their emotions as the call to Managua was confirmed. The people of both congregations filed up to express their love and support to Timo and his family. *This is the way it should be.* Omar sighed. He loved it!

How would God fill the vacancy in Jicaral that this decision would bring about? The bishop urged the Jicaral congregation to relax and trust. God would provide leadership for them.

They will probably ordain a brother from Waslala to replace Timo, Omar thought. *I have a feeling it will be Jona.*

55

LONGING TO BE FREE

THE BRAND-NEW PISTOL glistened on the table in Uncle Bato's dining room. Omar knew its sole purpose was to scare him. "Do you see my new .38 caliber pistol?" Uncle Bato sneered as he picked it up and tucked it into his belt.

Omar caught Bato's eye and held it. *I'm not going to let myself be intimidated by this man,* he vowed.

"I'm a bad man," Bato bragged. "You know I can use a pistol when I need to, right?"

Omar nodded. He knew what was coming next, but he wasn't afraid of Bato anymore. Jesus now ruled his life, and his uncle's raving and threatening wouldn't sway Omar from his resolve.

Before this meeting with Bato, Omar had traveled to Regadío, where his father had warned him about Uncle Bato's rage. "Omar, listen to my advice," Fermín urged. "Don't go near that man. He's dangerous!"

"He's scared stiff that I'll get him in trouble over the Andrés deal," Omar surmised. "He's afraid that I'll tell the U.S. authorities everything he's been into as well. But I'm not scared of him. He won't do anything to me."

"But son, if you turn yourself in, won't that get Bato in trouble too?"

"Not likely. If I turn myself in, I'll be confessing my own crimes, not other people's. Let Uncle Bato rant and rave."

"I don't know, Omar . . . I just wish you wouldn't stir things up with the authorities." Fermín moaned. "I'm afraid it's going to cause a lot of trouble—not just for you, but for the rest of our family too."

"Just wait till this evening," Omar had answered. "I want the whole family to see a video we made back in Waslala. It will explain why I'm planning to turn myself in."

That evening after Omar's family had watched his video of confession, everybody in Miriam's house was quiet and solemn. No one except Omar knew what to say.

"As you can see," Omar told his family, "I'm serious about giving my heart to the Lord. If being free requires me to turn myself in, I'm not only willing—I can't wait! You all know what a wicked sinner I was. I felt as if I was carrying a ton of stones on my back. Now, every time I make something right, it's like getting rid of another stone from my sack. I'm longing for the day when the stones are all gone!"

The family had been too stunned to answer. Some, including his mother, fully supported what Omar planned to do. But others did not. No matter—Omar's heart was set like a flint. It would take more than an angry uncle to change his plans. On his way back to Waslala, he stopped in to face Bato personally.

Once Omar knew he was armed, Bato plopped into a chair. "What in the world is going on with you?" he snarled.

"What do you mean, what's going on?" Omar asked.

"I've heard some crazy things—that you're planning to turn yourself in to the U.S. authorities," Bato growled. "What's the deal? Don't you esteem your life? If you're tired of living, tell me so, and I can take care of that with this pistol." Bato caressed his new weapon.

Omar answered carefully, "I knew this would be hard for you to understand, Uncle. But since I've given my heart to the Lord, I do His will, not man's will. Yes, I've decided to make right my wrongs of the past. I'm going to turn myself in."

Bato jumped up from his chair. "But if you do that, Omar, you'll get me in trouble too!" he yelled. "I won't put up with this nonsense. It wouldn't be hard at all to stop you with this pistol."

"Calm down," Omar ordered, sitting down. "I have a question for you. If you had a chance to be totally free of all the bad things you ever did in the past, would you accept it?"

Bato didn't answer.

"I'm getting close," Omar stated. "I'm determined to be free. I've set my heart on confessing and making restitution for all my sins, and that includes confronting the U.S. authorities. Once I'm done, I'll be a free man."

Bato was listening carefully.

"When I meet the authorities," Omar insisted, "I promise I'll confess my own sins, not yours. I'm only interested in freeing myself. Why would I mention your affairs?"

"I still think you're crazy, b-but if you promise to not get me in trouble..." Bato stuttered.

"You still haven't answered my question," Omar said, smiling. "If you had a chance to be totally free, would you accept it?"

Bato nodded. "I guess I would."

"Okay, that's all I'm doing. Even though you don't understand it, just believe me. God has given me the opportunity to be free. The peace I feel in my heart is already making this whole thing worthwhile!"

Bato sighed as the wind dropped out of his sails. "All right. Do what you have to do. I don't understand why it's so important to you, but I'm warning you—if you get me in trouble, I'll kill you!"

The meeting over, Omar said goodbye and hurried back to Waslala. His family was tugging at his heart, and he missed them.

A single bulb hanging from the rafters lit the simple living room enclosed by bare board walls. People filled the white plastic chairs that had been borrowed for this occasion. Pastor Pablo's whole family was present. So were the nurses from the church's clinic as well as Omar's family. Several other brethren from the church had also been invited.

Behind a small wooden table stood a man whose eyes shone almost as brightly as the bulb. He wore black dress pants and a white long-sleeved shirt. His hair was neatly cut, his face was clean-shaven, and for once, his hands were clean. *He sure doesn't look like the same man!* Omar marveled. He hadn't known Tomás could look so handsome.

"Brethren, I want to give my testimony this evening," Tomás announced, beaming. "You see, when I fought in the war as a Contra, I lived through very dangerous situations in the Nicaraguan jungles, and I prayed a lot. I had been a Christian before the war, and I vowed, 'Lord, if You get me out of this alive, I'll serve You forever.'"

Omar's eyes were glued to his friend. He was amazed at what he saw. Tomás was a new man. The joy of the Lord shone from his face.

"After the war, I forgot all about my promise and lived a life of sin. I was trapped in the vice of drinking whisky—not all the time, but every so often I would drink for a week or two."

Tomás paused, licked his dry lips, and plunged on. He wasn't used to public speaking, but the more he talked, the more freely the words came, gushing out of his very heart and blessing his listeners.

"Well, not long ago, my longing for God grew. I was so tired of sin that I knew I had to do something. So I went to Pastor Pablo, and from there you know the rest of the story.

"I gave my heart to the Lord a week ago. Since Marta and I were not married, we separated, and I moved in with Daniel. Then the Lord opened the door for us to get married quickly. That took place this morning. And now Pastor Pablo has promised to bless our marriage in the service on Sunday with a special prayer.

"Tonight I am very happy. My conscience is finally clean, and I have fulfilled my vow to God. That's why we're celebrating tonight, and I thank you all for coming. Pastor Pablo, could you come up here to ask the blessing on the food?"

After the blessing, Marta and Tomás's daughters served a delicious meal of chicken stew with a salad and plenty of hot tortillas. As they celebrated with heartfelt singing after the meal, Omar's heart was almost bursting. What a joy to participate in helping a man like Tomás come to the Lord! Omar glanced at Yuri and Karen. He was so glad that Yuri had followed him in the faith, and he hoped that Marta, too, would soon choose to follow her husband's example.

Just like it had been for Omar, Tomás couldn't hide his joy at being delivered from the vices of sin. Of course, Omar still had to face the authorities about the crimes he had committed. But that didn't matter. Soon he would be as free and happy as his dear brother Tomás. Praise the Lord!

Jona's cousin Mateo, pastor of the Nueva Armenia church, was a cattleman like Jona and Omar. When Mateo found out that Omar had a contact in Estelí for excellent breeding stock, he persuaded Jona to transport a load to his area, where good breeding stock was hard to find.

Omar did the wheeling and dealing for six young Holstein and brown Swiss bulls. Then Jona traveled to Estelí to meet Omar, where they loaded the animals and drove them the eight hours to Nueva Armenia.

When Omar and Jona arrived at Nueva Armenia, the eager dairymen, including Mateo, were waiting for their breeding bulls. After the deals were made and the money exchanged, Omar and Jona went home with Mateo for a good supper.

Omar was delighted to be back visiting the brethren in the place where he had been so inspired by God's Word the year before. That evening, Mateo, Jona, and Omar had a wonderful time talking about the Lord, and Omar gave his testimony again.

After a short sleep, Jona and Omar headed back to Waslala in the wee hours of the morning. The hum and rattle inside the truck box made it hard to visit, but it would take more than a little noise to keep Omar from sharing with his best friend. Through the long night hours, the two men's hearts knit as they shared intimately about their lives.

After several hours they fell silent. It was hard for Omar to grasp how Jonathan, raised in a Christian home and sheltered from the horrible world of sin, could have such confidence in him, an ex-criminal. Like Pastor Pablo kept explaining, Jona believed what the Bible said—that a man can become a new creature in Christ.

Glancing at Jona, whose eyes were glued to the road, Omar thought, *Someday I need to tell this man how much his friendship means to me!* He sighed. *I need to do it soon.*

Once again, the Jicaral and Waslala congregations filled the chapel. As Omar watched the proceedings from his usual seat on the third pew, his heart filled with wonder. This evening, April 20, 2008, a brother would be chosen to replace Timo Miller, who had moved to the new mission in Managua.

The ordination proceeded as usual. After several preparation messages the previous evenings, the church was now gathered to nominate the new leader. If more than one brother were chosen, there would be a lot the next evening.

After the message, Pastor Pablo and Tim Schrock disappeared into the schoolrooms behind the chapel. *How is Jona feeling?* Omar wondered, glancing at him occasionally. Surely Jona realized he was a prime candidate to take his brother's place. But Omar couldn't tell how Jona and Jéssica were feeling. On the surface, they showed no signs of emotion.

After prayer, the ushers directed the brethren through the rooms at the back to give their nominations. Omar's heart pounded in expectation. He had no doubt about who he would nominate, and Yuri was in agreement with him.

The ushers motioned to Omar and Yuri to file through the schoolrooms. Stepping up to the table where Pastor Pablo and Tim were taking the names, Omar smiled. "Jona," he said quietly.

Yuri nodded and said the same.

"God bless you." Pastor Pablo smiled, and Omar and Yuri returned to their seats.

The tension grew as the last brethren filed through to give their nominations. Omar felt as if his heart were about to burst. But very soon, after the brethren had all been through, Pastor Pablo and Tim returned. Pastor Pablo took his seat, and Bishop Tim stepped up to the pulpit and smiled. "Brethren, God has clearly shown us His will tonight. There will be no lot. Brother Jonathan Miller has been chosen by the church to be pastor of the Jicaral congregation, replacing his brother Timo."

The whole congregation sighed as one.

"Lord willing, tomorrow we will come together again to ordain our brother by the laying on of hands as the Bible teaches. Let's stand for closing prayer."

After the prayer, the brothers and sisters gave vent to their pent-up feelings. Jonathan's shoulders shook as he sobbed. Jéssica cried too as she hugged their baby Cesia close. Their two older daughters blinked, bewildered about what was going on. Everywhere Omar looked, people were weeping. Then he realized his own tears were running down his cheeks.

Such a combination of feelings! Omar realized soberly that both Jona and Jéssica knew the weight a minister carries on his shoulders—especially Jéssica, who had watched her own dad ever since she had been a baby.

Still, Omar rejoiced, because the choosing of a leader had been free of politics. No one doubted that God had clearly shown His people His will. Omar made his way to the front, and soon he and Jona were clinging to each other, their embrace saying much more than the words Omar stammered. God had called Jona; God would give him the grace he needed.

God would use Jona, Omar knew. He was such a humble young man who loved the Lord. Even though he had once told Omar that preparing a message was hard for him, he would do a good job in Jicaral. Omar, for one, would give Jona his full support.

I will watch for a chance to tell Jona how much I appreciate him and his testimony, Omar decided. *And I will pray for him daily.*

56

PACKING BAGS

"JESUS LOVES YOU; He really cares," Omar and Yuri sang, and little Karen joined in from the little red plastic chair where she always sat for family worship. "Jesus loves you," she hollered, several words behind, like usual. Omar and Yuri grinned at each other as they sang on.

Omar opened his Bible and began to read aloud from 1 Peter 5, which describes the devil as a roaring lion, sneaking around to see whom he can snatch. "That's why we need to be alert and vigilant at all times," Omar reminded his family.

Yuri, heavy with child, listened intently and nodded in full agreement.

"This is especially important for me right now, with my trial looming," Omar said pensively. "It seems the devil is eager to get me. But I also feel God's presence very close."

"It's especially stressful for you right now," Yuri agreed, her eyes full of compassion, "with Pastor Pablo in the United States lining things up for you to turn yourself in."

"You're right." Omar sighed. "I don't know what's going to happen next."

Just then Omar's cell phone rang, and he picked it up to hear Pastor Pablo's voice. "I'm here in Pennsylvania at my brother-in-law's place," Pablo explained. "We're discussing when we should phone Detective McKnight, whose number is on your wanted page. Here's our plan, if you approve it. If nothing interferes, I'll call this Detective McKnight tomorrow at 9 a.m. What do you say?"

"If that's the way God is leading, go for it!" Omar answered, determination welling in his heart. "In a way, I'm more than ready to get this over with. Just remember the three requests you have in exchange for giving my information."

"Yes," Pastor Pablo replied, "let me refresh my memory. First of all, we'll ask if it's possible for them to wait to process you till after November when the baby is born. Second, they should let you know before they arrest you, so you can turn yourself in. And finally, we want them to help us get the video of confession to Gema's family."

"That's right."

"Okay, Omar, I won't be back in touch with you till after the call, unless something new comes up. We'll be praying, brother. Be brave!"

"Thanks, Pablo. I will."

But as soon as he ended the call, Omar dropped his face in his hands and wept. The time had come. He would probably be facing prison time, separation from his family, and who knew what else? He was willing to accept the consequences for his past sins. But, oh, it would be hard!

Controlling his emotions, Omar turned to Yuri. "Well, this is it. Pastor Pablo plans to call the detective tomorrow morning. Knowing how detectives work, they might nab me right away."

"But aren't you going to bargain for time for me to have my baby?" Yuri asked, tears filling her eyes.

"Yes, Pastor Pablo plans to negotiate, but you can't trust those detectives. They might or might not give us time. Honey, do you realize that they could arrest me tomorrow?"

"What? How could they do that?"

"Those detectives are on the ball, Yuri. As soon as they know for sure where I am, they could call our local authorities, and I could be locked up within hours."

"But won't they have a little mercy in this case because you're turning yourself in?"

"Maybe and maybe not. Some of those fellows are pretty heartless. I know, Yuri. I was in jail one time in the United States for driving without a license and for running from the police. Some of those policemen are about as kind as angry jaguars." Omar shuddered. "God's in control, and He will take care of us. But today I'm going to act as though they are coming to get me, which means I'm going to have a busy day."

"So, what can you do to get ready?" Yuri asked, staring wide-eyed at her husband.

"First of all, I need to take care of my cattle and two horses. They need to be some place where they can stay for a long time, and I need to get their bills of sale put into somebody else's name.[30] That way, after I'm gone, they could be sold to help with living expenses for you and the children," Omar explained. "I think I'll put the cattle and horses all in Jona's name. He's a cattleman and can take care of things while I'm away."

"But, Omar, I hoped you wouldn't be going anywhere!" Yuri wailed. "Now you make it sound as if you're going to jail tomorrow. I sure didn't expect this."

Omar smiled. "To tell you the truth, I didn't either. But you never know. All I know is that if they come, they'll find me ready. Let's pray."

As soon as family worship was over, Omar left to get everything lined up. Jona, along with the rest of the brethren, agreed to take care of Omar's business and family in case he went to jail.

That evening, with Yuri's help, Omar packed his clothes, ready to travel. "If I get any inkling that they'll nab me," he explained, "I'll catch the first bus to Estelí. I want to turn myself in there. The prison conditions would be better than here in Waslala, and I would be close to my uncles who promised to help. Also, that's where the kind judge lives that I told you about. So depending on what Pablo tells me tomorrow, I'm out of here!"

Omar prayed extra hard that evening before he went to bed. He already missed the precious little family he was learning to love in a deeper fuller way. *Why must I leave my family now,* Omar questioned God, *just when I'm finally learning to live the way You planned for a man to live? But yet, if you need me to preach the Good News in jail, I am willing. Your will be done.*

---

30   In Nicaragua, each head of cattle has to have a bill of sale/ownership.

| 425 |

At ten o'clock the next morning, Pastor Pablo called again. "How do things sound?" Omar asked eagerly.

"Well, not too bad," Pastor Pablo replied. "I talked to Greg McKnight. He's very friendly and wants to work with us in this case. And guess what? He's the same detective who was investigating the murder that morning when you were crossing the border. He was happy to hear that I had information to share on you. I can tell they still want you pretty badly."

Omar was all ears. "Did you tell them that I'm a Christian now and part of your church?"

"Oh, yes. I told him that you're voluntarily making this restitution for Christ's sake."

"What about the requests?"

"He didn't promise anything. He wants to talk to me face-to-face. He did say they'll consider getting the video to Gema's family, but I soon detected that they mostly want to see the video for themselves. They're considering flying me out to California in the next several days. Or maybe they'll fly here to Pennsylvania to talk to me and to pick up the video."

"Do they seem interested in coming to Nicaragua to try me?" Omar asked next.

"Well . . ." Pastor Pablo hesitated. "They're trying to convince me that you're morally responsible to come to the United States for your trial, since your crime was committed in this country."

"What did you tell them?"

"I told them that it's your decision. And I reminded them of what they already knew—that Nicaragua has a non-extradition law for its citizens. I confirmed that we as a church will support you in choosing whatever you think is best. Guess why they would rather not try you in Nicaragua."

"Tell me!"

"Nicaragua can give you only thirty years!"

"So they want me to have a lot more than that?"

"That's exactly right. I think they would ask for a life sentence here in the United States. But Greg also said that they just recently tried another Nicaraguan citizen in Nicaragua who had committed murder in LA. He said that the officials had to make six trips down there, and it ended up being extremely expensive for the city, and the man ended up getting only a few years. It almost sounds like if you choose Nicaragua, they might just drop it."

"I doubt they'll give up that easily," Omar replied. "Did they talk about arresting me?"

"No. They don't seem to be in a terrible rush to arrest you. I told them that you aren't going to run anymore, and that you want to turn yourself in, preferably in Estelí. What they want right now is to talk to me personally and watch the video before they make any moves. I just praise the Lord that they aren't going to nab you right away."

After hanging up, Omar shook his head and sighed. "I can tell Pastor Pablo trusts those men. I sure don't. They could easily pull a trick on me now that they know where I am. But then again, it's all in God's hands."

The next several weeks were tense for Omar and his family as the detectives deliberated. Pastor Pablo kept calling with updates. After several days the detectives decided to send their agents to Virginia where Pastor Pablo was now visiting his wife's sister and her family. What they most wanted was a DVD of the confession video.

"They've decided to wait to do anything on your case until I'm back in Nicaragua," Pastor Pablo assured Omar in a final call. "They may fly down for a personal interview with you. For now, you can relax. We'll face the next step once I'm home again."

Omar was incredulous. "Pastor Pablo, do you really believe those men? Don't you think they'll still come pick me up?"

"Well," Pablo answered carefully, "I tend to believe them. They seem to be professionals who do things in the open. I sure don't get the feeling that they're swindlers. This Greg McKnight is really a nice person to deal with."

"Well, I'm not so sure," Omar replied. "I just can't trust them. I have my bags packed and ready." Omar told Pablo about putting his cattle into Jona's name. Pastor Pablo was touched to realize how serious this whole thing was for Omar and his family.

After the call, Omar wept again. How he appreciated that their pastor understood what they were going through! Omar and Yuri talked for a long time. They found comfort in knowing that God was with them through it all.

Time ticked by. The detectives didn't seem to be in a hurry.

Meanwhile, Nataly Montenegro got tired of waiting and made her appearance early one Sunday morning in November 2008. Omar had never been present at a birthing before, and he was moved to tears when the midwife placed his baby daughter in his arms.

After church that morning, Jona and his family stopped by to visit Omar and Yuri, who were still at the midwife's house. Omar and Jona swapped stories of their children's births, as did their wives. But what set Omar's heart on fire was when they shared their goals to love their children, to train them according to the Bible, and to raise them for the Lord.

Since Jona had been raised in a Christian family in a church setting, Omar felt blessed to have his example to follow. Jona was gentle and kind with his children, but he was also tough as nails on nonsense and disobedience.

That's the way I want to be with my children too, Omar purposed in his heart. *And that's exactly the way God is with me.*

"Greg McKnight is the detective in charge of my case," Omar explained to the brotherhood in one of their frequent meetings. "He says that since I have nothing against me legally here in Nicaragua, they can get me a visa and a ticket, and he'll come and personally escort me to the United States."

"And when you step off the plane, they'll handcuff you and put you in jail for the rest of your life!" Jona surmised.

"Exactly!" Omar agreed.

"Choosing to accept Nicaragua's non-extradition law is a little like the Apostle Paul saying, 'I appeal to Caesar,' " explained Pastor Pablo. "Omar is not refusing to be tried and condemned. He will turn himself in, he will be tried, and he will accept the sentence that a Nicaraguan judge pronounces."

"My family in Estelí would never agree for me to fly to the United States for my trial," Omar added. "The detectives clearly stated that they can't force me. So if I choose to fly to the United States, my uncles who are helping in my case would accuse me of breaking our law here and would never forgive me."

"One of those detectives claimed that if Omar were his son," Alvino drawled, "he would fly him to the States to face a life sentence in jail. But you know good and well that wouldn't happen if they had a local law that says you can choose to have your trial at home."

After a lot of discussion, a hush settled over the circle of brethren. They supported Omar in his decision to turn himself in to the local authorities rather than traveling to the United States to be tried. Even though the detectives claimed that going to the United States for trial was Omar's moral obligation, Omar chose instead to do what the laws of his own country allowed.

All the brothers involved felt peace, and joy filled Omar's house that evening as he told Yuri about their decision. Even little Karen seemed extra happy, though she did not understand what might happen to her daddy.

For the next several months, Omar and Yuri waited tensely. No detectives came to snatch Omar, but the U.S. officials continued to pressure him to come to the United States. After Pastor Pablo gave them Omar's clear answer, they agreed to meet with Omar in Nicaragua. The question was, where should they meet?

Again the Waslala brotherhood gathered, and Pastor Pablo reminded them, "Look, this is really Omar's choice. We're here because he's asking for our advice. But we'll respect his final decision."

"Here's the problem," Omar explained. "At first the detectives agreed to meet me here in Waslala. Now the American embassy says that Waslala is too dangerous. What shall we tell them?"

Should the detectives be willing to come wherever Omar was, or should Omar feel obligated to go to the place the detectives chose? The brethren discussed the question at length.

Omar finally stated his decision clearly. "Let's tell them that I'll meet with them in Estelí." Omar looked at each brother around the circle. "Estelí will be safe enough for them, and it's my hometown. That's actually where I want to be judged anyway. If I go to prison, I'll be right there to turn myself in." Again the brethren agreed.

As the date of the meeting approached, Omar was struck by anxiety. *What if they're setting up a trick to kidnap me and take me to the United States?*

Should he alert his uncles and the judge in Estelí to what could happen so they could stop it before Omar was taken out of the country?

Once more, Pablo assured Omar that the detectives were just doing their job—they weren't trying to deceive him. But every evening Omar would talk with Yuri about his fears.

Together, they would always come back to several things they knew for sure. "We know, Yuri, that what we're doing is right," Omar told her. "We have felt clearly that God led me to turn myself in. Ever since the trip to Nueva Armenia, I sensed that it was God's will."

Yuri nodded in full agreement.

"Secondly, every decision I make, I take it to the brethren first. The meeting never ends till the brethren are agreed, and I feel their full support. This gives me tremendous courage.

"Lastly, Yuri, we know that God is much bigger than those detectives from LA. Everything will work out for good if we love and obey God—and we do!"

One morning, as the countdown came to the last week, Omar sat on Pablo's porch. "Pastor Pablo, I got another call from Uncle Bato. Somehow he found out what day we're planning to meet with the detectives. Apparently, he forgot that he agreed to let me turn myself in as long as I don't involve him. But now he's angry and threatening me."

"Oh my, brother! That's the last thing we need right now, isn't it? What's he saying?"

"Well, he claims he might fly here from the States and stop my plans, and he tried his best to convince me not to go ahead. He claims the detectives will kidnap me, and I'll be sorry I ever tried to do this. He says if I get him in trouble, he'll shoot me."

"The poor man just doesn't understand, does he?"

"I told him once again that I'll confess my own crimes, not his. But it didn't faze him."

Pastor Pablo shook his head, clearly troubled.

"Guess what else he says, Pastor Pablo. He says that you're also trying to trick me—that you'll get a $25,000 reward for getting me into their hands."

"I'm sure glad you don't believe *that!*" Pastor Pablo sighed and looked at Omar. "Does anybody else in your family think that?"

"It doesn't matter what they think. Don't worry!" Omar assured his pastor. "You're right."

"I know you folks are genuine." Omar's voice broke. "You're helping me out of love from the bottom of your hearts, without any reimbursement except storing some more treasures in Heaven. I want you all to know how much Yuri and I appreciate your help. You love me much more than even my own family does."

"I'm glad you feel that way," Pastor Pablo answered. "Let's take courage and go ahead with the plans. God is much bigger than any Bato Montenegro!"

Omar raised his face and said through his tears, "I agree, the plan is on. Full force ahead! In the name of the Lord, I go to do what I know is God's will for me."

57

GO WITH GOD

A DRIZZLE HAD settled over Waslala, and a frisky wind swirled the rain in every direction. The streets were slippery with mud, and the potholes were full and running over. The flooded Waslala River roared its way through town, heading toward the sea. The afternoon seemed almost as chilling as Omar's future encounter with the detectives from Los Angeles.

Inside the chapel, an emergency brother's meeting was in full session. The room was filled with grim faces. Every eye was on Omar as he spoke.

"You all know I had agreed to meet the detectives on the fifteenth of December—that's the day after tomorrow. Everything was set, and Pastor Pablo and I were planning to head for Estelí tomorrow. Well, this morning Greg McKnight called, and he says the American embassy won't let him travel to Estelí due to the dangers during the Christmas holidays. They want to meet in Managua instead."

Pastor Pablo explained, "I tried to assure him that there is really no danger—at least not worse than traveling around in Managua. But he firmly stood his ground. So we need to decide. What should Omar do?"

"I think he should tell them again that he's willing to meet in Estelí," Alvino answered. "They can't just push him around at their whims. If they want a meeting with Omar, they should be willing to come all the way to Waslala."

"I'm afraid it's a trick," Omar added. "In Estelí, my relatives have connections. Snatching me onto an airplane would be a lot quicker and easier from Managua."

"I don't think it's a trick," Pastor Pablo contradicted. "I think they're just paranoid. And I'm sure it's not coming from the embassy! These detectives know this country is in firm control of the leftists, who aren't friendly toward the United States. So they really *are* scared. But there's no valid reason for their fear."

Alvino's opinion coupled with Omar's fear swung the group; the majority thought Omar should stick with Estelí. Reluctantly, Pastor Pablo agreed.

Omar felt for his pastor, who had talked personally with the U.S. detectives and trusted them. But he was worried. *All they need to do,* thought Omar, *is throw around some reward money for my arrest, and I'll be on the plane for the United States and in jail for life.*

Later, over at Pastor Pablo's house, Pablo called the detective in Omar's presence. "Omar is afraid of a trick," Pastor Pablo spoke frankly into the phone, "and the local church brethren support his decision to not go to Managua. I personally don't believe you're up to a trick, but I agreed to this plan since the brethren here support Omar's decision. I'm sorry, but if Omar has to go to Managua to meet you, the whole thing is off."

"It's hard for you to accept this, Pastor Pablo, isn't it?" Omar asked gently after the phone call.

Pastor Pablo nodded. "I just hate to see this prolonged. I'm going to pray that if God wants this to happen, they'll agree to meet in Estelí."

"Pastor Pablo, let's get a second opinion," Omar suggested. "Let's go ask Bishop Tim Schrock."

"Great idea! Tim has a lot of wisdom. He's in Jicaral this evening, so let's run down to see what he says."

Minutes later, Omar was in Pastor Pablo's jeep, bouncing over Papayo Hill toward Jicaral. They met Tim in Doña Lucia's thatched gazebo, along with Ernest Strubhar from Oklahoma. Ernest was an old friend of Pastor Pablo's who was in the country visiting his son. Like Tim, Ernest had experience and wisdom. As dusk fell gently, Omar and Pastor Pablo poured out their dilemma.

When they were finished, Ernest spoke. "I understand, Omar, why it's hard for you to believe the detectives. But I don't think they're up to a trick. If they would have wanted to get you by slinging money around or playing tricks, they would have whisked you off a long time ago. I'm not insisting you go to Managua, but I'm sure it's just as safe as Estelí."

Tim gave Omar a fatherly smile. "Omar, I want to remind you that since you gave your heart to the Lord, Jesus is your friend. If Jesus is your friend, He'll go with you tomorrow. He is bigger and stronger than any detectives. I'm also not trying to convince you to go to Managua. It's up to you. But if you do decide to go, I believe you're safe in His hands!"

The men got up. The meeting was over. Ernest led in a prayer for guidance. Tim placed his arm around Omar's shoulders and whispered, "Go with God!"

After crawling into the jeep, Omar was silent, overcome with emotion. They bumped along until finally Omar blurted, "Pastor Pablo, let's go to Managua! I'm ready to get this over with!"

Early the next morning Omar sat in the front passenger seat as Pablo's jeep bounced along the rough road toward Managua. The pastor himself was driving, and Ernest Strubhar was sitting behind them. Ernest would fly back to Oklahoma the day after Omar's interview. He had watched Omar's story unfold from the beginning, and he was keenly interested in the case. Omar had invited Ernest to accompany them to Regadío and then join the interview in Managua, if the detectives allowed it. Ernest had some experience with the U.S. authorities and a head full of wisdom that both Pablo and Omar needed.

The three stopped in Estelí first to meet the lawyer who had promised to defend Omar, and Omar explained the choice to meet in Managua instead of Estelí. The lawyer was polite, but he asked again why Omar needed to meet them at all. "They could meet with just me," he reminded Omar.

But Omar quickly responded that dropping the interview was not an option. He ran over the facts again, and then once more gave the lawyer his testimony.

Later that day as Pastor Pablo's jeep topped a rise on a dirt road, a green valley opened up amid the dry, rocky landscape. Gnarled acacia trees and cacti grew between the lichen-covered rocks at the upper edge of the valley.

"This valley is green because it has irrigation canals running along both sides," Omar explained. "The canals are fed by a spring that fills a pond at the edge of town. People raise vegetables here, especially corn and beans. The black soil is very fertile, and because of irrigation they can raise crops even in the dry season. That's why the town is called Regadío."[31]

"I love this place!" Pastor Pablo exclaimed, staring at the valley as they bounced down the road. "I've been here before, but every time I come, I like it better. Maybe someday there will be a church here, Omar. The people from Regadío are really watching you. They know your story well. If God would want a church started here, and if He would send me, I would love to plant vegetables in this valley."

"So this is the place you grew up?" Ernest asked, smiling at his friend and brother.

"Yep," Omar replied. "I lived in the United States and in Costa Rica part of my life, but most of my years were spent right here."

The first thing that the three men had to do, after meeting Omar's family, was calm his mother's fears.

"Why can't he just let the case rest?" Doña Miriam wailed, wringing her hands. "We're sure the detectives will pull off some trick and snatch Omar off to the States. You have to think of his wife and children!"

It took Ernest and Pastor Pablo a little while to convince Miriam that Omar was not crazy. Ernest's gray hair and wise demeanor helped Miriam understand that as a Christian, it was Omar's duty to make restitution for his crime.

After settling Miriam's heart, they had to start all over with Fermín. Though Fermín wasn't as expressive as Miriam, his fears were deeper, and he was harder to convince. Omar, watching the scene and knowing his father, concluded that Fermín was not really convinced, but he finally just let the matter rest.

Later that evening, Omar and Fermín took Pastor Pablo and Ernest to look around Regadío. "Let's go see my Uncle Bato's cow herd," Omar suggested as they walked down the stony streets.

---

31 Regadío: irrigation.

On a swinging bridge, the three men crossed a little creek, flanked with huge chilamate trees and brush. Walking upstream, they found a corral where a dozen scrawny head of cattle ate chopped grass from wooden troughs. "It would sure be tough to raise cattle in this dry place," Pastor Pablo drawled, shaking his head. "All their food has to be hauled in, because there sure isn't any grass left in these hills."

Omar was nodding when his phone rang. It was Bato. Omar strode toward the creek, separating himself from the group. For a good twenty minutes, he paced up and down along the creek, trying to reason with Bato.

"And who was that?" asked Pablo, after Omar ended the call.

Omar frowned and placed his finger to his lips. Fermín was coming along behind.

When they were alone, Omar told Pastor Pablo and Ernest about the call. "My uncle is determined to stop me from going to the interrogation tomorrow. He's threatening to fly down from LA tonight. But I stood my ground."

"He says he's coming down tonight?" Pablo asked, raising his eyebrows. "Do you think he'll actually do that?"

"With Bato you never know," Omar answered. "In many ways he's just full of hot air. But then again, he has pulled some pretty dirty stunts. He's so angry that he says if I get him in trouble, even if I'm locked up, he'll kill my family!"

"Well, let's not worry," Ernest concluded. "Regardless what this man threatens to do, God is still on the throne. Our plans are made, and tomorrow we head out, Lord willing."

"Let's go spend some time with your family again, Omar," Pastor Pablo suggested. "Ernest, you find some meaningful Scriptures that explain how we can trust in God."

A unique collection of people gathered in Doña Miriam's living room that evening. A few of Omar's brothers and sisters were there, wearing serious expressions. Some of the grandchildren hung around, all ears. Their attention was focused on Ernest, who occasionally stroked his bushy gray beard as he talked about the Book. Everybody could see that Ernest not only knew his Bible; he loved it. That evening he made it speak to the whole group, who listened reverently. And oh, how it hit the spot!

"The LORD is my light and my salvation; whom shall I fear? the LORD is the strength of my life; of whom shall I be afraid?

"When the wicked, even mine enemies and my foes, came upon me to eat up my flesh, they stumbled and fell.

"Though an host should encamp against me, my heart shall not fear: though war should rise against me, in this will I be confident."[32]

By the time the half hour was up, everybody in the room knew that God is a God who can be trusted. They knew He loved Omar and held him and his family's future safely in His hands.

Miriam gave the two Americanos the bedroom with the best bed, and they slept well. Omar slept in the bedroom with his brothers, but his sleep was restless and broken. Even though he trusted God and, like Daniel of old, believed the Lord would deliver him, what he was facing the next day was a huge load weighing heavily on his heart.

It was not until they started for Managua that Omar confessed what else Bato had said in that phone call. "He says some big mafiosos are angry that I'm turning myself in. They're afraid it will get them in trouble too—such as people that I used to buy drugs from."

"Do you think it's true?" Pastor Pablo wondered. "What if we're only seeing the tip of the iceberg?"

Omar sighed. "I just don't know what to think. At first I didn't believe a word he said. That's why I didn't tell you right away. But this morning I've been wondering. What if it *is* true? Bato also said that these men from the Mafia were going to fly down last evening to stop me. The last thing he said before he hung up was, 'I'll see you tomorrow!' "

Omar had another question that he didn't verbalize. Had the detectives come in on last evening's Taca flight? Who else had flown in on that same plane?

"That could be bad!" Pastor Pablo looked serious. "Just maybe the whole scheme behind this interview has more to do with mafiosos than Gema's death. Why is Bato so afraid and so determined to stop us?"

32 Psalm 27:1-3

"What did we get ourselves into?" Ernest whispered, staring down the highway. "What if they're waiting to ambush us here on this highway? I think we need prayer."

Pastor Pablo's fists clenched the steering wheel tightly, and his eyes watched the road as the jeep hurtled down the highway. Squinting in the glare of the morning sun, the three men's thoughts flew faster than their vehicle.

Suddenly Pastor Pablo picked up his cell phone and punched in his son Jacinto's number. "Jacinto . . ." Pastor Pablo stammered, "we are suddenly afraid. We didn't realize what we were getting into on this trip. We are wondering—"

"—if there's not a bigger fish to fry," Ernest filled in quickly from the back seat.

"Son, we need some extra prayers. Could you call around a little?"

"Yes, Daddy, I'll do that! We're praying!"

Seeing a vehicle parked up ahead, Omar wondered, *Could this be an ambush? Will armed men step out and gun us down? Might some big men do all they can to keep me from reaching the Crown Plaza Hotel for the meeting?*

They passed the vehicle without incident, but they were running late for the nine o'clock appointment. However, that wasn't the only reason Pastor Pablo was driving fast. All of a sudden they just couldn't get there fast enough—they were afraid! During the next hour, the men were silent as they buzzed along, but their prayers were constant and intense.

After entering the dense traffic of Managua, their fears subsided and they relaxed a little. A mile from Crown Plaza, Pastor Pablo asked, "Omar, do you still want to take the safety measures?"

In the last brother's meeting they had discussed a safety measure to help assuage Omar's fear of a trick. Pastor Pablo would drop Omar off several blocks from the hotel. Next, he and Ernest would meet the detectives and make sure everything was clear. Then they would call Omar, and he would walk over and the interview would begin.

"I've been thinking about that," Omar answered. "No, I've decided to just go on in with you. My fear is gone."

Pastor Pablo drove into the Crown Plaza parking lot and killed the motor. They were a half hour late, but Pastor Pablo had called to let Greg know about the delay.

The time had come to face the U.S. detectives. "Let's pray," Pastor Pablo advised. "If we ever needed God, we need Him now!"

The prayer was short but sincere.

Omar couldn't believe how calm he felt. How he appreciated the support of his companions! What if he had to face this all alone? *But I'm in God's hands—that's what makes the difference. Like David, I am ready to go meet my Goliath. Please go with me, God!*

Perhaps God jotted down the date in the heavenly chronicles— December 15, 2008. Then He sent his angels down to be at Omar's side and the Holy Spirit to fill his heart with courage. Omar was willing to face the detectives for Christ's sake.

58

HAVE MERCY, MAN!

THE SUN WAS shining brightly as the three men crossed the parking lot and walked toward the main lobby of the hotel. As usual, Managua was warm and humid, but chilling thoughts raced through their minds. Though apprehensive, they were also filled with holy boldness.

Pastor Pablo stepped into the lobby first, Ernest and Omar right behind him. Three men rose from couches in the lobby and came to meet them. Omar was glad that Pastor Pablo took the lead and shook hands all around.

Next Omar shook hands with the men. The short, white-skinned Americano was dressed in khaki shorts and a yellow sports shirt. He had a butch haircut and wore a big smile. The unsmiling, dark-skinned Latino was dressed formally. The third man was a strong, hefty Nica who stood in the background. He carried a satchel on his shoulder, and Omar identified him as the bodyguard. No doubt the satchel held more than one gun.

The short Americano led the way. Single file, they walked past a fancy restaurant and out onto a spacious porch. Turning a corner, they found themselves on a wing of the porch edged by a low concrete wall about fifty feet ahead. The porch was perched high above the hotel's gardens.

At the far end a table was set up with four chairs, obviously prepared for the interview. At the corner was another table where the bodyguard sat down, pulling out a newspaper to entertain himself.

The man in shorts pointed at Ernest and asked briskly, "And who is your friend?"

"He's a fellow minister and friend from Oklahoma whom Omar invited along," Pastor Pablo answered.

Pointing to the table where the bodyguard sat, the detective said, "He can sit at this table during the interview, but he may not be present in the interview itself."

Ernest obediently took his seat with the bodyguard and pulled out a book to read. Then the Americano motioned to Pastor Pablo and Omar to follow.

Arriving at the interview table, the Americano commanded, "Have seats."

Taking his seat, Omar noticed a camera eye placed in the center of the table. As soon as the Americano took his seat, he reached over and turned it on, saying, "This session will be recorded." The eye was played straight at Omar's face.

Omar and Pablo were seated with their backs turned, not only to the bodyguard and to Ernest, but also to the only available exit. *We are neatly trapped in the wing of this porch,* Omar realized. *These men don't trust me one bit. Regardless what I say, they'll never trust me. To them, I'm still the criminal who murdered Gema, and they sure don't want me to try to escape during this interview!*

Omar also noticed a huge folder and a stack of papers on the table. How had they managed to get so much information on this case?

Once seated, the Americano didn't waste any time getting to the point. Though he was smiling, his manner was businesslike. "I am Greg McKnight, a criminal investigator sent from Los Angeles to investigate this crime."

Turning to the man beside him, Greg continued, "And this is Joe, my translator."

Greg started the interview calmly, making everyone feel comfortable. Joe, his partner, translated efficiently. "When did you first meet Gema?"

The first hour of the investigation wasn't too difficult. Greg asked background questions that were easy to answer. Omar was fascinated by Greg, his intelligent questions, and his steel-blue eyes. This was almost fun. But as the questions grew closer to the day and night of the crime, the interrogation became more intense.

"Where did you eat lunch on the day of the crime?" Greg asked Omar.

Omar drew a blank. "I don't remember," he answered truthfully.

"Omar, would you say that this was a day you will never forget?" Greg asked for the second time.

Omar nodded.

"Why do you say that this was an unforgettable day in your life, but now you can't even remember where you had lunch?" Greg barked.

From that moment, the investigation became torturous for Omar. Greg knew that at noon on the day of the crime, Omar had taken Gema and Matias out to eat. Apparently, he and Gema had had an argument. Omar didn't remember a thing about it. The detective was sure he was lying.

From time to time, Greg allowed tidbits of information to slip out of his big book to refresh Omar's memory. It was coming back slowly. But the detective got impatient, and his steel-blue eyes turned icy.

The two men locked horns. The detective wouldn't let up, and there were various things that Omar couldn't remember. Soon Omar was almost ready to scream, "Have mercy, man! What happened that night was such a huge thing for me, how do you expect me to remember such a trifle as what I had for lunch?"

By the time they got to the crime scene, it was at least two hours into the interview and Omar wasn't sure if he should cry, scream, or get angry. Greg would ask the same question up to three times on different occasions or right after one another—back and forth, up and down, and all around. Omar had never experienced anything like it.

Greg kept pulling things out of his huge scrapbook and holding them across the table for Omar to see, such as a photo of the pistol he had used. Omar just nodded.

Greg had tons of evidence, and Omar didn't deny anything. He simply couldn't remember all the details, but Greg kept on acting as if Omar were lying. At the beginning of the interview, Omar had promised to tell the truth, and he considered each question carefully before answering. Now Greg claimed there were too many different versions of what happened, and the evidence at the scene didn't match Omar's story. The detective wore Omar to a frazzle, and still he wasn't satisfied.

In the middle of the toughest time, Greg held up a driver's license, the photo toward himself. "I want you to tell me if you recognize the person on this driver's license," Greg commanded, his steely eyes piercing Omar's.

Then Greg took his time telling Omar how important it was that he tell the truth, as though this was the most important question in the whole interview. *Here it comes!* Omar surmised. *It will be a photo of the big Mexican narco dealer who's threatening me through Bato. This is the big fish to fry.*

When Greg handed Omar the license, Omar took it and flipped it around. He held it between his fingers for a long time, staring at the photo. The girl was very pretty; her long black curls tumbled down over her shoulders. She had large startling green eyes.

"Do you recognize this person?" Greg barked.

Omar nodded numbly, continuing to stare at the photo. A tsunami of emotion threatened to smother him as tears filled his eyes. Finally he handed the card back.

"Who is it?" the officer demanded.

"Gema," Omar whispered.

How could they be so cruel? He had already confessed that he had killed Gema. He hadn't dreamed that they would force him to identify her photo ID. What was the point? Whatever it was, it must have been important for them.

But the worst was yet to come.

As the investigation of the crime scene continued, more details didn't match up. Even though Omar was determined to tell the truth, there were still some inconsistencies between the report from the crime scene and Omar's revived memories. So Greg relentlessly cross-examined him on countless details, many of which Omar had forgotten. In fact, God had helped him forget. It was heart-wrenching now to bring it all up—if not from Omar's memory, from the huge folder. He had to relive it all again.

The crime investigator showed no mercy. After three hours, Omar was tired, and his hackles began to rise. The old Omar started lifting up his head, narrowing his eyes, and stiffening his neck.

Pastor Pablo was concerned when he saw what was happening. He reached under the table and gently nudged Omar, whispering in Spanish, "Hey, man, humble yourself. It's okay!"

Omar nodded and relaxed a little.

Greg caught the pastor's gesture. Suddenly he popped up out of his chair, saying, "Hey, Omar, this isn't personal, okay? This is my job. I'm a crime investigator. I have to know if you're telling the truth or not. Let's take a break."

After a quick drink and a breather, they dove right back into the investigation. But again, it was almost more than Omar could handle when Greg pulled out several photos of Gema's body at the crime scene. As Omar sat stunned, he wondered what Pastor Pablo was thinking. His pastor had never been exposed to such violence, and now he was forced to see it in the raw.

Finally, the worst was over. The interrogation of what happened right after the crime went much better. Omar told them exactly what he had done, who he had called, what car he drove, and how he got to the Mexican border that night. Everything Omar remembered matched up with the evidence from the investigation. Praise the Lord.

Omar felt vindicated. He was telling the truth after all. At the end, Omar knew that Joe was convinced and fully believed Omar's story, and he hoped Greg did too.

At one stage in the interrogation, Greg had asked Omar, "Why do you keep saying you're changed? What changed you?"

That was Omar's signal to do what he and Pastor Pablo had talked about earlier. He gave his testimony of the day he was saved, and it was all recorded. Probably the detectives wouldn't agree, but to Omar and Pastor Pablo, this was the most important information in the whole interview! Omar was reminded of the Apostle Paul's testimony before Agrippa, and praised the Lord for this opportunity.

As the investigation came to a close, Greg and Joe again tried to convince Omar that since his crime was committed in the United States, it was his moral duty to go to the United States to be tried. Thankfully, they didn't pressure him, and they accepted his "No." But they both claimed that if they were in Omar's shoes, they would do it.

Omar felt like hollering, "Yeah, right! You detectives had better just be glad I was willing to be here today to go through this grueling four and a half hours when my local authorities and my family tried their best to convince me not to come."

When Greg claimed that he, too, was a born-again Christian, Omar wondered why he had asked for a beer at break, and how he could be so ruthless. When Greg challenged Omar about obeying the Scriptures that say we need to obey our authorities, Omar answered, "That's what I'm doing. The fact that I'm here for this interview is as close as I've come to not obeying the authorities of my own country, do you understand? Yes, it's my fault that I killed Gema. But it's not my fault that I am a Nicaraguan. I did not make the laws of my country."

Everyone was exhausted by the end of the interview, but Greg took time to inform the two men what came next. "Next step is to present this case to the Nicaraguan magistrates to see if Nicaragua is willing to open the case. Since it's over ten years old, they might refuse to accept it. If they approve it," Greg explained, "then the case goes over to Joe, here. He works with Interpol."

Oh! Wow! Omar thought, glancing at the quiet, seemingly gentle man.

"Joe will be in charge of the case from now on. This finishes my job. After that, Washington has to approve the case. If Washington approves it, then we put on a red alert internationally for Omar's arrest. That is when Omar should turn himself in. Soon after, there will be a trial here in Nicaragua. This whole process will probably take over a year."

Greg and Joe promised to keep Omar updated through Pastor Pablo. If the trial went through, they promised to let Omar know when it was time to turn himself in so he wouldn't be apprehended and have to sit in jail unnecessarily.

Then Omar also confessed to having been an active cocaine agent. Even as he did so, he was afraid they would start asking him about his contacts and many other details about the drug ring he had been a part of. But they didn't seem interested in those details.

However, what they did ask startled him. "Is anyone threatening your life right now?"

Omar stalled and glanced over at Pastor Pablo, who was also startled. *Here we go*, Omar worried. *This is the real thing!*

Omar told the truth. "Well, one person has been calling and threatening me from the United States."

Greg and Joe sat forward in their chairs. Pastor Pablo briefly told them that there was a case that Omar had been involved in, but not solely responsible for. The man responsible was angry and afraid Omar would turn him in.

"Is it related to Gema's case?" Greg asked, looking from Pastor Pablo to Omar.

"Not at all," Pastor Pablo assured them.

The two men whispered back and forth for a minute and then said, "Let's just drop it."

Omar knew then that the men believed him. They accepted his word that he was not the instigator of this other crime. He felt not only relieved, but also vindicated.

Pastor Pablo then asked if the detectives had given a copy of the video to Gema's family. "No, we haven't," Greg acknowledged. "We think it would be too traumatic for the mother and daughters to see a video of Omar happy with a new family when he ruined theirs. Doña Juana is having mental issues, and this would not help."

"Could you give us an address so we could send them things?" Omar asked. "We really would like to have contact with the girls."

"No, we can't do that. I don't even know where the girls live," the detective said. God would have to open a door for Omar himself to get the video to Gema's family.

The detectives thanked Omar for coming voluntarily to the interview, and they also thanked Pastor Pablo for his help. Omar sincerely thanked the men for their patience with him.

By this time, the atmosphere was happy and relaxed, and everyone was ready to say goodbye. Omar was amazed when Pastor Pablo readily gave the two men a farewell hug. Omar shook hands all around.

Suddenly Pastor Pablo asked, "Greg and Joe, would you allow me to take a photo of you two with Omar?"

"Sure!" Greg stood to attention.

"Sorry," Joe answered. "I am an International man. I can't afford the publicity."

Greg and Omar posed, their arms around each other, and Pastor Pablo snapped the photo. It was a great way to end the day.

Omar, Pablo, and Ernest regrouped by Pablo's jeep in the parking lot. Omar collapsed over the jeep's hood and sighed. "Man, am I tired! I never dreamed that just talking could make a man so tired. I feel as if I had just put in a hard day's work macheting a field!"

"Me too!" Pastor Pablo agreed. "It was the tense emotional part that sapped us. What a relief that it's over with. Omar, you did a wonderful job!"

"Let's thank God," Ernest suggested.

Standing in a circle, the three men lifted their hearts to the Lord in thanksgiving. Then the floodgates opened, and they all talked a mile a minute, going over the happenings of the day and telling Ernest how everything had gone.

Suddenly Pastor Pablo cried, "Omar, we need to call the people who are praying to let them know what's going on!" In a minute, Omar was calling Yuri. Then he called his mother and next his father. His father had news for him.

That morning Bato had driven into Regadío in a rented vehicle carrying two big guns, asking for Omar and threatening everybody in the family.

"He sure enough flew down last evening!" Omar exclaimed to Pablo and Ernest. "I didn't think he would do that."

"But he didn't stop us," Ernest added seriously. "Praise the Lord!"

"And do you know what happened this morning?" Pastor Pablo gasped. "Just like we suspected, we passed each other on the highway. He flew down on the same Taca flight as Greg did. But he was not able to stop us!"

"I so nearly had to tattle on his crimes." Omar sighed. "I'm sure it was from God that those men decided to drop it or Bato would be in big trouble. Or rather, *we* would be."

"Well," Ernest announced, "I need to get a taxi and find my hotel. I'm not nearly as tired as you brothers are, but nonetheless, I am tired. I am so glad I can leave, knowing that everything is all right. Omar, remember, you are in God's hands. As long as you're faithful, everything will work out for good."

The three men said their goodbyes, and Ernest left. Pastor Pablo suggested, "Omar, let's drive to Matagalpa and get a hotel. That will probably be the safest. No one will know where we are in case Bato is trying to track us. We'll get a bite to eat, and you can call Bato. Then we'll get some rest before we drive home."

As Pastor Pablo pulled out of the parking lot, Omar laid his head back on the seat and sighed. "I'm so glad this is over with! I feel as if a ton of bricks were taken off my back today."

"Yes, Omar, now you can say you are free indeed!"

Omar closed his eyes, and the tears rolled out between his eyelids and streamed down his cheeks—precious tears of cleansing, of release, of joy, of freedom. Pastor Pablo cried along with him. God smiled down from Heaven and blessed Omar, whose heart had been so shattered and scarred by sin, with immense peace.

59

BORROWED TIME

AS THE SUN set at the end of the long tough day, so Omar's heart slowly settled to rest. His thoughts became clearer, and he felt more relaxed than he had in a long time. Pastor Pablo's eyes were fixed on the highway ahead, and his hands cradled the steering wheel. *I wonder what Pastor Pablo thinks of the interview,* Omar pondered. *Does he doubt some of my story, since Greg wasn't satisfied with some of the discrepancies?*

As if prompted by Omar's thoughts, Pastor Pablo sighed. "Man, that was a tough interview, Omar, wasn't it? Greg had no mercy on you, and he wasn't happy because a few details didn't match. Maybe it was a mistake to send him my Prayer Support report on your crime. He had that thing practically memorized, and he knew some of the things in that report weren't accurate according to the evidence or what you shared.

"But I wrote that report in a hurry, then read it to you, translating quickly. I can easily see how some of those details got mixed up. We weren't so concerned about exact details back then—I just wanted to get your story out so people would pray. Then, as an afterthought, I sent a copy to Greg."

"It's all right," Omar said. "It's as much my fault as yours, because when you translated the report to me, I noticed some details weren't accurate, but I thought they didn't matter. But to Greg they did matter."

"Because he's a criminal investigator, and he's good at his job!" Pablo finished.

"You said it! He wore me down until he was sure I was tired enough to tell the truth!"

Suddenly Omar felt an urge to be honest with his pastor, to share the story again with someone who really cared about him. "Pastor Pablo, I know you might have some doubts as to what really happened that horrible night. When I first told you the story, I didn't feel it was necessary to tell you all the gory details. But today you got your ears full. So that you have no doubts, I want to tell you the story one more time, with the details."

"I don't doubt you, Omar, nor your commitment to Christ. But, yes, a lot of questions were raised today. I don't demand answers for them, but if you feel you need to pour it out one more time, we still have a good hour till Matagalpa. Go for it!"

Omar tackled the gruesome job, sharing details with Pastor Pablo that were too intimate to share with anyone else. "When I shot Gema, something within me snapped. I can never explain how much I idolized that girl. Truly, I never expected to recuperate and be normal again. But I'm so glad everything has changed since I found the Lord."

"Amen, brother!"

"For years after Gema's death, whenever I was in a crowd, I watched for those haunting green eyes. Day in and day out, I searched, but I never found them.

"Gema's blood haunted me for a long time. After she died on my lap, I showered to wash the blood off. But psychologically, I carried the blood on my body for a long time. I would bathe with all kinds of soap and detergents, but I couldn't wash away the lingering presence of her blood. It haunted me for months and didn't go away till the blood of Jesus washed me clean."

As they swung off the main highway into Matagalpa, Omar said, "Pastor Pablo, by the time you took the photo of Greg and me, I actually felt good toward the man who wore me down. It was just his job, not something personal against me, and I felt like hugging him because I understood they weren't pulling a trick on me after all."

Pablo chuckled too. "I wonder how Greg felt about that hug."

"He was as stiff as a fiddle string," Omar said, chuckling. "Pablo, that man will never trust me. In his mind I'll always be a dangerous criminal. But that's all right. I'm happy this whole deal is over with."

After getting a bite to eat, Pastor Pablo said, "Omar, I know that you're going through tremendous emotional turmoil. Do you want to sleep alone, or shall I book one room for both of us? If you want to sleep in the same room, that's okay with me."

But there were no rooms with two beds available. "That's fine, Pastor Pablo," Omar said. "I'll be okay in a room by myself." Before turning in, Pastor Pablo invited Omar into his room to pray. On their knees by the bed, the two men prayed earnestly for a long time, and Omar felt a lot better.

But Omar hardly slept as his mind rehearsed the events of the day and the events of his life. When he dozed, they even invaded his dreams. He kept the light on and continued to pray, but his nerves were overwrought, and he was afraid.

The next morning over breakfast, Omar confessed that he had been afraid during the night. "I wished a thousand times that I had accepted your offer to bring my mat over and sleep in the same room."

"You know what?" Pastor Pablo admitted. "I was afraid too! I didn't expect that. I spent some time awake, praying for you."

"What were *you* afraid of?" the two men asked in unison, and then they laughed.

Omar said, "I was struck with the fear that the detectives were still up to a trick and that Interpol had followed us to the hotel to snatch me away."

"I never even thought of that!" Pastor Pablo exclaimed. "I had an awful dream that Bato and his mafioso buddies ambushed this hotel. They were banging on my door, trying to get me to open up. They were planning to kill us both because we had talked to the detectives. Then I woke up to discover that a drunk was pounding on my door."

Omar was incredulous. "What did you do?"

"Nothing. I kept quiet, and the drunk soon gave up and left."

The two men laughed again. "What a night!" Omar said, heaving a sigh.

"Isn't it interesting how our cultural differences affected our fears?" Pastor Pablo mused. "I never once expected the detectives to be scoundrels. I trusted them. And you aren't afraid of your fellow Nicas like I was."

The next several weeks were some of the most peaceful Omar had experienced in his life. His past was settled, except for the Andrés situation that God would bring about in due time. It would be months till the detectives got back with Omar—*if* the trial went through at all. So Omar and his family enjoyed their borrowed time in a special way. Meanwhile, Omar prepared his heart to still go to jail if it were God's will.

The afternoon sun was peeking out from behind a big black cloud in the west. This celestial game of hide-and-seek not only brought a cool hush to the mountainside, but also created a rainbow across the cloud's dazzling face, as if saying, "Very good!"

"Look at that rainbow!" Pastor Pablo exclaimed. "That must be a sign of God's blessing on today, don't you think?"

The five brethren who were with him agreed. Omar, Tomás, Marcelino, Daniel, and Elmer were sitting on an assortment of rocks that adorned the lush green hillside. Below them lay acres of rolling foothills covered with coffee bushes and shade trees. The nearby creek sang a happy song as the pristine water gurgled over the rocks and gushed into the dells.

What a blessing they had experienced that afternoon! A brother from the United States had bought the piece of land stretching before them, and then asked the Nica brothers to use it as their own.

"He didn't even want to make any money on it," Tomás said, smiling. "All he expects is that we keep the place clean and maintained."

"Yes, the U.S. brother sees this fifty-acre farm as a good investment," Pastor Pablo said. "But mostly he wants to help you brethren."

None of the five brethren who were to use the land had land of their own. So that day they had divided the land fairly among them to use indefinitely. Since Omar was the only cattleman among them, he was especially glad to have the use of the grassland. He could buy cattle, fatten them, and then sell them for a profit. The four brethren with farming blood in their veins were glad to have a place to plant corn and beans and to harvest coffee and cocoa.

A thankful, joyful hush lingered over the brethren as they sat on the picturesque hillside. The day had gone well, and the decisions had been peaceful. The rainbow was fading, and a mild rain was falling on the distant hill.

"Boys, let's call this farming venture the Rainbow Farm Project," Pastor Pablo suggested. "It's a great blessing we have received, and it's from the Lord. Let's thank Him right here and now."

So they did.

It was evening, and the cubicle in Alvino's bookstore was full again. As usual, Jacinto was at the keyboard. Omar leaned forward in his chair, his eyes glued to the computer screen. A little to one side, Pastor Pablo, also watching the screen, was giving suggestions. Little Kenny hovered around, fascinated by the technology, but staying out of the way.

Google Earth had pulled up downtown Los Angeles and was zooming in on Huntington Park. "There's one of the Tacos Mexico restaurants where I worked!" Omar pointed, his voice laced with excitement. "The apartment where I lived was just down that street."

After locating his old apartment, Omar helped Jacinto find Doña Juana's place. After the virtual tour of Omar's old haunts—the parks, Long Beach, the dancing clubs, and the bars, the little group felt sad. There was no way to hide the fact that Omar had hung out in many wicked places.

Omar sighed, shaking his head slowly. "I'm so glad I don't live there anymore! That was one wild, wicked life!"

"Now you're just glad you live in Waslala and serve the Lord," Jacinto suggested.

"You're right!" Omar agreed, nodding. "Even the memories are horrible!"

After jotting down some addresses, Jacinto started another search, opening a web page called White Pages. Soon Pastor Pablo was jotting down the phone numbers for all the listings for Matías, Ramón, and Juana Munoz at Huntington Park.

By the time the search was over, the little cubicle hummed with excitement. "I'll take these phone numbers home and see what I can do," Pastor Pablo said. "Surely one of them will help us track down Gema's girls. Soon we should be in contact with Daiana and Noemi."

"And soon these two girls can hear my video of confession," Omar said. "It's another important step toward my complete freedom. Praise the Lord!"

But that didn't happen. Every time Pastor Pablo called a number, he hit a dead end. It seemed that the Munoz family, who had once lived at Huntington Park, had disappeared. But God knew the secret of Daiana and Noemi's whereabouts. If the video were to reach them, it would have to be according to God's perfect plan and timing.

60

THE COST OF FREEDOM

MARCH 3, 2009

The early morning was chilly, and the skies were clear as the bus bounced along toward Omar's home city. Omar and Pastor Pablo hugged their jackets and their own thoughts as they contemplated their mission for the day.

Pastor Pablo's phone rang, and he answered. "Yes, son, what's up?"

After hanging up, Pastor Pablo told Omar, "Jacinto suggests that we should find a cybercafe on the way."

"Why?" Omar wondered, puzzled.

"Remember I told you I'd put out a request on my Waslala Life report, asking for prayer for this job? Well, Jacinto says that responses are swarming in this morning. He was sure it would give you courage for the tough job ahead. They all promise to pray."

The two men smiled at each other, tears in their eyes. Pastor Pablo wrote regular email reports about life in Waslala, encouraging people to pray for the mission, and Omar knew that Pastor Pablo often reported on his case.

My fear is gone, cybercafe or no cybercafe, Omar realized happily. He knew God was in this, and that everything would be okay. But what a blessing to know that a lot of people were praying for him!

Andrés was back in Nicaragua. The week before, Omar had heard the news through his family, and he and Pastor Pablo had made plans to travel to Estelí so that Omar could confess his involvement in the crime against Andrés.

At twelve o'clock the bus roared into Estelí. Omar chuckled when Pastor Pablo reached over and felt his pulse, grinning. "Are you okay?" Pablo asked kindly.

"I'm a little nervous," Omar answered. "But I'm ready for anything, brother. Here we go!"

Omar had called ahead and asked Fermín, one of the few who knew about this crime, to help set up a private meeting with Andrés. "What have you arranged?" Omar asked his father.

"Look, Omar, I-I don't want to get involved," Fermín stuttered. "I haven't arranged anything. Actually, wouldn't it be wise to drop this whole thing? Your uncle Bato is furious."

Omar stepped to one side and whipped out his cell phone to call Andrés' mother. "Doña Irma, is Andrés around?" he asked.

Minutes later Fermín was left alone at the bus stop, because Omar had hailed a taxi and motioned Pastor Pablo to join him. As they buzzed down the street, Omar explained, "God had it all set up. Andrés just happened to be at home, so I told him we'd be right over. We don't really need my father's help."

Arriving at the house where Andrés lived, Omar, filled with holy courage, marched ahead and disappeared into the house. Pastor Pablo followed, and Omar introduced him. Omar was delighted that Andrés was there waiting for him, and a lot of his family members were with him.

Doña Irma served them Coca-Cola, and they visited for a half hour. Omar was amazed at how relaxed he felt, knowing what was coming.

Finally, Omar took the plunge. "Andrés, so much has happened since we last met. I would like to talk with you and give you my testimony. Could we find a private place?"

Andrés glanced at his watch. "Well, I have some appointments. Let's just talk here."

"I'd rather be alone," Omar insisted. "Let's go to a restaurant, just us three. I have so much to tell you."

"But I already had lunch," Andrés objected. "I really am pretty busy."

Pastor Pablo came to the rescue. "Andrés, you and Omar are not only cousins, but you have been good friends. It would be great if we could spend some time privately at a restaurant, over a cup of coffee. Just us three."

Andrés looked puzzled, but agreed.

On the way to the restaurant in Andrés' pickup, Omar told his cousin the story of his conversion, and Andrés nodded at the right places. It was a good foundation for what was coming next. Minutes later, the trio sat at a fancy restaurant over coffee.

Feeling troubled, Omar nevertheless took the plunge bravely. "Andrés, I have to tell you some things that will be hard for you to believe. You know what a hard man I was . . . and wicked . . ."

At thirty-eight, Andrés was a large man. His face had the mildly distorted look of one who had faced serious physical trauma. It wasn't obvious where or what, but his features were just a little twisted, even though he hadn't had a stroke. As Omar continued, Andrés pulled his bill cap down over his face, almost obscuring his eyes, though they were glued on Omar. It was obvious he was thinking hard, wondering what this was all about.

"Andrés, the reason I wanted to have a private meeting with you is because I did some very serious things that involve you." Andrés sat still and silent, as if carved out of stone.

"Andrés, I have carried a load of guilt for many years. You and your family have been so nice to me, and you had no idea what I did. This has been terribly hard for me. You see, I was involved when those thugs beat you up in LA. I did not instigate the crime, but I was involved."

Andrés jerked up straight in his chair and barked, "I knew it! I knew all the time it was Bato."

Omar held up his hand. "Wait, Andrés! I want to tell you the whole story."

The rest of the conversation moved fast, with Omar explaining things and Andrés asking key questions and exclaiming, "I knew it!"

On that dark night, Bato had called his sister Irma in Estelí, telling her that someone had killed Andrés, before the rescue squad had even been called and before any of the other relatives had been alerted. All this time Andrés had suspected Bato's involvement. But he hadn't really suspected Omar.

Though he had been right about Bato, Andrés had guessed incorrectly that the crime had been committed for money. The thugs had taken all of Andrés' valuables and money, and only Omar and Bato had known where his things were hidden.

Omar explained that the truck deal was the real motive for the crime. "Andrés, Bato told the thugs to kill you. But when I took them to the scene, I told them to not take your life."

After his confession, Omar broke down and cried, telling Andrés how sorry he was.

Andrés' response startled his cousin. "Omar, I forgive you. Actually, I had already forgiven you awhile ago. God has prepared me for this. But five years ago, I wouldn't have sat here as calm as I am now. I would be . . ." He did not finish the sentence.

Pablo thanked Andrés and congratulated him for his beautiful attitude. "Can you also forgive your uncle?" he asked.

At first Andrés shook his head, but after thinking a moment, he replied, "Yes, I could. I won't lift a finger against the man. But my family is another story. Just pray that my oldest son doesn't find this out!"

Then Andrés also broke down, buried his face in his hands, and wept. Omar reached over and placed a hand on his shoulder, and all three men wept together.

Lifting his head, Andrés looked Pablo squarely in the eye. "Pablo, this isn't easy for me."

Pastor Pablo nodded, his face troubled.

Jerking off his cap and lowering his head, Andrés instructed, "Feel my head." Pastor Pablo ran his fingers over Andrés skull. Omar knew what he was feeling. Andrés had asked him to do the same thing years earlier. Andrés' skull was a series of drop-offs and gaps—clearly the result of a crushed skull.

Plopping his cap back on, Andrés continued, "I've never been the same since that horrible day. I can't work normally. I constantly have headaches. Those thugs ruined my life."

"I realize that, son," Pastor Pablo whispered. "That's why I admire you for forgiving Omar."

Omar was weeping again. "I know it's hard, Andrés. I—" Omar began.

"Don't worry," Andrés said quickly. "I've always said that Bato is the one who ruined you. He influenced you to become what you were. It's all right, cousin."

Then Omar and Andrés discussed the future. Andrés refused to promise to keep Omar's confession a secret, but just now he needed to leave and take care of his appointments. Quickly he rose to his feet, and the two men from Waslala followed suit.

Andrés began to walk out of the restaurant, but he turned twice to thank the two men for braving their strange mission. It seemed hard for him to leave. He especially thanked Omar for telling him the truth, and then, as a beautiful afterthought, he said, "And thank you, Omar, for saving my life!"

As Omar and Pastor Pablo watched Andrés leave, Omar grinned. "Pastor Pablo, within the hour every Montenegro in Estelí will know this story."

"And it won't be long till Bato hears it too, right?"

"Ever since I turned myself in to the FBI, Bato has been fearing this. That's probably why he sold his properties in Estelí and Regadío. Just like Andrés said, 'Uncle Bato will never set foot in Estelí again.' And maybe never in Nicaragua."

Omar and Pastor Pablo felt like shouting hallelujah. They were also hungry, as they had had very little for breakfast, and it was now two o'clock in the afternoon. Pastor Pablo ordered two large expensive meals, and as they downed the delicious food, Pastor Pablo sighed. "I declare that this meal is one of the best investments I've ever made!"

Omar decided to go to Regadío for the night. No doubt his mother was sick with fear, and he wanted to tell her everything and also comfort his fearful father.

"Thank you so much for coming with me on this delicate mission," Omar told Pablo before they parted. "My own father was too afraid to go with me to meet Andrés, but you didn't bat an eye. You were right there for me. You are more than a father to me!"

CHAPTER 60

The front-page news in Waslala was that the robber Frank had been converted. Omar watched from a distance as Pastor Pablo took the new convert under his wing to disciple him. He would wait to see if Frank were truly sincere.

Then Pastor Pablo asked Omar to go with Frank to make some necessary restitutions. Omar gladly accompanied Frank as he confessed his robberies and offered to repay those he had wronged. Omar was surprised that the people in Waslala not only freely forgave Frank, but also encouraged him to be firm in the Lord. Pastor Pablo asked the brethren for advice on how Frank should make amends for his sins, just as he had done earlier for Omar. And Omar was convinced that Frank, the former thief, was serious about serving the Lord.

Frank, with Pastor Pablo's help, turned himself in to the local police and gave them a copy of all the restitutions. Frank had also listed the wrongs that he still needed to make right. The head policeman offered to let Frank remain out of jail so he could continue his restitution, and the whole police force promised to protect and support him.

Omar was dismayed to discover that Frank had once butchered four head of cattle on Pastor Pablo's farm, including one of Omar's own cows. But Omar freely forgave him, just like Pastor Pablo did, and loved Frank more than ever.

Frank found a job on a farm that Jona was responsible for, and Jona became Frank's friend and mentor just like he had been Omar's.

"This is wonderful!" Omar would tell Yuri after a good time with his new friend. "Now I can help someone else who was a bad person fix up his life and serve the Lord. Frank is a miracle, wrought by the hand of God, just like me! To be part of these miracles is what I was born for."

Pastor Pablo's barn was full and running over with people. Omar sat beside his wife among the rest of the church brethren on crude boards placed on stacks of cement blocks. The church brethren had gathered the day before and slaughtered a hog. Today, Omar and Marcelino had grilled a huge batch of meat, and the ladies had cooked yuca and prepared a salad. More than a hundred tortillas, hot and ready for the feast, waited on the table at the head of the barn floor.

Pastor Pablo made the announcement. "Brethren, we planned this evening meal so we can fellowship together as a church. But this is also a surprise farewell supper for Jona and Jéssica and their little daughter."

A hush fell over the group as they looked at Jona and his little family. They were, indeed, surprised to know the gathering was especially for them. Jona looked over at his wife and smiled as Pablo continued, "As you know, Jona and his family have been traveling to Jicaral to pastor the church there. But now they are almost done building their new house on their farm in Jicaral and plan to move soon. We are going to miss them.

"We'll have a time of singing and testimonies. After that, we'll eat." Pastor Pablo smiled, motioning to the table laden with food.

Omar was the first to stand and share encouraging words with Jona and his family, but he wasn't the last. The testimonies were many and heartfelt, interspersed with songs.

Where would I be today without the family of God? Omar thought. *Where would I be if it weren't for Jesus' salvation and a brotherhood who loves and accepts me? Praise the Lord!*

Omar watched intently from the door of his house. *What does that man think he's doing?* he wondered irritably. Don Pedro, his next-door neighbor, was scurrying along the property lines, first measuring the frontage of his own lot, and then Omar's that lay adjacent.

Minutes later, Pedro accosted Omar. He claimed that the fence between them was at the wrong place. Omar found his own deed and patiently showed Pedro that his lot had fifteen yards of frontage, and that is what it measured. But Pedro adamantly claimed that the fence would have to be moved a whole yard in, stealing a section of Omar's land. Pedro had already driven in a stake to where he claimed the fence would have to be moved.

Omar restrained himself from arguing, but he went inside and spewed off to his wife. Yuri listened, worried that her man would get in trouble with this unhandy neighbor. "Just let it go, Omar," she suggested, as Don Pedro kept on measuring and driving in stakes.

Pedro stopped by later, wondering when they could move the fence. Omar refused to argue, but his anger surged inside. *That man just wants to pick a fight!* he fumed. *Don Pedro had better be glad that I'm a Christian now, or I would easily take care of this situation. I'd take it to the law immediately.*

"I'm going to talk to Daniel," Omar informed Yuri. "He'll have some good advice that I need right now."

Deed in hand, Omar left the house. As he walked through town, the battle raged in his heart. *This kind of case is what the law is for,* Omar fumed. *I wonder if Daniel will agree that I should go to the police station to set this neighbor straight.* But Omar knew what the Bible said—that Christians should not fight, but love their enemies. He was pretty sure Daniel would tell him, "Let it go. Leave it in God's hands."

As Omar meditated on Jesus' teachings, his anger subsided. *Why should I lose my salvation for a yard of land? I won't fight this deal. It's just not worth it. I'll help Pedro move the fence tomorrow.*

But when Omar told Daniel the story, he didn't give Omar an answer right away. Instead, he said, "I'll go with you, Omar. Let's go see the lot and talk to Don Pedro. I know him personally."

Just before Omar and Daniel arrived at Omar's house, they saw a young man sitting on a motorcycle, talking to a fellow beside the road. The man on the motorcycle worked for the county seat as a surveyor. Omar told him briefly about his problem. To Omar's amazement, the man answered, "I'll be right over after I finish talking with this fellow."

Minutes later, the surveyor arrived. Don Pedro didn't flinch when the surveyor took over, looking at both deeds and carefully measuring both frontages while Daniel, Don Pedro, and Omar watched. When he finished, the young man looked squarely at Don Pedro and said, "The fence is at the right place. Everything is as it should be."

To Omar's surprise, Don Pedro grinned his agreement, and Daniel smiled as he nodded at Omar knowingly. The fellow from the county seat jumped on his cycle and disappeared.

Later Omar related the story to Pastor Pablo. "I just couldn't believe it!" he exclaimed. "God fixed the problem so easily once I had given it up. I was ready to go help Don Pedro change that fence the very next day, but it wasn't necessary."

"Beautiful!" Pastor Pablo agreed. "That's God for you. I've seen things like that happen again and again. But has the relationship between you and Don Pedro healed?"

"No," Omar admitted. "Relationships are strained. Yuri hardly talks to Don Pedro's wife, and I find myself avoiding him. I never knew Pedro could be so selfish."

"Well, then, it's time for the next step," Pastor Pablo suggested. "It's time to show them love. You won a great victory by not fighting, Omar. But God wants something more. Show them that you love them and forgive them. Watch for an opportunity to do them a favor."

Omar sighed. *Is that even possible?* he wondered. "I'll try, Pastor Pablo," he said. "And I'll pray about it. It seems a bit hard, but yes, that is what the Bible says."

"I'll be praying for you as well," Pastor Pablo assured him. "God will give you an opportunity soon."

61

TWO NEEDLES IN A HAYSTACK

NOEMI AND DAIANA had begged a little money off their grand-mother, and now they sat at an internet café in Jalisco, Mexico, googling things that interested them. They often did this in the evenings after school, but this research had nothing to do with their studies. The sisters, now sixteen and eighteen, giggled as they sat close together on two chairs, using one computer.

"Let's do a search on the man who was Mama's boyfriend when she died," Daiana suggested. "It's been a long time, but I still remember his name."

"Why would you want to look up such a horrible man?" Noemi growled, her large green eyes snapping. "I can't even bear the thought of him!"

"But what if something would show up?" Daiana insisted, reaching for the keyboard. "I've seen his wanted page on the web. Maybe something new has been posted about him. He probably still lives in Nicaragua."

Even as Noemi frowned beside her, Daiana typed in the name—Fermín Omar Montenegro.

"Here's his wanted page," Daiana announced, looking at the monitor intently. "I see a new post here—it's apparently somebody's blog. His last name is Miller, and he appears to be an Americano who lives in Nicaragua. Let's read it."

The two girls became silent. Eyes fastened on the screen, they read Omar's side of the story of their mother's death for the first time.

Daiana was reading faster than Noemi. "Look at this," Daiana said. "It says Omar has become a Christian and changed his ways."

"If so, he would be the most horrible kind of Christian who could exist!" Noemi shook her head emphatically. "That man could never be good!"

"This is ridiculous!" Daiana exclaimed angrily. "Here it says that Mama aborted Omar's baby because she was a dancer and didn't want to lose her shape! I have never heard anything so crazy in my life!"

"That is not true!" Noemi objected, seizing the keyboard from her sister. "Those people are lying! I'm going to send this Mr. Miller a message right away and set him straight!"

In a matter of minutes, Noemi's message winged its way to Waslala and waited in Mr. Miller's inbox till someone would read it.

The next day, Omar stopped in at Pablo's farm, waving a paper. "Pastor Pablo! You'll never believe this, but we found Gema's daughters!"

"You can't be serious!"

"Brother Miller got a message from Noemi on his blog!" Omar explained excitedly. "And guess where they live."

"In Los Angeles, we thought."

"No, they're back in Jalisco, Mexico, where Gema was from, with their paternal grandparents."

"How in the world did they get hold of Miller's blog?"

"All I can figure out is they went to some cybercafe and googled my name," Omar guessed. "Daiana, especially, would have remembered my name. The blog pops up with my wanted page."

"And we tried to find them in LA! No wonder we couldn't find them, since they were in Mexico."

"Probably since Doña Juana had mental problems, and Matías and Ramón weren't willing to take the girls, they were sent back to their father's parents."

"What did Noemi have to say?" Pastor Pablo asked eagerly. Omar handed him the paper.

> *To Mr. Miller:*
> *Hello! My name is Noemi, and I am Gema's daughter.*

Noemi's message to Omar was skeptical, letting him know that she didn't think his story on the blog was true. She did say she wanted to see the video of confession, but that if she ever met Omar face-to-face, she would tell him how much he had made her and her sister suffer by murdering their mother. She hoped Omar would go to jail to pay for all the damage he had done.

> *PEOPLE LIKE YOU, OMAR, SHOULD NEVER*
> *EXIST BECAUSE YOU STEAL THE VERY OXYGEN*
> *THAT WE BREATHE. I HATE YOU, FERMÍN OMAR*
> *MONTENEGRO!!!!*

Pablo handed the letter back to Omar. He shook his head. "She's very angry!"

"I would be angry too," Omar told his pastor, "if someone had shot my mother. If I weren't a Christian, I would be a lot more angry than they are. Pablo, could you please start this contact for me? Could you write Noemi an email, explaining that she has all the right in the world to be angry? It's too soon for me to contact them directly. And don't forget to mention the video."

Excitement flared as the good news spread, and Omar testified to the church about finding these two precious needles hidden in a haystack. It was a miracle from God.

"Finally," Omar testified to the church, "I can be in contact with these two girls who suffered so much because of my sin. Hopefully they will watch the video. Whether or not they forgive me doesn't really matter. The important thing is that I have the chance to say I'm sorry and show them the love of Christ. This is an answer to prayer!"

That evening, Pastor Pablo wrote:

> *Dear Noemi and Daiana,*
>
> *Receive a big greeting from the pastor of the Waslala Christian Brotherhood. I am Omar Montenegro's pastor.*
>
> *Ever since the first day I heard about you two girls, my heart was moved. From day one I tucked you into my heart and have prayed for you often. You were victims in a horrible situation, and though innocent, had to suffer so much.*
>
> *Omar doesn't resent the fact that you two are angry at him and hate him. That is to be expected. He told me he would be angry too if someone had killed his mother. So don't feel bad if you have to cry, express your anger, or lash out at him. He accepts that reaction.*
>
> *At the same time, I would encourage you to start opening your heart to the possibility, though seemingly impossible, that Omar has repented. Omar has made a video in which he asks you two for forgiveness for his horrendous crime against you. Somehow we want to get this DVD to you so you can listen to it.*

In a short time Daiana sent an answer to Pastor Pablo's letter:

> *Thanks for caring about us, pastor. I am Daiana, the oldest of Gema's daughters. I am eighteen years old.*
>
> *Yes, I remember Omar well. Even though he has done bad things, I am not a bitter person. I could never deny someone's pardon if he is truly repentant.*
>
> *My family here in Mexico (father, grandparents, and uncles) don't want us to have any contact with any of you that have anything to do with Omar Montenegro. They were really upset when they found out that we contacted you folks. But I do want to have contact. If it's a mistake, I want to commit my own errors and learn the lessons they bring.*

I am Catholic, and I even sing in our church's choir. I will listen to the video because I don't believe in judging people. I am good at listening and enjoy dialogue.

Tell Omar that I still remember when he would help me with my homework.

Reading this, a tsunami of emotion washed over Omar's soul, and he wept. Bright memories from the past flashed through his mind. Those two little girls that he had loved and wanted to be part of his family had grown up and were now trying out their own wings. They wanted to contact him, even though their family was totally against it. Best of all, one of the two victims most affected by Omar's awful crime was willing to forgive him.

Omar's shoulders shook as Pastor Pablo embraced him and put his feelings into words. "Omar, if this isn't a miracle, nothing is. What a sweet gift God has given you today!"

In a later letter, Daiana briefly told what had happened after Gema died.

The truth is that I would like to forgive Omar. But do tell him that ever since we lost our mother, nothing has been the same. We are not happy here. After Mama died, we were kept in a foster home for two years. We were happy there, but then we were sent back here to Mexico. We did not want to come, but we were forced to.

Noemi's response was bitter. She wanted Omar to know how much he had hurt the two little girls and how sad and depressed she often felt because of what he had done to their mother. She wanted him to think about how such a crime would affect his own children if his wife was murdered. She said she was actually pleased for this contact with Omar, however, so she could tell him exactly how she felt.

Pastor Pablo's daughter Luana started writing to Noemi and Daiana, and they became friends. After several weeks, and after reading Noemi's letter, Omar finally knew that the time had come for him to write to the girls personally.

Dear Daiana and Noemi,

> *First of all, I want to tell you that the fact that we found each other is a miracle from the Lord! I am very grateful for this opportunity because ever since I gave my life to Christ, I have longed to get in touch with you. I have prayed to God many times for the opportunity to ask you for forgiveness for what I did and for how much I damaged you. This truly is an answer to prayer.*
>
> *That horrible night when your mother died was a nightmare not only for you, but for me too. We both lost everything that we loved, didn't we? I was a man crazed that night. Forgive me!*
>
> *I was also planning to kill myself that night, but I couldn't make myself do it. So I ran for my life and was a fugitive for years, on the brink of going crazy. I wanted to die. I couldn't sleep, and at night I would search for your mother in the darkness. I often asked God to take my life. I knew I was running away from myself. The wickedness of my sin was consuming me, body, soul, and spirit. I think that our suffering, though different, was in some ways the same.*
>
> *While I was running away from God, His hand was on me as He punished me with loneliness, rejection, hunger, sickness, accidents, a snakebite, and much more.*

Then Omar told the girls the story of his conversion. He told them how he had turned himself in to the U.S. officials and was waiting on a possible trial in which he would probably be condemned to prison.

> *But now, since I have repented of my sins, I am free. I belong to a new family, the best family in the world—the family of God. You also need that family.*
>
> *I realize that by asking you for forgiveness, I can't give back what I took from you—not even if I could hand my flesh over to you in a gunnysack or spend the rest of my life in jail. I will never be able to pay for what I did. But God Almighty has chosen to forgive me. So maybe you can forgive me as well.*

I am sure you remember those beautiful moments we shared as a family, when we would go to the park or to the beach. I loved you as my own daughters, and I longed to have a true family.

Omar was delighted when Daiana responded to his email warmly and forgave him freely. Noemi did not express her forgiveness as Daiana did, but Omar sensed that she was ready to lay down the issue. He was pretty sure that the girls were now ready to watch his video of confession. Together, he and Pastor Pablo packed the video, several books that Pastor Pablo had written, and a gift of money from Omar, and mailed the package to the girls. After that, all Omar could do was wait and pray.

Omar was relaxing on a hammock in his living room after a hard day of work. How peaceful his life was now, compared to the life he had lived before following Jesus.

Suddenly he heard a commotion on the rocky street outside his front door. His neighbor Don Pedro and Pedro's adopted son Wilmer were bringing in a cow and her calf from a neighboring community. Don Pedro, like Omar, was a cattle jockey, and Wilmer was his right-hand helper. Omar admired little Wilmer. Though only eight years old and skinny, Wilmer was as tough as nails. He was a better help to Don Pedro than some adults could have been.

Don Pedro was leading the cow, a lariat securely attached to her huge horns. Little Wilmer came along behind, whacking the cow with a stick and prodding the calf so he would keep up. Just as they approached the house where Don Pedro planned to tie the cow to a tree, Wilmer got too close to the cow's back end. *Wham!*

Omar leaped out of his hammock and raced outside, where he found little Wilmer lying on the street, limp and unconscious. Don Pedro jumped off his horse and knelt over the little boy, sobbing, "My little boy is going to die!"

"Let's take him to the hospital!" Omar cried. They climbed into the Suzuki Omar had recently bought. Don Pedro tenderly held the boy on his lap as they sped toward the hospital.

The next day, Omar told Pastor Pablo the story. "Wilmer was okay," he reported joyfully. "But it's like I told Yuri. God sure answered our prayer quickly. Now that I did this favor for Pedro, our friendship is back."

"Isn't it wonderful how the Bible way always works?" Pablo exclaimed.

"That's exactly right," Omar agreed. "Love is stronger than hate."

———

Daiana wrote to Omar several weeks later.

> *Yesterday the package you sent us arrived in the mail. We've already watched the video, and the books are spectacular. I started reading one of them right away!*
>
> *My sister Noemi's reaction to the video was insignificant. She didn't seem very concerned about the whole thing. But I felt like Omar's words were very sincere.*
>
> *Omar has a very lovely family. His daughter is very cute, and his wife is pretty as well.*
>
> *Your church looks a lot different than mine, though the songs are very beautiful!*
>
> *Thank you very, very much!*

Omar raised his hands to the sky and exclaimed, "Praise the Lord! God has answered our prayer! It is done. My restitution for my crime is taken care of. These two girls have heard my confession, and now I am free."

"Not only were you able to free yourself, brother," Pastor Pablo added, "but obviously they have forgiven you! Praise the Lord!"

62

DEATH OF A FRIEND

THE JANGLING OF his phone woke Omar from a deep sleep. He rolled over and picked it up from the stand beside the bed. It was 5 a.m.

"Hello, this is Omar."

"Omar, this is Pastor Pablo. Have you heard the news?"

Concern gushed into Omar's heart. It was unusual for his pastor to call him this early. "No. What's up?"

"Jona died," Pastor Pablo answered bluntly, his voice breaking.

"What . . . who died?" Omar stuttered.

"Jona."

"Which Jona?"

"*Our* Jona!" Pastor Pablo choked. "He died this morning at 1 a.m. I tried to call you then, but you must have cut your phone off."

Omar was crying hard now. *Not Jona. He's been my best friend!* his heart screamed. He was as healthy as an ox!

"What-what happened, Pablo?" Omar stammered. "What did he die from?"

"We don't really know, but he must have had a heart attack or something. He just stopped breathing. When you come out, we'll give you more details."

"I'll be right there!" Omar gasped.

"Look," Pastor Pablo said. "You might as well milk your cows first. There are tons of people here, and things are all taken care of. Nothing you can do will change anything. Come whenever you can."

All during the milking, Omar wept. *Why did Jona have to die? His three little girls and Jéssica need him so much. The Jicaral church needs him. And most of all, I need him!*

As soon as the milking was finished, Omar loaded up his family in the Suzuki and then, with heavy hearts, they drove down to Jicaral.

Jona's place was teeming with people. Since it was the heart of the rainy season, the yard was squishy where all the feet had stamped the grass into a muddy mess.

Many of the church people were already there. Omar had expected that. But what he couldn't believe was how many others had come. Rich ranchers who had done cattle business with Jona huddled together. Poor folks from far and wide who had worked for Jona or had contact with him in other ways stood dumbfounded. Everyone shook their heads, wondering about this strange, sudden death and talking about how kind Jona had been to everybody.

Omar and his family approached the house timidly. How did one act at a time like this? Omar had never been to a funeral where the people were Christians.

Pastor Pablo met Omar's family in front of the house. He invited them in and led the way into the living room where Jéssica and her three little girls were surrounded by church sisters. Jéssica was repeating the story of what had happened at one o'clock that morning.

"I woke up because Jona was thrashing around and making noise," she said. "It was dark, and the electricity had gone off, so I said, 'Jona, where is the flashlight?' But he didn't answer. So I asked him again, thinking he was teasing me. Finally, I found the flashlight and shone it in his face. It was then I realized he wasn't breathing anymore, and there was blood on his lips."

Omar was too shocked for words. So quick. So final. So sad. He looked at the young widow, surrounded by her precious children, and he trembled as he tried to control his emotions.

"That's when I called my dad," Jéssica continued. "By the time the family got here, I knew that my husband was gone."[33]

After Jéssica's account, Omar shook her hand and expressed his condolences. But Yuri flew into her arms, and they wept together.

At that moment, Pastor Pablo motioned Omar to follow him upstairs. Stepping into Jona's bedroom, Omar's heart almost stopped. There was his dear friend, lying on his bed, covered up to his chest by a sheet, his pale face peaceful.

"He looks alive!" Omar whispered. "As if he were just sleeping."

Pablo nodded. "That's what everyone says. I guess it's because he died in the Lord."

Pastor Pablo gently took Omar's hand and laid it on Jona's hand that lay still at his side.

Omar sighed sadly. "He's cold."

"He's gone," Pastor Pablo said reverently. "His body is still here, but his spirit is gone to be with God." Omar's head dropped as he covered his face and wept.

Later that morning, Omar told Jéssica how he had often felt an urge to tell Jona how much he appreciated their friendship. "Now it's too late," Omar lamented, wiping his eyes. "I'll never have a chance to tell him what was on my heart."

"Don't you worry," Jéssica replied. "Jona knew how much you loved him, and I know how much he appreciated you. Your friendship was a little like David and Jonathan in the Bible, right?"

Omar smiled through his tears. As he and his family joined the crowd to wait for the burial, he thought about his friendship with Jona. That friendship had included correction when Omar needed it. In his love, Jona had not spared his friend, but he had also given Omar many kind words of encouragement as well. Yes, Jona had been a real friend!

The second-story balcony of Jona's house faced the yard, which was full of people milling about. Pastor Pablo closed in the balcony by hanging up sheets

---

33 Because no autopsy was performed, Jona's family will never know for sure how he died, but the doctors thought that a blood clot took him home. Jona had flown the week before for a quick trip to the United Staes due to his job with Christian Aid Ministries' SALT project. Apparently the altitude change dislodged a blood clot in his leg that traveled to his heart, blocking his heart suddenly.

to block the view from curious eyes. He placed a bench in the center of the balcony on which to lay Jona's body for washing and dressing before placing it in the coffin. Pastor Pablo, Omar, and Frank, the former robber, carried Jona's stiff, cold body out gently and laid it on the bench. But when Pastor Pablo and Frank started to strip the body, something happened in Omar's heart. Even though he badly wanted to help, an immense sadness gripped him.

He whispered, "Pastor Pablo, I can't do this."

Pablo's eyes spoke compassion. "It's okay, Omar."

Omar slipped outside to find a quiet corner alone where he could cry out to God. Something strong and strange was clutching at his heart, almost choking him. *God is speaking to me.* Omar wept. *Why does my conscience strike me so? Why did I wait until my friend died? Jona was ready to go. But if it had been me, I wouldn't have been ready.*

Omar took his family home and then returned to Jicaral. The all-night watch in the Jicaral schoolhouse was interrupted when Jona's extended family arrived, and everyone rose to receive them. Some of Jona's nine siblings came from El Salvador, but most of them had come from the States.

The rest of the night was spent watching, singing, and visiting. The Laguna family who lived close to the schoolhouse prepared food for the people who had come from afar. Two couples from a sister congregation arrived to help with cooking for the crowds.

Again and again the evening activities were interrupted as people poured in, mostly from Nicaragua, but also from Honduras, from Costa Rica, and from the States. Omar was amazed again to witness how these Christians responded in crises. *If I had died,* Omar realized, *the Christians would have responded in the same way.* This was genuine love being expressed in the family of God!

It rained during the night, and by morning, several hundred people milled around, waiting for the funeral and burial. The schoolyard and even the road became a muddy mess, but people didn't seem to mind. They stopped by to view Jona's body or visit with others. When the time came for the funeral to begin, the brethren in charge stood at the end of the school building beside the coffin. Folks were still crowding in.

During the chaos, Pastor Pablo had been able to have a word with Omar. "Brother, we are asking four Nicaraguans who were close to Jona to give testimony during the funeral service. Would you be willing to share?" Omar nodded.

Edwin Hershberger, who had served as a schoolteacher in Waslala, led the songs. Never before had the singing in Waslala been so vibrant and intense. Though tears streamed down many faces, no one could miss the joy and the hope as Edwin led favorite songs about Heaven. Oh, how the people sang!

This is incredible! thought Omar as he sang along with the rest. *This is possible because we have God in our hearts and we know without a doubt where Jona is right now. This is what the Bible means when it talks about the hope of eternal life. This is real! This is wonderful!*

Omar's heart throbbed as he worshiped. *This is just like when the glory of God came down on Mount Sinai, and now I know what I must do. I must confess my hidden sin.*

After the singing, Bishop Tim Schrock gave a brief, warm welcome. "Recently Jona has preached a sermon about death several times. He preached it in Jicaral. He preached it in the States recently. The last time he preached it was in Zapote Kum only a week ago. Toward the end of the message, he asked this startling question, 'Who will be next to die? Will it be you? Will it be me? Will we be ready?'

"Yes, this time it was Jona's turn to go to be with Jesus. And yes, we believe that he was ready to go. He believed in keeping his life up-to-date with God. May God's name be praised!"

After Tim's meditation, the four Nicaraguan brethren gathered at the front—Elmer, Frank, Julio, and Omar. Packed from all sides by the crowd, they shared what Jona's life had meant to them.

Elmer was a young, fatherless boy from the Waslala congregation who often worked for Jona and whom Jona had taken under his wing like a daddy. Elmer could hardly talk because of his sobbing. Everyone could see how much Elmer had loved Jona.

Frank was also a member of the Waslala congregation. He had worked on Jona's brother's farm and learned to know Jona well. Like Elmer, Frank had found more than a friend in Jona. Strong bonds had formed as Jona had helped to disciple these two young men.

Julio gave his testimony next. Julio was a converted delinquent and a member of Jicaral. Jona had been his pastor and confidant. Julio, the only one in his family to serve the Lord, felt Jona's death acutely. In spite of Julio's horrible past, he now served Christ faithfully and was known to be Jona's right-hand man.

Omar was glad to testify to so many people about Christ. He also confessed that he had missed the chance to tell Jona how much his friendship meant to him. "Let's not put it off any longer, brethren," he admonished. "Let's tell the people we are close to how much we love them!"

Along with five other brethren, Omar shouldered the coffin, slipping and sliding down the mud-covered hillside toward the grave site. It was pouring rain again. The crowd, some clinging to their umbrellas, opened the way for the men carrying the coffin as they surged along in the mud.

The gravediggers had covered the grave with several old pieces of tin to keep the rain out. People crowded so tightly around the grave that the Yoder and Miller families couldn't get close. The neighbors who had arrived first didn't want to give up their precarious spots. People were slipping and falling in the mud, and Omar feared that someone would crash through the tin and fall into the grave.

Alvino and Pastor Pablo finally placed a chair for Jéssica right beside the grave. Her children, wet and cold, huddled around her.

As soon as the pallbearers placed the coffin on a set of chairs beside the grave, the rain stopped. From their spots in the crowd, the visiting brethren joined the local brethren in singing—songs that were heartfelt, joyous, and sad.

A Salvadoran pastor of a church in Costa Rica scrambled up onto the pile of dirt beside the grave. From there he had a good view of the people, and everyone could see and hear him. Bible in hand, Chente Mejia was ready to preach, and preach he did!

"Set thine house in order!" Chente cried, raising his Bible high. "Set thine house in order; for thou shalt die, and not live."

It was a scene that Omar would never forget. Even as Chente preached, God continued to speak to Omar's heart, and what Omar had decided was confirmed. He needed to make right some things that had been deeply hidden in his heart. God would tell him when and how.

The day after Jona's death, Omar's heart was heavy, his nerves raw. Yuri noticed his sad spirit and figured that it was the pain of losing his best friend. But something more was eating at Omar, and it was time to clear it.

After the burial, the people went home, and most of the nonresident visitors left. But Chente and several families stayed in Waslala for a few days to comfort the Yoder and Miller families.

Who would comfort Jona's other friends? It was Jacinto who came up with a plan that Omar appreciated. "Right now the Millers have the Millers for comfort," he reminded the brethren. "We Yoders have the Yoders. But many of Jona's friends have no one to comfort them. Let's get together so we can all comfort each other."

The word spread. "There will be a special service in the Waslala chapel tonight. Come join us as we face the loss of our brother and seek healing together."

The chapel was packed that evening as people poured in from all three churches. There were still some visitors around, and even a scattering of neighbors showed up. Jacinto took charge, and again the chapel rang with songs about Heaven. Then Jacinto opened it up for the brethren to share words of comfort, teaching, or inspiration. Many of the brethren went forward.

The time had come for Omar to clear his conscience. He walked to the pulpit and faced the crowd. "Brethren," he began slowly, "Jona did not die in vain. His example has spoken to me in a mighty way. Jona was ready to die, but if it would have been me, I would not have been ready. I have been hiding sin."

The crowd waited patiently as Omar took time to wipe his tears. Then he plunged on boldly. "What breaks my heart is that my best friend had to die to get me ready to make this confession. But when Chente preached at the burial yesterday, calling us to set our houses in order, I knew what I had to do."

Taking a deep breath, he continued, "This happened three years ago, while I was still in instruction class, and Yuri and I were living separately. On one occasion we were not faithful to our promise to live apart until we were married. We both felt awful and confessed our sin to God, and it didn't happen again. But we decided to not confess it to you brethren, and that was another sin heaped upon the first one. Now Yuri is agreed that I confess to you as well, so we can clear our hearts before God."

Omar paused again to regain control over his emotions. "Also, I want to confess that soon after I was converted, I fell into one of my old sins of immorality during a visit to Regadío. Again, I begged God for forgiveness, but He has often reminded me that I should confess these two sins to the brethren. I pushed His voice aside, making the excuse that confessing to God was enough. But since Jona died and Chente preached that message, I have become desperate for complete peace. I sinned. I hid my sin, and I was not ready to die. But today, I can already feel freedom and the peace of God flooding my heart."

A great hush hovered over the congregation as Omar continued, "I also ask my wife for forgiveness for hiding my sin from her, and I ask each one of you, my brethren, for forgiveness, because my sin was also against the church of Jesus Christ."

As soon as Omar was finished, Pastor Pablo came to the pulpit and put his arm around Omar. "How many of you forgive Omar?" he asked in a loud, clear voice.

Every hand was raised high.

"Let's pray for our brother that God will cleanse him and restore him from having hidden these sins."

Chente was the first to join them at the pulpit, and many other brethren poured up the aisle. The group wept with Omar and prayed with Pastor Pablo as the Lord God Almighty flooded each one with His forgiveness and joy. The Waslala church walked on holy ground that evening.

The next morning Chente visited Omar at his house to bless him for confessing publicly and to encourage him in the Christian life. Pastor Pablo and his wife spent some time helping Yuri work through her hurt of finding out that Omar had hidden sin from her.

What had seemed like a blow for God's people in Nicaragua was actually a threatening blow to Satan and his deceptive kingdom, and time would continue to prove it.

63

ROUGH EDGES

OMAR STOOD AT the window beside Pastor Pablo's desk, clenching the iron bars that kept prowlers out. He could hardly believe what Pablo had just said. Annoyed, Omar mumbled a quick goodbye, jumped on his horse, and rode out the lane.

How dare Pastor Pablo say that? he complained inwardly. *He's just as bad as the rest of the brethren who are talking about me!*

Omar had been part of the church for several years now. With his strong, outgoing personality, he sometimes clashed with some of the other Waslala brethren. Because Omar hated all the sins he used to revel in, he had little patience with other brethren who were careless. When he corrected them, his manner was not always as kind as it should have been.

Whenever Omar clashed with a brother, he would pour out his woes to Pastor Pablo or Daniel. The leaders always listened and then helped Omar to also see his own faults. They encouraged Omar to talk with each brother personally. The amount of time Omar spent with Pastor Pablo bothered a few of the brethren.

On this day, Omar had approached Pastor Pablo's window with another issue he had just discovered. Pastor Pablo was at his desk working on a book he was writing, but like usual, he took time to hear Omar out.

"And guess what else he is saying about me," Omar complained. "He said that I must think I'm a gringo, because my family and I don't ever visit the nationals, only the gringos."

Pastor Pablo hesitated only a minute. "Omar, what the brother is saying is partly true. You hardly ever visit the national brethren, but you visit my family, Jona's family, and Jacinto's family regularly."

Omar was so shocked at this candid answer that he turned on his heel, leaving the bewildered pastor at his desk. As he rode to work that morning, his anger began to subside. *Pastor Pablo is always frank with me. But it seems like he could have at least a little mercy. It's hard for me to hear such comments from the brethren. I was looking for a little compassion, not a sermon!*

Omar sighed. It was true that every Wednesday, Omar and his family spent several hours with either Pastor Pablo's family or Jéssica's family before the evening service. They always served coffee and sweet bread. It had become an important part of Omar and Yuri's social life. But maybe it was time to think about visiting others as well.

By the time the day was over, Omar was eager to get back to that window to ask his pastor forgiveness for being angry at him. Pastor Pablo forgave him on the spot.

"You're right—we mostly visit the gringos," Omar admitted, looking at his shoes. "But you also realize why, right?"

"Yes, Omar, I understand," Pastor Pablo agreed. "You visit us because you have confidence in us, and we get along. It's also true that a few of the brethren have a little of the Older Brother Syndrome from the story of the prodigal son. But, Omar, you have been a Christian long enough now, and have grown enough spiritually, that you should be able to build bridges with the brethren who rub you the wrong way. A shortcut to that goal would be visiting them even if they don't visit you."

Omar nodded.

Pastor Pablo smiled. "When you left this morning, I saw that you were hurt. I'm sorry, because I *was* kind of blunt, wasn't I? But the time has come that God wants you to wean yourself from us and start reaching out. I don't want you to feel bad for having visited us a lot. I have been your counselor, and you needed it. But now it's time for you to not depend on others so much and to reach out to others yourself."

Omar nodded again, understanding very well what God wanted of him. Thanking the pastor, Omar went home and shared with Yuri. They purposed to visit other families in the church and to build bridges instead of walls.

As time pressed on, Omar's family grew. Little Omarcito, Omar's first son, made his appearance, bringing Omar much delight. Several years later little Lucy was born, making the fourth Montenegro child. Omar's longing for a happy family was finally becoming a reality, and his cheerful wife Yuri shared his enjoyment.

Omar keenly felt his responsibility and the challenge of raising his four children for the Lord. Two things spurred him on—the teaching Mark had given in Nueva Armenia, and Jona and Jéssica's example. Even though Omar still missed Jona so much that his heart ached, Jona's example of a firm hand of love in the home encouraged Omar in his efforts.

But Omar was not perfect, and he made blunders. Impatience and his continuing battle with anger caused him many struggles. But Omar was quick to realize his faults and tried his best to overcome his weaknesses.

When little Karen was old enough for school, Omar started to pray about moving closer to the church building, where she would attend school. It was almost too far for little Karen to walk all the way across town. God answered Omar's prayer, and he was able to buy a lot close to the chapel. He sold some cattle to bring in money for building a house on his new lot. The church organized two frolics to help him pour the concrete floor, and Omar appreciated their help. He also spent many hours building on his own.

God also blessed Omar by helping him find a buyer for his old house. After moving into the new house, Omar was sure his joy was full. But the devil was not happy.

Omar and Yuri began experiencing stress in their marriage. Early one morning, Omar came to Pastor Pablo's window with a troubled heart and trembling lips. "Pastor Pablo, please come to our home to help. My wife and I have been arguing, and we can't seem to get to the bottom of our problem."

"What's happening?" Pastor Pablo nudged gently.

"I'm not sure, but Yuri seems irritable all the time and lashes out at the children for every little thing. And she won't say she's sorry. We went to bed last night without making up, even though I've always tried to not let the sun go down upon our wrath."

"So did you say *you* are sorry?" Pastor Pablo probed.

"Yes, but really, I don't think I've done anything wrong."

"Except that you got angry," Pastor Pablo finished for him. "Right? And Omar, that's bad enough."

The truth was beginning to sink in, and Omar felt numb.

"The reason I'd like for you to come," Omar continued, "is because Yuri is in her room and doesn't want to come out to talk. We need some help."

Minutes later, Omar and Yuri and their pastor sat together in Omar's living room. Yuri was finally ready to talk. The man who couldn't see that he was at fault had to listen to his wife pour out her frustrations. Omar didn't have enough patience around the house. He took Yuri and all her hard work for granted and hardly ever gave compliments. Omar didn't always take Yuri into consideration when making decisions, and his demands were sometimes hard to live up to.

Pastor Pablo looked at Omar kindly. "Is there any truth to what Yuri is saying?"

Omar hung his head and nodded. "She's right. And I'm sorry. I want to do better."

"Yuri, was Omar repentant last evening when he asked you for forgiveness?"

"No, he wasn't!" Yuri answered firmly. "His eyes were angry, and his face showed clearly that he was still upset."

Pastor Pablo asked Yuri, "Are the things he is saying about *you* true?"

Yuri answered, "Yes, and I am truly sorry now. I wasn't before. But this morning I realize I'm more at fault than Omar is."

Suddenly Omar's face lit up. "Pastor Pablo, this is nothing else than the work of Satan!"

Omar had been so busy building the house that he had neglected his personal time with the Lord, and for a time they had even stopped having their family devotions. Yuri confessed the same, and suddenly life looked bright again.

"The devil saw that we were going to be happy living closer to the chapel in a nicer house," Omar reasoned. "He saw that the dream I had longed for all my life was coming true. So he set a trap to make us angry instead of appreciative." Then, looking at Yuri, Omar declared, "If we're sorry and ask God to help us, He'll foil the devil's plans and we'll be happy!"

Pastor Pablo beamed. "I think the victory is won, and my job is done. I'll leave the two of you here to talk."

The next half hour went by too fast as Omar and Yuri once again united their hearts to serve the Lord and to raise their family for God. Omar called the children together, and he and Yuri both apologized for their irritability and for being a bad example. The children heard their parents set new goals, and peace reigned in the home again.

Omar and his family were sitting in Jéssica's spacious living room, Jéssica surrounded by her little family. Jéssica had served them bread and glasses of *pinol,* and Omar shared about the marriage struggles he and Yuri had just overcome.

Jéssica nodded vigorously. "Jona and I had our rubs too." She smiled pensively. "At times it got tough. But whenever we made up, things were always better than ever."

Omar smiled and nodded, glancing at Yuri. She was smiling too.

"I'm healing slowly." Jéssica sighed. "But I still miss my Jona so much." Then, smiling mischievously, she added, "Now I almost wish I could have a clash with Jona so we could make up and be together again. Taking on the responsibility of raising our family alone has not been easy. Oh, I miss Jona so!"

After a minute of silence, Jéssica turned to Yuri and said, "I had my first ultrasound today, and guess what? My baby is going to be a boy!"

"Wonderful!" Omar cheered, tears filling his eyes.

"I can still remember where we were standing the day Jona told me how much he wanted a boy," Jéssica reminisced. "And now I will have a little boy . . . but Jona's gone."

"I remember," Yuri said, "that you found out you were expecting just before Jona died, right?"

"That's right," Jéssica answered, overcome with emotion. "It was only two weeks before, and he was so excited."

As Yuri and Jéssica continued to discuss the upcoming birth, Omar's mind wandered, and homesickness for Jona gripped his soul. *That little boy will be one special little fellow! I sure hope they call him Jonathan after his father.*

Before they left for home, Omar told Jéssica about his plans to accompany a group of brethren to Regadío for an evangelistic trip. "It will be such an opportunity for my people to hear the Gospel!" Omar rejoiced. "We're planning to have a service on the street, and Pastor Pablo asked me to give my testimony. I wonder how many people will show up."

The dim rays of the streetlight embraced the small group of singers. Ladies in colorful clothing stood on the sidewalks, and others sat on the curb. A sprinkling of men stood in the background, fingering their bill caps as they listened. Pastor Pablo had preached a message to about twenty-five people as a group of brethren from Waslala stood behind him to show their support. When the group had sung their last song, it was time for Omar to step forward and give his testimony.

"Friends and relatives from here in Regadío," Omar began slowly, "you may never know how much it means to me to share my testimony with you. Every one of you knows about my past. I don't have to remind you of all the bad things I did when I lived here. Then I became involved in even more wickedness in Los Angeles. But what you don't know is that although I had all the money I wanted and lived in this world's pleasures every day, I was a very unhappy and lonely man. But that all changed when I found Jesus."

Doña Miriam was there, surrounded by a few of Omar's brothers and sisters. Don Fermín was there as well, but not Doña Eva. The others in the group were either related to Omar or knew him well. They listened intently as Omar explained how God had pursued him over the years, how his heart had softened, and how he had finally yielded to Jesus.

"Tonight I invite you to also give your hearts to the Lord," Omar pleaded. "You can't go wrong if you surrender your life to the God who made you. He loves you very much. Tonight, even if you've been a great sinner, He invites you to come to Him so He can clean you up."

Later that evening Omar found a moment to talk with Jacinto alone. "I'm so glad I had the opportunity to give my testimony to my friends and relatives," he said, heaving a deep sigh. "I have longed for this moment. I can't seem to be able to shake the call I feel to preach to my own people."

"Maybe someday God will start up a church here in Regadío," Jacinto answered, smiling. "Then maybe God will call you to be one of the brethren to move here and help usher souls into the kingdom. Wouldn't that be exciting?"

Omar nodded, tears brimming in his eyes. "I admit that I feel the call," he answered. "May God's will be done."

Then Omar remembered a commitment he had made and not fulfilled. "Jacinto," he said, taking the plunge. "Before Jona died, I planned to tell him how much I appreciated him. But as you know, God snatched him away, and I still hadn't done it."

Omar paused, his head bowed. Jacinto nodded and waited.

"I don't want that to happen again. That's why I want to tell you how much I appreciate you and what our friendship means to me. Thanks for always being there for me."

"God bless you, brother," Jacinto responded, placing his arm around Omar's shoulders. "I appreciate you as well. It's a great blessing to have you as a brother!"

"Pastor Pablo," Omar asked one morning, "have you heard anything from Daiana and Noemi recently?"

"No, I haven't," the pastor answered with a little frown. "Their silence is loud. I really think we spooked them, don't you?"

"Yes, I'm afraid we moved too fast, or the grandparents discovered their communication with us."

"Well, we did it out of love," Pastor Pablo said. "We did what we could. If we don't hear from them again, we have no regrets."

After Omar and Pastor Pablo knew that Daiana and Noemi had received the things they had mailed, Pastor Pablo had offered to try to make the first personal contact. Omar agreed.

Pastor Pablo and his wife were traveling to Belize to their Latin America ministers' meeting, and they offered to bus over to Guadalajara to meet the girls in person. Omar hoped Pastor Pablo would be able to help them spiritually. But the girls had not answered the email that Pastor Pablo sent, offering to meet.

"I sure hope this won't be our last chance to communicate with them." Omar sighed. "But at least I'm free. Both of them heard my video of confession and forgave me. That's what really matters."

God loved Daiana and Noemi regardless of their lot in life. He could use their past communications to work in the girls' hearts. He alone knew when it would bear fruit in their lives, and Omar rested in that assurance.

64

HELPER MINISTER

THE SKY ARCHED like a canopy above Omar as he walked slowly in the long lonely lane. The bus had dropped him off at Las Pilas, on top of the mountain between Matagalpa and Jinotega. *What am I doing on my way to a ministers' meeting if I'm not an ordained man?* he wondered. But both Daniel and Pastor Pablo had encouraged Omar to attend, since he had been chosen as the helper minister for this year. Would this meeting do him any good?

As Omar wound his way around the last curve in the rocky lane, he gasped and almost broke stride. *What in the world?* Pastor Pablo had told him that quite a few ministers from all over Latin America usually came to these meetings. But Omar had not been prepared for this—it looked like hundreds of people down there!

Several buildings sprawled amid the green jungle. Milling around the dining hall, a multitude waited for the noon meal. Omar's heart warmed and swelled as he drew closer. "These men are all ministers of the Gospel of Jesus Christ!" he whispered reverently.

He felt conspicuous. He was probably the only brother who had come to the meetings half a day late. He was sure he felt the stares as he arrived, walking briskly. In the sea of faces, he recognized various brethren who had visited Waslala. He knew them by name—Ernest Strubhar from Oklahoma, Ben Stoltzfus from Belize, Jesse Brubaker from Jinotega, Richard Burkholder from Leon, Nicaragua, Chente Mejia from Costa Rica, and many more.

Omar had arrived just in time to participate in the prayer for the noon meal. This was like a homecoming! Omar realized that the three days he was to spend in prayer, fellowship, and hearing God's Word was a God-orchestrated plan, timed perfectly to meet his emotional and spiritual needs. He would never be sorry he had come.

A ringed kingfisher slammed into the pond's surface as he snatched a young tilapia. Then he flew up and landed on the electric line high above the pond to swallow his catch. Omar smiled as Pastor Pablo observed the drama through his ever-present binoculars. Even in the middle of a ministers' meeting, Pablo took time to sit under the thatched-roof gazebo and watch a bird find his lunch.

The afternoon sun struck the pond's surface on a slant, making the brackish water glisten. Pastor Pablo's wife Euni approached the gazebo carrying a tray. *Coffee time,* thought Omar. Every time Pablo called a ministers' meeting, his wife served the men rich black coffee. Today she even had some sweet bread to go with it!

The three brethren gathered around a small table in the gazebo. After the cups were filled and the bread dispersed, Pastor Pablo resumed the meeting. "Okay, Omar, you make a list of the different homes and who will visit who this month. Then, Daniel, you can hand out the visitation slips on Sunday after the message."

After Pastor Pablo had corrected Omar for not visiting in the homes of his fellow Nicaraguans, Omar had come up with the idea of a visitation plan. Pastor Pablo was preparing to preach a message on the importance of visiting each other, and then Daniel would give out the slips.

"I'm eager to see what the brethren will do," Omar said. "Will this actually help us get started visiting each other more?"

"It would be better if we would visit each other without having to be nudged," Daniel reasoned. "But I do think the slips will help us get started."

After the visitation plan was taken care of, the three brethren discussed many other things related to the church administration. After several hours the three men dispersed.

The kingfisher had long since flown off to look for better fishing on the Waslala River, and Omar hurried home to spend the evening with his precious little family.

As he walked home, his thoughts were happy and rewarding. Being part of the leadership team was not only a great responsibility, but a great privilege. What a blessing it was to be useful in God's kingdom!

65

THE CALL

OMAR WAS SITTING at the tiny table between the living room and dining room of their new house. Baby Lucy was sitting on his lap and little Omarcito stood at his knee, jabbering about the day's activities. Omar enjoyed these family times after a hard day's work.

When a phone call interrupted their conversation, Omar wasn't surprised to hear his father's voice. Fermín had been warming up to Omar recently. He would call and tell Omar about his financial woes, especially his mounting debts. As long as Omar listened, everything was fine. But when he tried to witness to his father, Fermín resisted. Omar didn't really expect anything different this time, but he listened.

After telling Omar about his financial distresses, Fermín's mood changed. "Omar," the older man said humbly, "I really need to change my life. I want to seek the Lord."

Jumping up from his chair and motioning to the children to wait, Omar stepped outside and paced the yard as he talked with his father. "Well, Dad, I'm so glad to hear that! But do you know what that means?"

The conversation was long and intense. As soon as the call ended, Omar headed for Pastor Pablo's house to share the good news. "Pastor Pablo, it's really hard to believe that my proud father is actually repentant. But by the sound of his voice, it seems genuine."

"Why don't you travel to Regadío and talk with your father personally?" Pastor Pablo suggested. "It's always so much better to see a man's face when you share Jesus, isn't it?"

"One thing that concerns me..." Omar hesitated. "Dad has always been such a con artist. What if he's doing this for financial help? I'm actually willing to help him, because he's in debt so deeply right now that some people are about ready to stick him in jail."

"Well, Omar," Pastor Pablo admonished, "let's be careful. But I think we should give the man the benefit of the doubt. As long as we can see that he's not playing a game, let's do what we can to help, especially spiritually."

The next week Omar traveled to Regadío. As he had sensed on the phone, his father seemed genuinely humble. Omar explained what it meant to take up the cross, and then with gladness led his father to the Lord. Omar was overjoyed to have this opportunity to be an ambassador for Christ.

During the next several months, as groups of Waslala brethren traveled to and from Regadío with Omar to hold services, two more older gentlemen gave their hearts to the Lord. Soon it was obvious that the Waslala Christian Brotherhood needed to send somebody to Regadío to give spiritual direction to these three men. God was opening the doors for a church in Omar's hometown. Another one of his dreams was coming true.

The question was, who should go?

What a surprise it was for Omar to learn that the whole Zapote Kum church, where his dear friend and brother Jacinto was pastoring, had evacuated to Waslala because of a robber band that had been harassing them for a year. Some of the brethren soon returned to Zapote in spite of the difficulties. However, Pastor Jacinto and over half of the church made Waslala their temporary home.

The Waslala brotherhood asked Jacinto if he would consider moving to Regadío temporarily. After the Zapote brethren agreed, Jacinto was willing to move to Regadío for a few months to disciple the three older gentlemen who wanted to serve the Lord.

But the Waslala brotherhood knew they also needed a support family to join Jacinto and his wife Kendra. The church prayed and decided to handle the choosing like an ordination.

As the day for the nominations approached, Omar and Yuri experienced a roller coaster of emotions. They knew the church would consider them since Regadío was Omar's hometown. But they also knew that other brethren would be capable of the job.

"On one side, I feel a call to preach," Omar confided to Daniel. "Especially to my own people. But in another way, I don't feel worthy or capable of taking on this task."

Daniel smiled. "Just allow yourself to be very soft, like soft clay in the potter's hand. Then it will be easy for God to show you what His will is."

"You know, Daniel, that I will take a real beating financially if we move to Regadío." Omar sighed. "Making a living in that rocky place makes anybody sweat."

Daniel nodded.

"But again, I know God will take care of us."

"Look at it this way," Daniel suggested. "You could have the chance that you've always longed for, to reach your family and your old friends. Maybe God will give you that gift. Or He might ask you to stay at home and send someone else. God knows what's best. Just trust Him."

That evening Omar talked to his family once again. "We're going to be very soft," he proclaimed, with a huge smile for his wife and children, "so that God can do His will."

A holy hush embraced the Waslala chapel that Sunday morning as the brethren and sisters gathered. Omar sat in his usual spot by the aisle on the third bench on the men's side, his little son Omarcito at his side. Yuri sat toward the middle of the chapel surrounded by her three little girls. At 9:30 sharp, the brethren burst into song as Tomás led the church in five hymns.

One of the songs, "I Have Decided to Follow Jesus," was Omar's favorite. As the Spirit conveyed the words up to God, Omar's heart again sealed his vow. *I will follow Jesus until the end,* he promised. This morning, he was willing to do God's will, whatever that might be. Go or stay—Omar wanted only His will.

After Pastor Pablo preached the message, he announced, "Let's pray, brethren. The time has come to nominate a support family to move to Regadío."

After the prayer, Pastor Pablo explained the procedure to the members. "Each of you will file through the back to the schoolroom to give your nomination to Daniel and me. If a brother gets more than eight nominations, he'll be a candidate for a support family for Regadío. If there is more than one candidate, we'll cast a lot."

The church sang again as the brethren filed through, the husbands with their wives. When it was Omar's turn, he and Yuri felt peace as they gave the name of their choice. Though their hearts thumped faster than usual, they knew they were in God's hands. They returned to their seats, and the singing and nominating continued.

When Pastor Pablo and Daniel returned to the auditorium, Daniel took his seat on the front pew, and Pastor Pablo made his way to the pulpit. "Brethren," he announced, his voice laced with emotion, "there will be no lot this morning. God has clearly shown His will through the brethren. Omar Montenegro has been chosen to take his family to Regadío as a support family, along with Jacinto and Kendra."

The hush intensified. Pastor Pablo continued, "Jacinto and Kendra are planning to move to Regadío temporarily. But after Omar and his family move, if a church is established, they will stay permanently, and Omar will be part of the team that presents the Gospel to his hometown. God bless you and your family, brother, as you prepare to make the move."

Omar hung his head. Wave after wave of emotion washed over him. He was overwhelmed that God could use him, who had been such an awful sinner and criminal, to preach His Gospel to the people in Regadío. Indeed, God's hand was upon him!

I have been chosen—chosen from among the worst. Chosen to go and preach the Gospel to all nations, starting with Regadío. Thank You, thank You, God!

EPILOGUE

SEPTEMBER 2020

Fifteen years have gone by since Omar gave his heart to the Lord. Readers may want to know, among other things, what became of the impending murder trial by the Los Angeles Police Department.

The first year after turning himself in, Omar and his family lived in constant tension, expecting that any moment Pastor Pablo would get a call from Detective McKnight, telling Omar when to head to Estelí for the trial. But the call never came. Was the case too old after ten years? McKnight had told Omar that Gema's family wasn't pushing for the case anymore. Also, McKnight had explained that traveling to Nicaragua to process a case was expensive for Los Angeles. In that case, the trial might be dropped. Though Omar may never know why, the Los Angeles Police Department apparently dropped his case.

After two years with nothing happening, Omar realized he was a free man, and he could get on with life like any other Waslala citizen.

What about the Costa Rican drug dealer, "Tony," who was shot by Omar on Jaco Beach? Omar has always been open to making restitution for that crime also. However, he knew only the man's nickname, and almost nothing else about him. Omar knows of no one he could contact who would have known who "Tony" really was, or anything about his family. God never opened the doors in this case like He did with Gema's. With no leads, Omar decided to drop it unless God gave him the nudge.

Omar still has contact with Daiana by WhatsApp. She has forgiven him completely. She takes a real interest in Omar and his family and shares tidbits of her own life. Noemi is still too hurt to actually become a friend.

What happened to the work in Regadío? Jacinto's and Omar's families moved there with the dream of planting a church in Omar's hometown. After a year, Pastor Pablo's family replaced Jacinto's. They also lived in Regadío for a year. Omar and his family remained for the full two years.

During that time, three people were discipled. But Omar's father and one of the other men fell back. The third brother attended services faithfully, but was never willing to be baptized. Therefore, after two years and no serious commitment to the church, the Waslala brotherhood closed down the outreach, and Omar and his family moved back to Waslala. Omar is still in contact with his family in Regadío, and the dream of someday planting a church there has not totally died.

One of the happiest days of Omar's life was when his daughter Karen was baptized. Omarcito is growing up to be Omar's right-hand man on the farm. For Omar, that is another dream come true.

For three years in succession, the Waslala church has chosen Omar to be a helper minister. Though he still has some rough edges that God faithfully keeps honing, his hatred for sin and his determination to follow Christ till the end is as strong as ever. Omar knows that he was chosen from the worst—chosen by the God who loved him even when he was a wicked criminal, and faithfully welcomed him home to His heart.

Omar and his family, September 2020
Left to right: Nataly, Karen, Omarcito, Yuri, Lucy, Omar.

MORE BOOKS BY PABLO YODER

Home on the Rock Pile and *Home on the Blue Ridge* describe the childhood adventures of Pablo and his siblings in the hollows near Faith Mission Home in Virginia. *The Long Road Home* tells of Pablo's growing-up years in Costa Rica. *Angels Over Waslala* and *Angels in the Night* describe the experiences of Pablo, Euni, and their children after they moved to Nicaragua.

Pablo has written two books of nature stories and photography, *The Work of Thy Fingers* and *The Work of His Hands,* as well as the following true stories:

Death of a Saloon: God's work in the lives of a soul-sick Costa Rican family.

La Catracha: how God saved a despised, ill-treated, and love-starved Nicaraguan girl.

From Contra to Christ: a Nicaraguan fighter's journey to the foot of the cross.

These books are available from Christian Light.

ABOUT THE AUTHOR

Pablo lives with his wife Euni in Waslala, Nicaragua. They have six children—Jacinto, Jéssica, Janie, Luana, Cynthia, and Kenny—and a growing number of grandchildren. Pablo enjoys hearing from readers and can be contacted through Christian Light Publications.

PABLO YODER
c/o Christian Light
P.O. Box 1212
Harrisonburg, VA 22803
Email: office@christianlight.org

Christian Light is a nonprofit, conservative Mennonite publishing company providing Christ-centered, Biblical literature including books, Gospel tracts, Sunday school materials, summer Bible school materials, and a full curriculum for Christian day schools and homeschools. Though produced primarily in English, some books, tracts, and school materials are also available in Spanish.

For more information about the ministry of Christian Light or its publications, or for spiritual help, please contact us at:

ADDRESS :: P. O. Box 1212
Harrisonburg, VA 22803
TELEPHONE :: 540-434-0768
FAX :: 540-433-8896
E-MAIL :: info@christianlight.org
WEBSITE :: www.christianlight.org

CHRISTIAN LIGHT
PUBLICATIONS